CONTENTS

Includes Part D Practice

Introduction

This review handbook has been designed to help you prepare for the Regents Examination—Living Environment. Before you begin reading this handbook, take a minute to flip through the pages, scan the sections, and examine how information is organized.

The first part of this handbook explains what you can expect on the Regents exam and offers test-taking strategies. Read these pages before you begin reviewing and again a few days before you take the exam. Use this information to create your own plan of action.

The content sections contain living environment, review material. They include major topics such as "Life Processes" and "Ecology." Each major topic is divided into subtopics that provide in-depth concept coverage and explanations. "Biodiversity" is a subtopic of "Ecology."

Each section includes a list of vocabulary words. Scan the list and write down terms that are unfamiliar to you. Check the glossary at the end of this book for their definitions and write them in your review notebook. As you read this handbook, you will see the vocabulary words in boldface type. In your notebook, add supporting details and related facts after the word's definition.

Graphs, charts, and illustrations reinforce the content of each section. If a concept is difficult for you, copy the chart, graphic, or illustration in your notebook. Drawing ideas may help you remember them.

Within each section, you will find a Regents exam question with explained answer choices. This feature is to help you practice analyzing multiple-choice answers. In addition, there are questions periodically in the text for you to check your understanding of content. The questions after a subtopic called "Quick Review" also help you check your understanding of content. Each section ends with practice questions for the Regents exam: Parts A–D.

What to Expect on the Regents Exam

The Regents Exam—Living Environment consists of a three-hour written test in four parts, A, B, C, and D. There are no optional sections; you must answer all questions.

Part A consists of content-based multiple-choice questions that assess your ability to apply, analyze, synthesize, and evaluate your knowledge of the Living Environment core curriculum. Part A is 30–35% of the exam's raw score.

Part B includes content-based and skills-based questions that are 25–35% of the exam's score. There are multiple-choice and simple constructed-response items that test skills and understanding of the Living Environment core curriculum.

Part C contains extended constructed-response questions that assess your ability to apply science knowledge and skills to real-world conditions. These questions require detailed answers written in complete sentences. Answers must include examples and applications that support your response. These questions are 15–25% of the exam's raw score.

Part D assesses your laboratory skills through multiple-choice and open-ended questions based on laboratory activities you have performed in class. Part D is 10–20% of the exam's raw score.

Test scorers use a table to convert raw scores to final scores.

Test Strategies for Success

Multiple-Choice Questions

Have you ever thought about what you do when you take a multiple-choice test? Do you read the question and then look for the right answer among the choices? Do you read the choices first, and then the question? No one strategy works for everyone, but the following suggestions might give you more confidence with multiple-choice questions.

- Read the entire question before reading answer choices.
- Carefully study any photo, diagram, or other graphic associated with the question. Be sure you understand what is shown, then reread the question.
- When you read a question, circle or underline key words or phrases. Consider key words when thinking of an answer to the question. When you are certain of the answer, read the choices. Select the answer that most closely matches yours.
- If no answer is similar to the one you thought of, eliminate those answers that you know are incorrect. Select an answer from the remaining choices.
- If you cannot decide on an answer after eliminating one or two choices, read the question again. If you still cannot choose an answer, make a mark beside the question then go on the next question. Sometimes, there is information in other exam questions that can help you with an answer. When you reach the end of the exam, return to unanswered questions. Reread each unanswered question and its answer choices. Again, eliminate answers that you know are wrong. Make an educated guess from among the remaining choices. There is no penalty for guessing, so do not leave any blanks.

Constructed-Response Questions

Some of the questions in Part B and all of the questions in Part C of the Regents Examination—Living Environment require you to construct a response. For some questions, you may need to write only a sentence or two. Others will require you to write a unified, coherent paragraph. Again, no one strategy works for everyone, but the following suggestions may help you with constructed-response questions.

- Carefully read the entire exam question.
- Underline or circle key words and phrases. Constructed-response questions contain words that instruct you on how to answer the question, such as *compare, contrast, explain, define, describe,* and *analyze.*
- Once you understand the question, write down what information you will include in your answer. You may create an outline and/or a concept map, chart, or other graphic tool to help you organize your thoughts.
- Be specific. Remember that you are not writing an essay. Use key terms and thoroughly explain any processes. Include relevant details such as the names of processes.
- Make it easy to find your answers. For example, if a question consists of two parts, respond in two paragraphs. Be sure that the first paragraph answers part one of the question and the second paragraph answers part two.
- Write clearly and concisely. You will not lose points for incorrect grammar or mechanics, but poor handwriting can make it difficult for the scorer to read and understand your answers.

Preparing for the Exam

- Before you take the exam, review your class notes and the information in this book. If there are concepts you do not understand, reread the corresponding chapters in your textbook. Ask a teacher or a classmate to clarify confusing concepts.
- Set aside a notebook just for test preparation. Write down key terms and their definitions. Illustrate important concepts and processes.
- Study with friends and be tutors for each other. Quiz each other on content and skills. Take previous exams together and compare your answers.
- The night before the exam, get a good night's sleep. On the morning of the test, eat a good breakfast.

Taking the Exam

- Be on time and prepared. Have several sharpened number 2 pencils.
- Read through the directions carefully.
- Periodically during the exam, check to be sure that the question number you are currently answering matches the number on the answer sheet that you are filling in. This is especially important if you have skipped a question to answer later.
- Pace yourself. Do not rush through the exam, but do not linger on difficult questions either. Answer the questions you know first, and then return to those you are not sure about.
- If there is time remaining, look over your answers, but do not change them without a reason. Often, your first choice is the correct one.

The Nature of Science

control
data
dependent variable

experiment
hypothesis
independent variable

scientific methods
theory

Have you ever wondered why on a cool, dry day you often can receive an electric shock after walking on a carpet and touching a metal object? Why plants facing a sunny window grow toward the window? Why your leg muscles ache the day or two after you run around the track at school? Scientists explore these and other questions so that we have a greater understanding about our world. In this section, we will explore the methods that scientists use to discover and develop these explanations.

What Is Science?

Science is both a body of knowledge and a way of understanding how the world works. Science involves the application of human intelligence and creativity to explore, discover, and explain how the natural and physical world works. Scientific explanations are developed when people make observations and then describe them based on what they already know about the world. An observation is a careful inspection of an object or an event in which the observer uses his or her senses. This leads to asking questions, which can lead to experimenting, collecting and organizing data, and drawing valid conclusions. Scientific explanations are subject to change whenever new observations challenge existing explanations. By exploring the historical development of scientific concepts and the individuals who contributed to scientific knowledge, you can better understand scientific inquiry and the relationship between science and society.

Early Science

At one time, scientific discovery and knowledge was based on opinions and ideas that attempted to explain observations. An example of this is the account of Jean Baptiste van Helmont, a sixteenth-century Dutch physician. He supported the theory of spontaneous generation—that nonliving material could produce living organisms. A **theory** is an explanation of natural phenomena supported by a large body of scientific evidence obtained from many different investigations and observations. Van Helmont devised an experiment similar to the one in Figure 1.1, to demonstrate the spontaneous generation of mice. The procedure involved throwing some grains of wheat and a soiled shirt into an open container, and then placing it in a damp cellar for about 21 days.

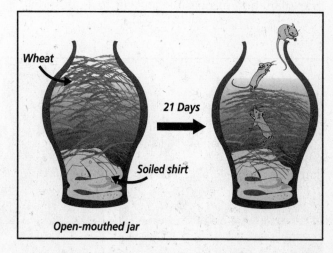

Wheat

21 Days

Soiled shirt

Open-mouthed jar

Figure 1.1 Van Helmont's experiment was designed to prove the theory of spontaneous generation.

After the 21 days, van Helmont discovered that there were mice in the container. Also, the amount of wheat was less, so van Helmont concluded that the wheat, not the soiled shirt, spontaneously became mice.

The experiment that van Helmont conducted failed to recognize the origins of living matter. If van Helmont had conducted his experiment in a location other than a damp basement, his results probably would have been different. It might seem silly to believe that wheat combined with an old soiled shirt would produce baby mice in a damp cellar. However, the theory of spontaneous generation seemed reasonable at that time based on van Helmont's observations and those of others, existing ideas on the origins of life, and available scientific tools. In the modern view, a scientific explanation is accepted when it is consistent with experimental and observational evidence, and when it leads to accurate conclusions.

✅ **CHECK FOR UNDERSTANDING** What experiment did van Helmont devise to prove the spontaneous generation of mice?

Scientific Inquiry

Scientific investigations are used to answer questions and explain how things operate in the natural and physical world. Scientific investigations generally use **scientific methods** that involve the following:

- Observing
- Developing questions based on observations
- Developing a **hypothesis**—a testable explanation or possible answer to a question
- Developing an **experiment**—a set of procedures that lead to testing a hypothesis
- Collecting and organizing data from the experiment
- Developing inferences—explanations based on the observable results of an experiment
- Publishing results for peer review

The Scientific View of the World

The scientific view is founded upon direct observation of the world around us. To think scientifically one must critically examine events and explanations and attempt to avoid all sources of bias. Keep in mind that scientific explanations are subject to change. No matter how well one explains a set of observations, it is possible that another explanation will fit just as well or better. In science, this testing and improving of explanations occurs continually.

The scientific view involves many individuals doing many different kinds of work, such as those in Figure 1.2. These people include scientists, engineers, mathematicians, physicians, technicians, computer programmers, librarians, and others. They contribute to the scientific view with data gathering, the building of science tools and instruments, and/or communicating. It is appropriate in science to turn to knowledgeable sources of information by seeking people who specialize in different disciplines. Well-accepted scientific explanations have been supported by the process of scientific testing and involve the contributions of many different individuals.

✅ **CHECK FOR UNDERSTANDING** Why does a scientific discovery involve the assistance of many people besides scientists?

Figure 1.2 The scientific view of the world involves a variety of individuals who support scientists in their work.

Testing Proposed Explanations

Suppose your teacher brought in several brands of paper towels and asked the class the following question: *Which brand of paper towel is most absorbent?* This is the beginning of a scientific inquiry. Your teacher then instructed the class to think about ways to answer this question. The teacher also brought in magnifiers, rulers, beakers, cylinders, plastic tubs, eyedroppers, and balance scales. Applied thinking skills will be used to design a plan to test the absorbencies of the different brands of paper towels.

Scientific Inquiry and Testing

Inquiry involves asking questions. These questions should lead to forming a plan or plans to test the paper towel samples. Among the questions the class might consider before developing a testing plan are:

- What is absorbency?
- What aspects of paper towel absorbency can be investigated using the available materials?
- What factors need to be controlled in order to compare testing results?
- Will you buy the most absorbent brand of paper towel after you complete your tests?

Inquiry involves examining the questions used to formulate a good experimental design. The class might consider testing the various brands of paper towels to determine which paper towel absorbs the greatest volume of water, or absorbs the most water in a given period of time, or has the greatest change in mass when immersed in a specific amount of water. Solutions to each of these investigative possibilities can be explored through a research plan and the development of a hypothesis to test methods being considered.

Development of a Research Plan

When a scientist defines a problem for investigation, such as exploring the absorbency of several brands of paper towels, it usually is followed by a search for information about the topic to be investigated. It is important to know what other people have learned about the topic before beginning research. This involves the development of a research plan in which background information can be obtained that will assist in developing a hypothesis and devising an experimental design. Most research plans begin with a thorough library

Figure 1.3 Using the Internet allows a scientist to research a topic quickly and from worldwide sources.

search that can include a review of the literature contained in scientific journals, and a search of library databases and the Internet, as shown in Figure 1.3. Research in the classroom on the topic of paper towel absorbency can even include contacting the various companies that manufacture each of the brands being tested. In addition, it can include a careful review of the tests and results that each company has conducted on their brand of paper towel. Familiarity with the existing research on a topic allows a scientist to avoid repeating investigations already done and to plan the best approach for investigating the problem. In the course of their research, scientists must make judgments about the reliability of and relevance of the information they uncover.

✓ **CHECK FOR UNDERSTANDING** Why is it important to develop a research plan before fully investigating a problem?

Developing a Hypothesis

Next, a scientist will formulate an explanation for the question or problem that can be tested. This explanation is known as a hypothesis. In a cause-and-effect relationship, such as the paper towel absorbency problem, the hypothesis is an educated guess about the outcome of the investigation about which paper towel will absorb the most liquid. Experiments that follow either will or will not support the hypothesis. A hypothesis can never be proven or confirmed with absolute certainty.

In formulating a hypothesis, a scientist should know what is involved in solving the problem based on his or her previous observations and research. The hypothesis is often written as an "if–then" statement or as a statement where you can add, "I think that" to the beginning. If we were to investigate the problem of paper towel absorbency based on the amount or volume of water that a paper towel sample can absorb, a possible hypothesis would be: *If you soak several brands of paper towels in a specific volume of water, then the brand that is most absorbent will soak up the largest volume of water.* This statement is testable and can lead to designing an experiment that will either support or fail to support the hypothesis.

✅ **CHECK FOR UNDERSTANDING** Why is the statement of a hypothesis so critical to the experiment that will follow?

For the paper towel problem, the proposed hypothesis will not prove which paper towel is most absorbent. Additional hypotheses based on surface area absorption and rate of absorption could lead to other experiments, which might indicate another brand of paper towels as being the most absorbent. A hypothesis sets the groundwork for designing an experiment to support or not support it. The following are examples of hypotheses.

- If you exercise strenuously for 10 minutes, then your heart rate will increase.
- If you place a plant near a window, it will grow toward the window because a plant responds to light.
- Wheat and a damp shirt in a cellar do not create mice in 21 days. Only mice can reproduce to make more mice.
- Rotten meat does not turn into flies. Only flies can reproduce to make more flies.

Experimenting

Once a scientist has completed background research on a problem and has developed a hypothesis, he or she designs an experiment to test the hypothesis. An experiment is an investigation consisting of procedures that test a hypothesis by collecting information under controlled conditions.

Controls and Variables

Science experiments usually have a control component. A **control** is the standard in which all conditions are kept the same. This is in contrast to an experimental, or test group. In an experimental group, all conditions are kept the same as the control except for the condition being tested. The condition that is tested in an experiment is known as the **independent variable,** because it is the only variable that affects the outcome of the experiment. When changing the independent variable, the scientist observes or measures a second condition that results from the change.

REGENTS EXAM
Strategies for Success

STEP 1 **READ the Regents Question . . .**
Tomato plants in a garden are not growing well. The gardener hypothesizes that the soil is too acidic. To test this hypothesis accurately, the gardener could do which of the following?

(1) Plant seeds of a different kind of plant.
(2) Move the tomato plant to an area with less sunlight.
(3) Change the pH of the soil.
(4) Reduce the amount of water available to the plant.

STEP 2 **ANALYZE each choice . . .**
(1) Planting seeds of different kinds of plants adds an additional variable to be tested.
(2) Moving the tomato plants to an area of less sunlight will change the light conditions and add an additional variable to be tested.
(3) Changing the pH of the soil will lead to comparing the effect of soil with a higher pH (less acidic) on plant growth.
(4) Reducing the amount of water available to the plants would add an additional variable to be tested.

STEP 3 **CHOOSE the best answer . . .**
Because the gardener's hypothesis is based on the effect of soil pH on tomato plant growth, the correct answer is number 3.

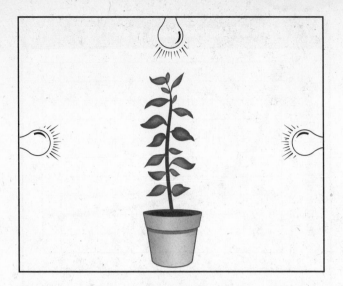 

Figure 1.4 In testing the effect of light on the growth of plant stems, there must be only one variable—the direction of the light source.

This condition in known as the **dependent variable** because it "depends" on the changes made to the independent variable.

If we were to continue our paper towel exploration to determine which of several brands would soak up the largest volume of water, we also would have to control several factors in designing an experiment. Variables to control might include:

- testing each brand with the same volume of water and in the same size beaker or tub;
- testing the same size of toweling;
- soaking each towel for the same amount of time;
- allowing each soaked towel to drip water back into the beaker for the same amount of time.

The brand of towel that leaves the least amount of water remaining in the beaker or tub would be rated the most absorbent. In this case, the independent variable would be the various brands used, while the dependent variable would be how much water each towel absorbed.

If we were to investigate the hypothesis of plant stems growing toward the source of light, we would set up a controlled experiment, such as the one in Figure 1.4. The controls in this type of experiment would include plants of the same species and size, planted in the same type of soil, maintained under the same temperature and soil conditions, and subjected to these conditions for the same length of time. Both groups of plants would be placed in opaque containers of moist

soil. The independent variable, or factor that would vary, would be that one group would receive light only from one direction. We would then compare this group to the control group that received the same total intensity of light, but evenly distributed around the plant. If after a set period of time, the plants receiving directed light demonstrated growth toward the light, while the control plants did not exhibit any measurable change, we have supported the hypothesis. Remember that there should be only one variable tested at a time.

✔ **CHECK FOR UNDERSTANDING** What is the dependent variable in the experiment where we investigated the effect of directed light on plant stems? Explain your answer.

Carrying Out an Investigation

When carrying out an investigation, scientists need tools that enable them to record information as accurately as possible. Selecting scientific equipment and considering the safety precautions required to use it, and planning how to maintain the accuracy of the results are important parts of carrying out an investigation.

The safe and proper use of scientific tools is a key factor in determining accurate results in any investigation. In addition, the number of samples and trials conducted also help determine the accuracy of an investigation. Consider the plant study described previously.

Would the information from testing a plant from the control and a plant from the experimental group provide accurate results?

Proper testing would include using multiple plant samples. In addition, several trials should be conducted to determine if your results are consistent. The same factors apply to paper towel testing. Multiple samples and trials involving each brand would have to be tested to see if the results of the testing were consistent. Repeated trials with large sample sizes provide information that is more accurate and reduce the probability that errors are due to chance.

Observing, Analyzing, and Concluding

During experiments, scientists collect data based on the observations they make. **Data** are all of the information obtained from an experiment, and sometimes are referred to as experimental results.

Gathering and Organizing Data

Scientists organize and analyze data. Scientists make decisions based on their analysis of data. Data can be organized into diagrams, charts, graphs, equations, matrices, and tables, such as Table 1.1 shown below. Sometimes data are expressed in verbal or written form that describe observations. Often, data are expressed in numerical form based on measurements such as time, temperature, length, mass, area, volume, or numerical counts of matter.

To collect the quantitative data from the plant experiment, a scientist would have to measure the length and angle of the stems of the control plant group and the experimental group. These measurements will be taken at the beginning and end of the experiment for comparison. These results can then be recorded. A data table is one way to record and organize the results of

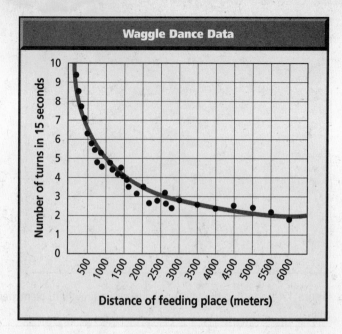

Figure 1.5 Graphs permit scientists to interpret data. This line graph shows an inverse relationship between the distance of food and the number of turns in worker bees' waggle dances.

testing the volume of water absorbed by several different brands of paper toweling. Data tables also can help scientists examine information collected while doing an experiment.

Another way that scientists examine data is to construct a graph. A graph allows the scientist to represent data visually, often making it easier to make comparisons of the data collected. It also can allow scientists to see patterns in data such as those shown in Figure 1.5.

✓ CHECK FOR UNDERSTANDING Describe three ways in which a scientist can collect and organize data.

There are three basic forms of graphs: circle graphs, bar graphs, and line graphs. A scientist must decide which type of graph will be the most effective means of presenting data.

Table 1.1 • Water Absorbency in Different Brands of Paper Towels			
Brand	Amount of Water in Container Before Soaking	Amount of Water in Container After Soaking (60 s)	Amount of Water Absorbed by the Paper Towel
A	150 mL	126 mL	24 mL
B	150 mL	118 mL	32 mL
C	150 mL	132 mL	18 mL

When constructing a graph, there are several rules that should be followed.

- Create a title for your graph.
- The independent variable is plotted on the horizontal or *x*-axis. This is the factor you altered or varied.
- The dependent variable is plotted on the vertical or *y*-axis. This variable is what you discover or measure because of the experiment.
- Create a scale on each axis by marking off equal spaces on each axis. Make sure that each scale covers the range of data collected for each variable. Label the units on each side.
- Make sure your *x*-axis and *y*-axis are titled and units are labeled.
- Data points in a line graph are connected and the lines should not go beyond the data points plotted.

The data collected from the paper towel absorbency testing also can be represented in the form of a bar graph like the one in Figure 1.6. A careful examination of the experimental results represented in the bar graph would indicate that Brand B is the most absorbent brand when absorbing a specific volume of water.

Developing Valid Conclusions

Careful analysis of data collected in an experiment allows a scientist to make decisions about the outcome of the experiment. Those decisions often are referred to collectively as a conclusion.

A scientist will need to determine if the stated hypothesis was supported by the actual results of the experiment. Scientists usually consider data from an experiment valid after that experiment has been repeated several times and yielded similar results. Statistical analysis techniques are often used by scientists to determine if their results were affected by errors in measurement, differences among test samples, or by chance. Once a pattern or relationship can be supported through repeated testing, a scientist then tries to explain these results.

Reporting Results

Because of the nature of science, it is possible that other individuals could have conducted similar experiments and arrived at similar conclusions. Experiments that cannot be repeated, or do not yield similar results, cannot be considered valid.

Research among scientists must be reported clearly and in detail so that other scientists can repeat the investigation and duplicate the results.

The results of investigations are reported in scientific journals or are shared with colleagues during professional meetings. A report describes the hypothesis, including a literature review of previous studies and how the experiment was performed. It also describes data and states the scientist's conclusions. Public discussion and review of an experiment may result in a scientist revising his or her explanation and thinking about additional research.

Peer review is a process in which scientists evaluate the results of scientific investigations and the explanations proposed by other scientists. A peer review can be a presentation, as shown in Figure 1.7 on page 8. It generally includes analysis of experimental procedures, careful examination of evidence, identification of faulty reasoning and statements that go beyond the evidence, and suggestions for alternative explanations for the same observations. Peer review serves as a system of checks and balances for scientific research.

Evidence is a collection of facts offered to support the validity of an idea. Scientific claims must be supported by a large collection of evidence before they are considered valid. Scientific claims that are based on small data samples, biased or inadequately controlled data, and misleading use of numbers, usually come under question.

In science, a hypothesis that is supported by many separate observations and investigations over a long period of time becomes a theory.

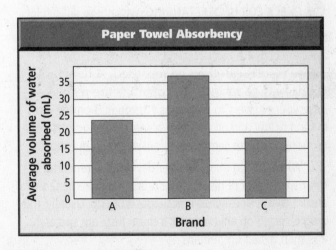

Figure 1.6 Data from the paper towel experiment is represented in this bar graph.

Figure 1.7 A presentation before other scientists is one form of peer review.

A theory results from a continuing process of verification and refinement of many related hypotheses. A valid theory often raises more questions. Theories can change or be refuted as new information and data are derived from experimentation. The theory of evolution began with the observations of naturalists. Over the years, many scientists and others have researched the many aspects of evolution to form one general theory.

✔ CHECK FOR UNDERSTANDING Why is it so difficult for the results of an experiment to become a theory? Explain.

Quick Review

Base your answers to questions 1 through 3 on the information below and on your knowledge of biology. Use one or more complete sentences to answer each question.

When a drug manufacturer develops a new drug to treat some form of disease, the drug should be tested to ensure that it does what it is supposed to do. Usually, the drug is tested on animals and, if these tests are successful, it is then tested on humans.

A drug called Lowervil was developed by a drug company to lower blood pressure. Lowervil has been tested successfully on animals, and the drug company is now ready to test it on humans. The drug company claims that one dose of Lowervil per day will decrease blood pressure in individuals experiencing high blood pressure.

A researcher has been hired to determine whether or not Lowervil lowers blood pressure. Answer the following questions related to the experimental testing of the new drug Lowervil.

1 How should the experimental group and control group be treated differently?

2 Why would it be important to use a large number of people in this experiment?

3 How could the researcher determine if the drug is effective in reducing blood pressure?

Base your answers to questions 4 through 6 on the information and data tables below and on your knowledge of biology. Use one or more complete sentences to answer each question.

Drinking alcohol during pregnancy can cause the class of birth defect known as fetal alcohol syndrome (FAS). Scientists do not yet understand the process by which alcohol causes damage to the fetus. There is evidence, however, that the more the pregnant woman drinks, the greater the chances that the child will be affected and the birth defects will be intellectual and behavioral problems.

Infant Characteristics		
Characteristics (Average)	Alcohol Use During Pregnancy	
	Drinker	Nondrinker
Weeks of development before birth	36.9	38.7
Birth weight (g)	2555	3094
Birth length (cm)	46.8	50.1
Head circumference (cm)	32.1	34.5

Physical Abnormalities Detected in Infants at Birth		
Physical Abnormality	Alcohol Use During Pregnancy	
	Drinker (% of 40 infants)	Nondrinker (% of 40 infants)
Low birth weight	73	12
Small brain	33	0
Flattened nasal bridge	8	0
Abnormal facial features	15	0
Spinal defects	8	0
Heart defects	8	0

4 Do the data in the tables justify scientists' conclusions that alcohol causes physical abnormalities at birth by interfering with the normal development of the fetus? Defend your position with supporting data.

5 What additional data would be needed to better support the scientists' conclusions?

6 Explain why alcohol consumption by the mother is especially harmful during the early stages of pregnancy.

Part A

1 A scientist tested a hypothesis that white-tailed deer would prefer apples over corn as a primary food source. The findings of the test, in which the scientist claimed that the deer preferred apples, were published. Which research technique, if used by the scientist, might result in this claim being questioned?

(1) The scientist observed four deer in different locations at various times of the day.

(2) The scientist observed a total of 500 deer in 20 different locations at various times of the day.

(3) The scientist observed 200 deer in various natural settings, but none in captivity.

(4) The scientist observed 300 deer in various locations in captivity, but none in natural settings.

2 An experimental design included references from prior experiments, materials and equipment, and step-by-step procedures. What else should be included before the experiment can be started?

(1) a set of data

(2) a conclusion based on data

(3) safety precautions to be used

(4) an inference based on results

3 The current knowledge concerning cells is the result of the investigations and observations of many scientists. The work of these scientists forms a well-accepted body of knowledge about cells. This body of knowledge is an example of a

(1) hypothesis   (3) theory

(2) controlled experiment   (4) research plan

4 In his theory, Lamarck suggested that organisms will develop and pass on to offspring variations that they need in order to survive in a particular environment. In a later theory, Darwin proposed that changing environmental conditions favor certain variations that promote the survival of organisms. Which statement is best illustrated by this information?

(1) Scientific theories that have been changed are the only ones supported by scientists.

(2) All scientific theories are subject to change and improvement.

(3) Most scientific theories are the outcome of a single hypothesis.

(4) Scientific theories are not subject to change.

5 The data table below summarizes the results of an investigation in which seeds from the same plant were grown under different conditions of temperature and relative humidity.

Temperature: 20° C Relative Humidity: 20%		Temperature: 31° C Relative Humidity: 95%	
Genes Present in Cells of Organism	Appearance of Organism	Genes Present in Cells of Organism	Appearance of Organism
AA	red	AA	white
Aa	red	Aa	white
aa	white	aa	white

Which conclusion can be drawn from the information in the data table?

(1) Color in this species is determined by genes, only.

(2) Many characteristics are not inherited.

(3) Mutations occur only when plants are grown at low temperatures.

(4) There is an interaction between environment and heredity.

6 Diagrams, tables, and graphs are used by scientists mainly to

(1) design a research plan for an experiment   (3) organize data

(2) test a hypothesis   (4) predict the independent variable

7 The use of technology often alters the equilibrium in ecosystems. With which of the following statements would most scientists agree?

(1) Humans should develop new technology to expand the influence of humans' natural communities.

(2) Humans should learn how to control every aspect of the environment so that damage due to technology can be spread evenly.

(3) Humans should use their knowledge of ecology to consider the needs of future generations of humans and other species.

(4) Humans should develop the uninhabited parts of Earth for human population expansion.

8 Scientific studies have indicated that there is a higher percentage of allergies in babies fed formula containing cow's milk than in breast-fed babies. Which statement represents a valid inference made from these studies?

(1) Milk from cows causes allergic reactions in all infants.

(2) Breast feeding prevents all allergies from occurring.

(3) There is no relationship between drinking cow's milk and having allergies.

(4) Breast milk most likely contains fewer substances that trigger allergies.

9 An experiment was performed to determine the effect of different mineral salts on plant growth. Forty pots containing genetically identical plants were divided into four equal groups and placed in a well-lighted greenhouse. Each pot contained an equal amount of nonmineral potting soil and one plant. Minerals were then added in equal amounts to each experimental group of pots as shown below.

Control Group	Experimental Groups		
	Water + Nitrogen salts	Water + Potassium salts	Water + Phosphorus salts

For the experiment to be valid, what should be added to the control group of pots?

(1) water

(2) nitrogen salts

(3) potassium salts

(4) potassium and phosphorus salts

Part B

10 What is the dependent variable in the experiment summarized in the graph below?

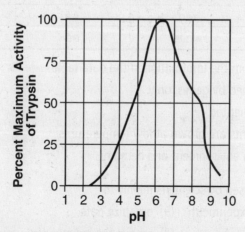

Base your answers to questions 11 through 14 on the data table and information below and on your knowledge of biology. The data table shows water temperatures at various depths in an ocean.

Water Temperatures at Various Depths	
Water Depth (meters)	Temperature (˚C)
50	18
75	15
100	12
150	5
200	4

Directions (11–14): Using the information in the data table, construct a line graph on the grid following the directions below.

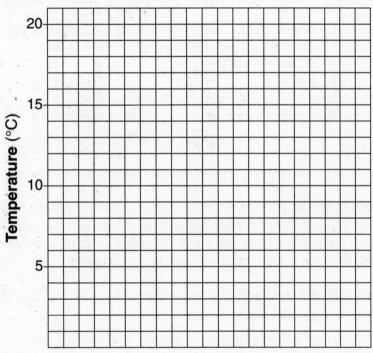

Water Depth (m)

11 Mark an appropriate scale on the axis labeled "Water Depth (m)."

12 Plot the data on the grid. Surround each point with a small circle and connect the points.

Example:

13 State the general relationship between temperature and water depth.

14 The approximate water temperature at a depth of 125 meters would be closest to

(1) 15°C   (3) 8°C

(2) 13°C   (4) 3°C

15 A student designed an investigation to determine the effect of temperature on the rate of seed germination. The student placed moist filter paper in each of four culture dishes. Ten bean seeds were placed on the filter paper in each dish. The four dishes were numbered and placed in the dark at different temperatures as follows: Dish 1: 10°C, Dish 2: 15°C, Dish 3: 20°C, Dish 4: 25°C. The total number of germinated seeds in each culture dish was counted each day for two weeks. Which data table is best for recording the results of this investigation?

(1)

Petri Dish	Day	Temperature	Amount of Light
1			
2			
3			
4			

(3)

Day	Temperature			
	Dish 1	Dish 2	Dish 3	Dish 4

(2)

Petri Dish	Amount of Water	Number of Germinated Seeds	Amount of Light
1			
2			
3			
4			

(4)

Day	Number of Germinated Seeds			
	10°C	15°C	20°C	25°C

Part C

Base your answer to question 16 on the information below and on your knowledge of biology.

You are the head of the research division of the Leafy Lettuce Company. Your company is experimenting with growing lettuce using hydroponic technology. Hydroponic technology involves growing plants in containers of growth solution in a greenhouse. No soil is used. The growth solution that the company uses contains water, nitrogen, and phosphorus. The company wants to know if adding iron to this formula will improve lettuce growth.

16 Briefly describe how to test the effect of the formula with iron added. In your description, be sure to:
- state a hypothesis to be tested in the new experiment
- state how the control group will be treated differently from the experimental group
- identify *two* factors that must be kept the same in both the experimental and control groups
- state what type of data should be collected to support or refute the hypothesis

17 With only the materials list supplied below and common laboratory equipment, design an investigation that would show how a change in pH would affect the activity of enzyme *X*. Your design need only include detailed procedure and a data table.

> *Materials*
> Enzyme *X*
> Sugar *C* solution
> Indicators
> Substances of various pH values—
>   vinegar (acidic)
>   water (neutral)
>   baking soda (basic)

Procedure:
Data Table:

Answer all questions in this part.

Directions (18–20): Base your answers on the information and data table below and on your knowledge of biology.

You are going to devise an experiment to determine if a person can squeeze a clothespin more times in a 1-minute period by exercising first or by NOT exercising first.

18 State a hypothesis for your experiment.

19 Complete the data table below with the correct column name.

Trial 1	Pulse Count at Rest	
Student 1		
Student 2		
Student 3		

20 Identify a tool or tools needed to collect these data.

Directions (21): Base your answer on your knowledge of biology.

The diagram below shows a partial setup of a laboratory activity used by a student during an investigation of diffusion. The U-shaped tube contains sugar solutions separated by a membrane. The concentrations of the sugar solutions are not equal. Water can pass through the membrane, but sugar cannot. The first drawing shows the tube at the beginning of the activity. The second tube shows the tube after time has lapsed.

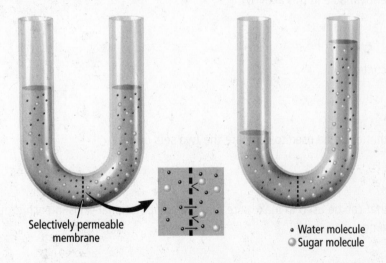

Selectively permeable membrane

• Water molecule
○ Sugar molecule

21 Which statement best explains why the liquid levels are not equal on each side of the U-shaped tube after a period of time has lapsed?

  (1) Water molecules diffused to the side with the greater sugar concentration.

  (2) Pressure was applied to the surface of the liquid on the right side of the tube.

  (3) Water molecules diffused to the side with the smaller sugar concentration.

  (4) The U-shaped tube was submerged into a hot-water bath.

Directions (22–26): Base your answers on the information and data table below and on your knowledge of biology.

A biology class wanted to conduct an experiment to determine if exercise affects their ability to think. They planned to divide the class into two groups. In Group 1, the students would use a stop watch to calculate the time required to complete a page of simple math problems. In Group 2, the students would run in place for a 2-minute period and rest for a 1-minute period. Then, the students would use a stop watch to determine the length of time required to complete the same page of simple math problems. The data collected are shown below:

Data Table		
	Time Required to Complete Math Page (minutes)	
Student 1	Group 1	Group 2
Student 1	4.5	3.4
Student 2	5.2	4.0
Student 3	5.0	3.7
Student 4	3.7	4.5
Student 5	4.3	3.0

22 What is the independent variable in this activity?

23 What is the dependent variable in this activity?

24 Which group is the control?

25 Describe a method that could be used to compare the two sets of data.

26 Describe a method that can be used to make sure that the computational skills in each group are approximately the same.

active transport
cell
chloroplast
cytoplasm
cytoskeleton
diffusion
homeostasis

lysosome
mitochondria
nucleus
organ
organelles
organism
organ system

plasma membrane
response
ribosome
selective permeability
stimulus
tissue
vacuole

Everything in our world is either living or nonliving. However, telling the difference between a living thing and a nonliving thing is not always easy. Why is a tree considered a living thing, while a rock is not? How are living things similar to and different from nonliving things, and how are living things similar to and different from each other?

Living Versus Nonliving

How do you know that something is living? You might say that living things grow. Yes, living things can increase in size, but so do some non-living things like gases, foams, and the flames in Figure 2.1. So how do you decide whether a thing is living or nonliving?

Over time, biologists have established that all living things share certain characteristics. These characteristics include:

- a cellular organization,
- reproduction that passes hereditary information to offspring,
- growth and development, and
- adjusting to surroundings to maintain internal stability.

An **organism** is anything that possesses all of the characteristics of life. Sometimes, nonliving things have one or more of these characteristics, but to be considered living, something must have all of them.

Living Things are Organized

An orderly cellular or organismal structure is one of the characteristics that biologists use to determine if something is living or nonliving.

Figure 2.1 Although a flame can increase in size and produce more flames, it cannot adjust if its surroundings change.

All living things are made of one or more cells. All cells contain the information needed to carry on the processes essential for life. All living things maintain this cellular organization. This orderly structure enables the parts of an organism to work together as a living system.

Living Things Reproduce

The ability to produce offspring is another characteristic of life. While an individual organism cannot live forever, the hereditary information for that organism can be passed to its offspring by reproduction. The offspring, in turn, pass this information to their offspring, and so on through subsequent generations. Life continues because hereditary information is passed on by reproduction.

Living Things Grow and Develop

All organisms begin life as a cell. A unicellular organism remains nearly the same size all of its life but can undergo development. For a multicellular organism, a cell divides into new cells, these cells increase in size and divide, and new structures form. A multicellular organism also goes through many developmental changes during its life.

The amount of time required for growth and development varies greatly among organisms. A bacterium might exist only hours before dividing into two new cells. Some insects complete their lives in a few months. However, a redwood tree might grow for centuries.

Living Things Adjust to Their Surroundings

Organisms constantly interact with the nonliving and living things in their surroundings. For example, a sunflower's "face" turns toward the Sun as it appears to move across the sky throughout the day. You might shiver when stepping outside on a cold winter morning. A bony fish, as shown in Figure 2.2, can sense living and nonliving objects in its surroundings. Anything in an organism's external or internal environment that causes the organism to react is a **stimulus.** A reaction to a stimulus is a **response.**

All living things have the ability to respond to stimuli in their environments. Even as organisms adjust to changes in their environments, they also must be able to maintain internal conditions in order to carry out life-sustaining processes. For example, in humans, a nearly constant internal

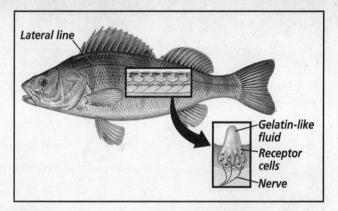

Figure 2.2 A fish's brain receives signals from the lateral line that allows the fish to locate living and nonliving things in its environment.

temperature and the proper amount of water in cells must be maintained in order to function properly.

✓ **CHECK FOR UNDERSTANDING** Identify the stimulus and the response in the following situation: A dog sees a rabbit and chases it.

Regulation of an organism's internal environment to maintain conditions suitable for its survival is known as **homeostasis.** Without the ability to regulate its internal environment, an organism would die. Homeostasis occurs in all living things—another characteristic of life.

Quick Review

1 List the four characteristics of life shared by all organisms.

2 Anything that possesses all of life's characteristics is called a(n)
   (1) stimulus   (3) homeostasis
   (2) organism   (4) reproduction

3 How do most organisms ensure continuation of life?

4 An organism's regulation of its internal environment to maintain stability is called
   (1) homeostasis   (3) organization
   (2) structure   (4) stimulus

5 What is the difference between a living and a nonliving thing?

6 What is a response?

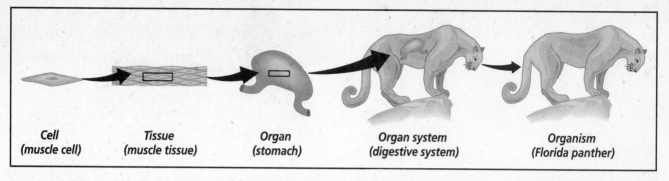

Cell
(muscle cell)

Tissue
(muscle tissue)

Organ
(stomach)

Organ system
(digestive system)

Organism
(Florida panther)

Figure 2.3 The levels of organization for a complex multicellular organism are cell, tissue, organ, organ system, and organism.

From a Cell to an Organism

Cells are the basic units of all living organisms. They perform functions necessary to sustain life. In multicellular organisms, groups of cells that work together to perform a specific function are called a **tissue.** Two or more tissues that work together are called an **organ.** An organ performs specific complex functions within the organism. For example, cells make up cardiac muscle tissue. Cardiac muscle tissue works with other tissues in the heart, which is the organ that pumps blood. Multiple organs that work together form an **organ system.** The heart, arteries, veins, and capillaries are parts of the circulatory system that carries blood throughout the body.

✅ **CHECK FOR UNDERSTANDING** Arrange the following from smallest to largest: *organ, cell, organ system, tissue.*

All organ systems work together for the survival of the organism. An example of cell specialization and organization for a complex organism is shown in Figure 2.3. The digestive system works together with other organ systems to ensure the survival of this panther.

Cellular Organization

Just as organ systems are coordinated and work together for the survival of an organism, the parts of a cell also must be coordinated and work together for the survival of the cell. A cell is covered by the **plasma membrane.** It is a flexible boundary between a cell and its environment. All cells contain small structures called **organelles** that perform specific functions. Organelles work together to carry out metabolic processes necessary for a cell's survival. Membranes surround many organelles. The absence or presence of

membrane-bound organelles determines cell type, as shown in Figure 2.4. A cell that does not contain membrane-bound organelles is called a prokaryotic cell. Bacteria are prokaryotic organisms. A cell that has membrane-bound organelles is called a eukaryotic cell. Some unicellular organisms and most multicellular organisms are composed of eukaryotic cells.

The Plasma Membrane

Phospholipids, proteins, and carbohydrates are the primary components of the plasma membrane. The structural model of the plasma membrane is called the fluid mosaic model. Like a fluid, the phospholipids move within the membrane.

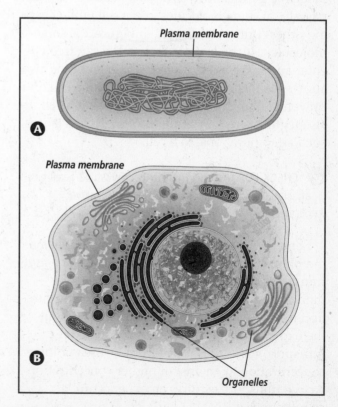

Plasma membrane

Ⓐ

Plasma membrane

Ⓑ

Organelles

Figure 2.4 Cell types are either prokaryotic **A** or eukaryotic **B.**

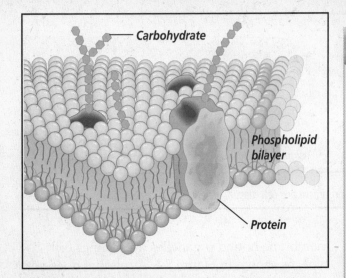

Figure 2.5 The phospholipid and protein molecules are free to move sideways within the boundaries of the plasma membrane.

The proteins also move easily among the phospholipids and create a "mosaic," or a pattern, on the plasma membrane's surface.

The plasma membrane, shown in Figure 2.5, separates a cell from its environment, controls which molecules enter and leave a cell, and recognizes chemical signals. It maintains homeostasis within a cell by being selectively permeable. **Selective permeability** is a process that allows the passage of some molecules into a cell while keeping others out. As indicated in Figure 2.6, some molecules, such as water molecules, can freely enter and leave a cell. The plasma membrane also allows for the excretion of wastes from a cell and prevents other substances from entering a cell. It also regulates certain amounts of other substances, such as sodium ions, in a cell.

✅ **CHECK FOR UNDERSTANDING** How would a cell be affected if the plasma membrane lost its selective permeability?

Some molecules can pass through the plasma membrane by the processes of diffusion or active transport. **Diffusion** occurs when molecules randomly move from an area of higher concentration to an area of lower concentration without the expenditure of cellular energy. In **active transport,** molecules move from an area of lower concentration to an area of higher concentration. Active transport requires an expenditure of cellular energy.

Strategies for Success

STEP 1 READ the Regents Question . . .
Which statement best describes the plasma membrane of a living plant cell?

(1) It is composed of proteins and carbohydrates only.

(2) It selectively regulates the passage of substances into and out of a cell.

(3) It has the same permeability to all substances found inside or outside a cell.

(4) It is a double protein layer with floating lipid molecules.

STEP 2 ANALYZE each choice . . .

(1) The make up of a plasma membrane includes proteins, carbohydrates, and phospholipids.

(2) A living plasma membrane is selectively permeable allowing the passage of some substances but not others.

(3) Small molecules, such as water, can pass through a cell's plasma membrane but larger molecules cannot.

(4) A plasma membrane is composed of a phospholipid bilayer with proteins embedded in it.

STEP 3 CHOOSE the best answer . . .
After considering all of the options, the correct answer is number 2 because only living membranes are selectively permeable.

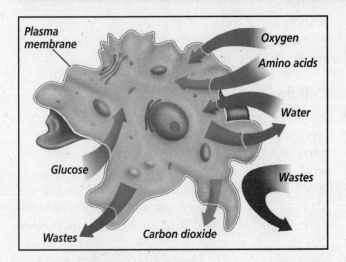

Figure 2.6 The plasma membrane regulates the movement of substances into and out of the cell.

In a multicellular organism, cells communicate with one another. Embedded within the phospholipid layer of the plasma membrane are proteins that serve as receptor molecules. These receptors identify and bind with specific chemical signals, such as hormones and antibodies, to aid in cellular communication. These signals generally give some kind of instructions to a cell that might modify cell function.

Transport of Materials Inside a Cell

You have learned that the plasma membrane regulates the movement of materials into and out of a cell. How does material move inside of a cell?

The **cytoplasm** is the main component inside of a cell. It is a clear, gelatinous fluid. However, unlike dessert gelatin, cytoplasm flows and moves around a cell. In a prokaryotic cell, most of the metabolic processes take place in the cytoplasm. In a eukaryotic cell, organelles suspended in the cytoplasm perform the metabolic processes.

The cytoplasm contains a framework called the **cytoskeleton.** It is composed of microtubules—thin, hollow rods made of protein—and microfilaments—solid protein fibers. This network of rods and filaments helps maintain the shape of a cell and allows for cellular movement. It also provides a system by which materials and organelles move within a cell. Figure 2.7 shows how the cytoskeleton connects organelles.

Information Storage in a Cell

Just as a computer needs a hard drive to store the information used to make it operate, a cell needs a storage unit to hold all of its operating information. The **nucleus,** as shown in Figure 2.8A on page 18, is the organelle in a eukaryotic cell that contains DNA—hereditary material. DNA contains the instructions for making proteins. Every part of a cell depends on proteins. Since the nucleus holds the instructions for making proteins, it manages cellular function by controlling the activities of all the organelles.

Building Proteins in a Cell

The nucleus contains an organelle called the nucleolus, which makes ribosomes. **Ribosomes** translate the directions from DNA and build proteins. Unlike many other organelles, ribosomes are not membrane-bound. In order to build proteins, ribosomes and copies of the hereditary material must leave the nucleus and enter the cytoplasm of a cell.

In the cytoplasm, ribosomes remain free or attach to the endoplasmic reticulum, an organelle that is the site of cellular chemical reactions. Endoplasmic reticulum (ER) with ribosomes attached is called rough ER, as shown in Figure 2.8B. The proteins made in the rough ER carry out particular functions. They may be released from a cell, bound in the plasma membrane, or move to other organelles. Free-floating ribosomes produce proteins that perform functions in the cytoplasm itself.

Proteins are transferred from ribosomes to another organelle called the Golgi apparatus. The Golgi apparatus, as shown in Figure 2.8C, is a system of flattened tubular membranes that sorts and packs the proteins before sending them to their appropriate destinations.

Storage in a Cell

Vacuoles are membrane-bound spaces in the cytoplasm used for the temporary storage of materials. Vacuoles store materials needed by a cell, such as food and enzymes. Some vacuoles are used for the temporary storage of wastes. Plant cells usually have one large vacuole, while some animal cells contain a few small vacuoles.

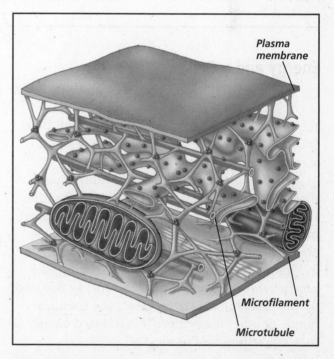

Plasma membrane

Microfilament

Microtubule

Figure 2.7 The cytoskeleton of a eukaryotic cell acts like a highway for the movement of organelles.

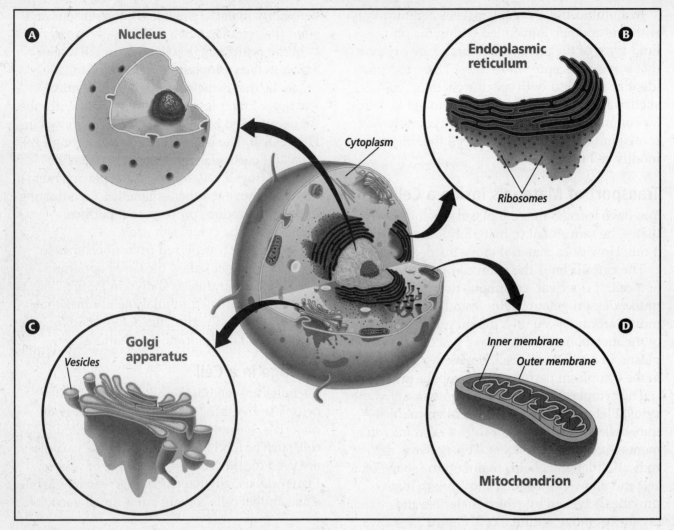

Figure 2.8 Organelles, such as **A** the nucleus, **B** endoplasmic reticulum, **C** Golgi apparatus, and **D** mitochondrion, have specific cellular functions.

Energy and a Cell

All of the metabolic processes that occur in a cell, such as protein building and transportation, require energy. Two organelles—mitochondrion (plural, *mitochondria*) and the chloroplast—can transform energy for use within a cell.

Mitochondria are membrane-bound organelles that transform energy stored in food molecules. Each mitochondrion is surrounded by a double membrane that consists of an outer membrane and a highly folded inner membrane, as shown in Figure 2.8D. Molecules that store energy are produced on the inner folds. The energy released by the mitochondria comes from the chemical bonds of other molecules. This released energy fuels all activities of a cell.

✅ **CHECK FOR UNDERSTANDING** What organelles transform energy stored in food to perform metabolic processes?

Chloroplasts are found in some protists and some cells of plants. A chloroplast has a double membrane, consisting of an outer membrane and a folded inner membrane, as shown in Figure 2.9 on page 19. The inner membrane is arranged into stacks called grana. The grana contain the structures called thylakoids that can trap the energy in sunlight. The chloroplasts transform light energy to chemical energy during the process of photosynthesis. This chemical energy is stored in the bonds of sugar molecules produced by some plant cells or protists.

The number of chloroplasts or mitochondria in a cell depends on the function of a cell. A cell that requires a high amount of energy to function can contain many mitochondria. For example, muscle cells require much energy and contain a high number of mitochondria. In contrast, skin cells use little energy and contain few mitochondria.

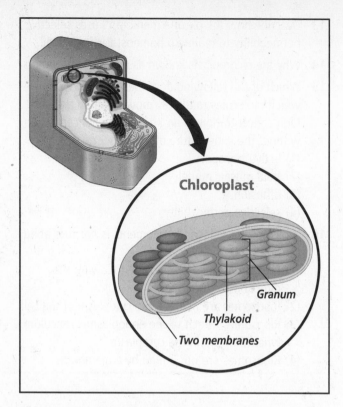

Chloroplast

Granum

Thylakoid

Two membranes

Figure 2.9 Chloroplasts are surrounded by a double membrane and function during photosynthesis.

Waste Disposal in a Cell

How does a cell dispose of any waste products? In an animal cell, the process begins with **lysosomes**—organelles that contain digestive enzymes. Lysosomes help digest food particles, trapped viruses, or bacteria and excess or worn out organelles. What prevents a lysosome from destroying the cell it is in? The membrane surrounding the lysosome separates the lysosome's digestive enzymes from the rest of a cell. After materials are broken down by a lysosome, the waste exits a cell through the plasma membrane.

✔ **CHECK FOR UNDERSTANDING** How does a cell break down waste materials?

Prokaryotic Cells and Eukaryotic Cells

You have learned that most unicellular organisms consist of a prokaryotic cell and multicellular organisms consist of eukaryotic cells. You also know that eukaryotic cells contain membrane-bound organelles that perform cellular metabolic processes. In addition, a complex organism has tissues, organs, and organ systems that work together for the survival of the organism. How does a unicellular organism function despite lacking the levels of organization present in more complex organisms?

As mentioned earlier, many metabolic processes in prokaryotic organisms are performed in the cytoplasm, not in membrane-bound organelles. Unicellular eukaryotic organisms have structures that act in a manner similar to the tissues, organs, and organ systems found in multicellular organisms, enabling them to perform all of the life processes needed to maintain homeostasis. To help you understand this concept, Table 2.1 compares prokaryotic cells to eukaryotic cells, their cell parts, and what those parts do.

Table 2.1 • Comparison of Prokaryotic and Eukaryotic Cells			
Cell Part	Function	Prokaryotic	Eukaryotic
Plasma membrane	Maintains homeostasis	Present	Present
Cytoplasm	Transports materials	Present	Present
Nucleus	Cell control center	Absent	Present
Nucleolus	Makes ribosomes	Absent	Present
Ribosome	Builds proteins	Present	Present
Endoplasmic reticulum (ER)	Chemical reactions	Absent	Present
Golgi apparatus	Sorts and transports	Absent	Present
Vacuole	Storage	Absent	Present in some
Chloroplast	Transforms energy	Absent	Present in some
Mitochondrion	Releases energy	Absent	Present
Lysosome	Digests material	Absent	Present in some

7 Which of the following organelles builds proteins?
   (1) lysosome   (3) nucleus
   (2) ribosome   (4) vacuole

8 Compare the number of vacuoles in plant cells and animal cells.

9 Which of the following is a group of cells that works together to perform a specific function?
   (1) organ system   (3) tissue
   (2) organ   (4) organism

10 Brain cells require a large amount of energy to function. Which organelles might be numerous in a brain cell?

11 The digestive enzymes in lysosomes break down food particles and worn out organelles. Why don't these enzymes digest the cell itself?

12 What is the structural model of the plasma membrane called? Explain.

13 Describe how the plasma membrane uses selective permeability to maintain homeostasis in the cell.

14 Why are chloroplasts known as energy transformers?

15 Which of the following describes the process by which molecules randomly move from an area of high concentration to an area of low concentration without the expenditure of energy?
   (1) active transport
   (2) fluid mosaic model
   (3) diffusion
   (4) selective permeability

16 Which of the following statements is *not* true about ribosomes?
   (1) Ribosomes build proteins by following the directions of the DNA.
   (2) Ribosomes are made in the cytoplasm of the cell.
   (3) Ribosomes attach to the endoplasmic reticulum when they are in the cytoplasm.
   (4) Ribosomes are not bound by a membrane.

Part A

1 The diagram below represents a cell in water. Formulas of molecules that can move freely across the cell membrane are shown. Some molecules are located inside the cell and others are in the water outside the cell.

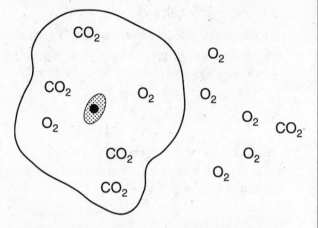

Based on the distribution of these molecules, what would most likely happen after a period of time?

(1) The concentration of O_2 will increase inside the cell.

(2) The concentration of CO_2 will remain the same inside the cell.

(3) The concentration of O_2 will remain the same outside the cell.

(4) The concentration of CO_2 will decrease outside the cell.

2 Which statement describing the cells in a body system is correct?

(1) Each cell in the system is identical to the other cells in the system, and each cell works independently of the other cells.

(2) Some cells in the system may be different from the other cells in the system, but all cells are coordinated and work together.

(3) Each cell in the system is different from the other cells in the system, and each cell works independently of the other cells.

(4) All cells in the system are identical to each other and work together.

3 Every single-celled organism is able to survive because it carries out

(1) metabolic activities

(2) autotrophic nutrition

(3) heterotrophic nutrition

(4) sexual reproduction

4 Which of the following is a structure that performs a specialized function within a cell?

(1) organ system

(2) tissue

(3) organelle

(4) organ

5 Both a deer and a tree react to changes in their external surroundings, helping them to maintain a constant internal environment. This statement describes

(1) predation

(2) homeostasis

(3) antibiotic resistance

(4) autotrophic nutrition

6 While viewing a slide of rapidly moving sperm cells, a student concludes that these cells require a large amount of energy to maintain their activity. The organelles that most directly provide this energy are known as

(1) vacuoles

(2) ribosomes

(3) chloroplasts

(4) mitochondria

7 In a cell, all organelles work together to carry out

(1) diffusion

(2) active transport

(3) information storage

(4) metabolic processes

8 Which statement regarding the functioning of the cell membrane of all organisms is *not* correct?

(1) The cell membrane forms a boundary that separates the cellular contents from the outside environment.

(2) The cell membrane is capable of receiving and recognizing chemical signals.

(3) The cell membrane forms a barrier that keeps all substances that might harm the cell from entering the cell.

(4) The cell membrane controls the movement of molecules into and out of the cell.

9 An example of a reaction to a stimulus is

(1) a boy smelling a flower

(2) eyes blinking due to smoke in the air

(3) a person tapping on the shoulder of a friend

(4) a loud clap of thunder following lightning

10 Which life process is indicated by the arrows in the diagram of an amoeba shown below?

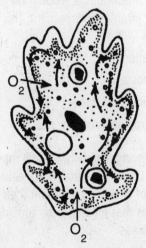

(1) digestion   (3) fermentation

(2) excretion   (4) transport

11 Anything that possesses all of the characteristics of life is called

(1) an organ   (3) a stimulus

(2) an organism   (4) a vector

12 In multicellular organisms, cells must be able to communicate with each other. Structures that enable most cells to communicate with each other are known as

(1) pathogenic agents

(2) chloroplasts

(3) antibiotics

(4) receptor molecules

13 Which of the following statements does *not* describe a characteristic of life?

(1) All living things maintain a cellular organization.

(2) All living things pass on hereditary information through reproduction.

(3) All living things grow and develop.

(4) All living things move.

14 Which letter in the diagram below indicates the structure that is most closely associated with protein building?

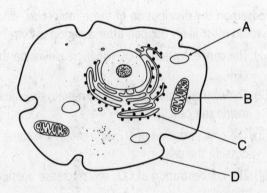

(1) *A*   (3) *C*

(2) *B*   (4) *D*

Base your answers to questions 15 through 17 on the diagram below, which shows some of the specialized organelles in a single-celled organism, and on your knowledge of biology.

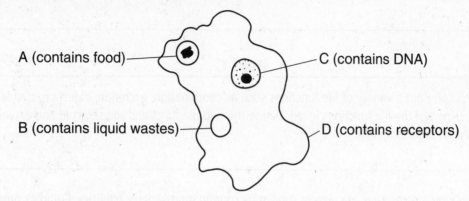

A (contains food)

C (contains DNA)

B (contains liquid wastes)

D (contains receptors)

15 Write the letter of *one* of the labeled organelles and state the name of that organelle.

16 Explain how the function of the organelle you selected in question 15 assists in the maintenance of homeostasis.

_____

17 Identify a system in the human body that performs a function similar to that of the organelle you selected in question 16.

_____

18 In desert environments, organisms that cannot maintain a constant internal body temperature, such as snakes and lizards, rarely go out during the hot, sunny daylight hours. They stay in the shade, under rocks, or in burrows during the day. Explain how this behavior helps maintain homeostasis in these organisms.

_____

19 Substance *X* has a unique characteristic in that it fluoresces (glows) when exposed to ultraviolet light. An investigator added substance *X* to a dish containing a culture of cells. The investigator exposed the cells to ultraviolet light and found that substance *X* was highly concentrated only within mitochondria (cell organelles). Which assumption could the investigator make regarding the results of this experiment?

(1) Substance *X* could be used to identify mitochondria in living cells.

(2) Substance *X* could be used to stain nuclei of living cells.

(3) All fluorescent substances will be absorbed by mitochondria.

(4) All mitochondria synthesize fluorescent substances.

20 A student filled a bag of dialysis tubing with a milky-white starch solution and placed the bag in a beaker of iodine-water solution as shown in the diagram below. An hour later, the student observed that the starch solution had turned blue-black (positive test for starch). What is the most probable explanation for the change?

_____

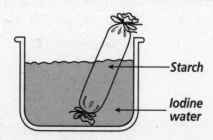

Starch

Iodine water

21 Describe the role of the Golgi apparatus in a eukaryotic cell. _____

_____

_____

_____

Part C

22 All living things carry out a variety of life functions such as coordination, excretion, digestion, circulation, and synthesis. Select *two* of the life functions listed. Define the two life functions you selected and explain how they interact to keep an organism alive.

_____

23 Just like complex organisms, cells are able to survive by coordinating various activities. Complex organisms have a variety of systems, and cells have a variety of organelles that work together for survival. Describe the roles of *two* organelles. In your answer be sure to include:

- the names of *two* organelles and the function of each
- an explanation of how these two organelles work together
- the name of an organelle and the name of a system in the human body that have similar functions

_____

Base your answers to questions 24 through 26 on the graph below and on your knowledge of biology. Use one or more complete sentences to answer each question.

A group of students designed an experiment to study rate of diffusion vs. temperature. The students recorded the time required for fruit drink crystals to dissolve and diffuse evenly throughout four beakers of water at various temperatures.

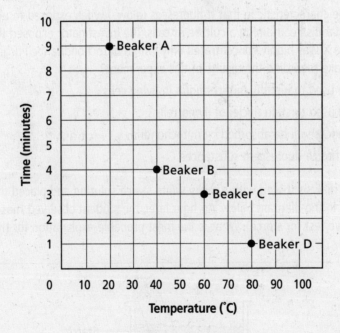

24 Do the data in the graph justify the students' conclusions that rising temperatures speed the process of diffusion? Defend your position with supporting data.

_____

25 Write an appropriate title for this graph on your answer sheet. _____

_____

26 Explain what would be most likely to happen to the diffusion rate of the crystals if the students lowered the temperature in one beaker from 20°C to 0°C.

_____

27 Explain how a one-celled organism is able to function despite lacking the levels of organization present in more complex organisms.

_____

Part D

Answer all questions in this part.

Directions (28–32): Base your answers on the information and diagram below and on your knowledge of biology. The diagram represents some cells on a microscope slide before and after saltwater solution was added to the slide.

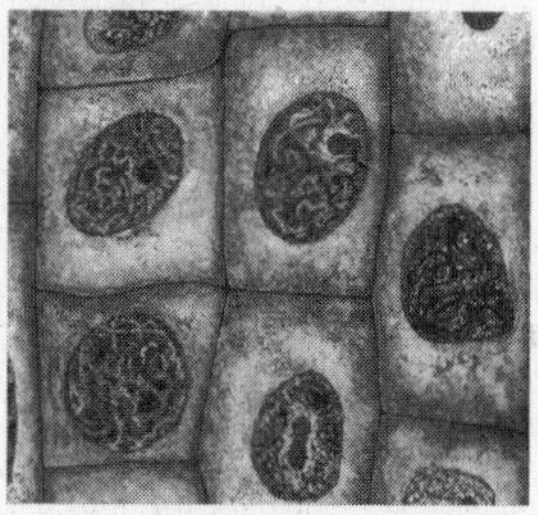

Before    After

28 Describe the process that occurred when a saltwater solution was added to the red onion cells shown on the slide.

_____

29 Why is it desirable to add the saltwater solution to the cell without removing the coverslip? _____

_____

30 Which structure in the cell controls the movement of molecules in and out of the cell?

(1) chloroplasts

(2) endoplasmic reticulum

(3) Golgi apparatus

(4) plasma membrane

31 How does homeostasis of a cell depend upon selective permeability of the plasma membrane? _____

_____

32 Describe what would happen to the onion cell if distilled water were added to the cell. _____

_____

Directions (33–35): Base your answers on the information and diagram below and on your knowledge of biology. The diagram represents a procedure or technique often used in biology laboratory activities.

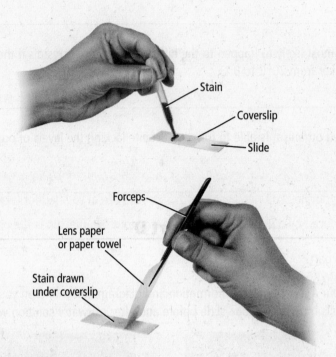

33 Explain what is occurring in the procedure shown. _____

_____

34 Identify a scenario in which this procedure might be used. _____

_____

35 How does staining aid the investigation of cells when viewing them under a microscope? _____

_____

A ll living things—from bacteria to complex organisms like humans—require energy to perform the processes necessary for life. You need energy to digest the cereal you had for breakfast. The cereal was made from grain produced by a plant that needed energy to grow. The Sun is the primary source for all of this energy.

Obtaining Energy

An organism must maintain a stable internal environment to survive. This stable state is called homeostasis and is maintained by a dynamic equilibrium that keeps the internal environment within certain limits. The biochemical processes that are involved are termed *dynamic* because they are not constant. Instead, they fluctuate continuously within a narrow range of conditions.

In order for these biochemical processes to function in living organisms, there must be a source of energy. The energy for most living organisms comes directly or indirectly from the Sun. The Sun's energy is transformed and then is used in living systems.

Photosynthesis: Trapping the Sun's Energy

Certain cells in some organisms can trap the energy in light, transform it, produce energy-rich organic compounds from inorganic compounds, and release oxygen to the environment. This process is called **photosynthesis** and is summarized in the following equation.

$$6CO_2 + 6H_2O \xrightarrow[\text{Chlorophyll}]{\text{Light}} C_6H_{12}O_6 + 6O_2$$

Figure 3.1 The carbohydrates in these foods result from photosynthesis.

The energy-rich organic compounds, called simple sugars, are produced from inorganic raw materials—carbon dioxide and water. Light energy is transformed into the energy in chemical bonds of each simple sugar molecule of glucose—$C_6H_{12}O_6$. Simple sugars then are converted by cells into other organic compounds, like those that make up the foods in Figure 3.1. These organic compounds store energy for cells.

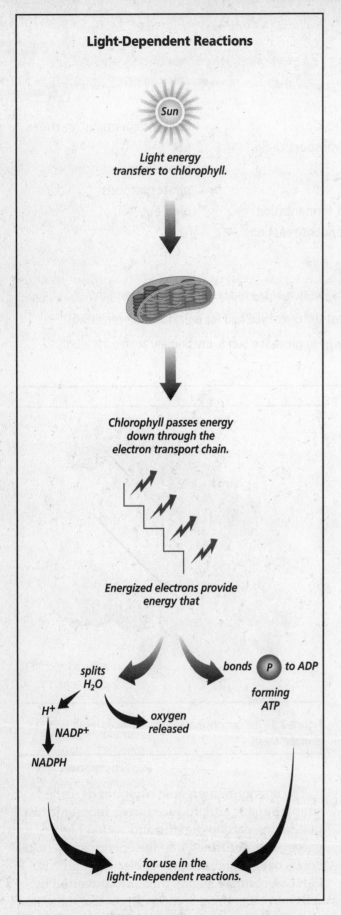

Light-Dependent Reactions

Sun

Light energy
transfers to chlorophyll.

Chlorophyll passes energy
down through the
electron transport chain.

Energized electrons provide
energy that

splits
H_2O

bonds P to ADP

forming
ATP

H^+

oxygen
released

$NADP^+$

NADPH

for use in the
light-independent reactions.

Figure 3.2 Chlorophyll traps light energy that energizes electrons that results in the production of ATP and NADPH.

Photosynthesis is a series of chemical reactions that can take place in some bacteria and in chloroplasts of some plant cells and protists. Recall that chloroplasts are cell organelles that transform light energy into chemical energy. Some reactions of photosynthesis require the presence of light—**light-dependent reactions**—and other reactions do not—**light-independent reactions.**

Light-dependent Phase of Photosynthesis

For cells with chloroplasts, the light-dependent reactions take place in the membranes of the thylakoid discs within the chloroplasts, as shown in Figure 3.2. The thylakoid membranes contain molecules called **pigments** that absorb specific wavelengths of light, thus, trapping the energy in light. Pigments are arranged within the thylakoid membranes in networks called photosystems. The most common pigment found in the photosystems is **chlorophyll.** Chlorophyll absorbs most wavelengths of light except green. Plants appear green because chlorophyll reflects this wavelength instead of absorbing it. If chlorophyll production stops, other pigments that are present can be seen. That is why some leaves seem to change color in autumn.

The light energy absorbed by chlorophyll is transferred to electrons during a process called **photolysis.** Photolysis occurs in thylakoid membranes and results in the breakdown of water molecules into highly energized electrons, hydrogen ions (H^+), and oxygen. This is the oxygen released into the environment. The electrons become part of an **electron transport chain,** a series of proteins embedded in the thylakoid membrane.

The energized electrons are passed along the protein chain, similar to the way that a line of people might pass buckets of water from person to person to put out a fire. The electrons release energy at each step along the chain, just as some of the water might spill from the bucket as it is passed from person to person. This energy can be used by a cell to form **adenosine triphosphate (ATP),** a molecule that stores energy in its chemical bonds. A cell can reuse the energy in ATP molecules when they are broken down. A phosphate group is released and the resulting molecule is ADP. The energized electrons then pass down a second electron transport chain. At the end of this chain, the electrons are still highly energized.

The energy is conserved when these electrons are transferred to the stroma—the fluid surrounding the thylakoid membranes in the chloroplast.

This transfer occurs with the help of an electron carrier molecule called $NADP^+$. When combined with two energized electrons and a hydrogen ion, $NADP^+$ becomes NADPH. NADPH stores the energy until it can transfer it to the stroma. In the stroma, NADPH is used in the light-independent phase of photosynthesis.

Light-independent Phase of Photosynthesis

The light-independent reactions use carbon dioxide, CO_2, and produce a complex carbohydrate, glucose, and additional ATP molecules. This series of reactions—the Calvin cycle—

is called a cycle because one of the molecules formed during the final reaction of the cycle is needed for the first reaction in the cycle.

✓ **CHECK FOR UNDERSTANDING** Why are the light-independent reactions of photosynthesis called a cycle?

The Calvin cycle, as shown in Figure 3.3, begins with carbon fixation. In this process, one molecule of carbon dioxide is "fixed," or added, to a five-carbon sugar called ribulose biphosphate (RuBP) and forms a six-carbon sugar. A series of reactions breaks down this sugar and converts it to two PGAL molecules. PGAL is a three-carbon sugar. Six molecules of PGAL are produced after three cycles. Five of the PGAL molecules are used to form three molecules of RuBP, the material used at the beginning of the Calvin cycle.

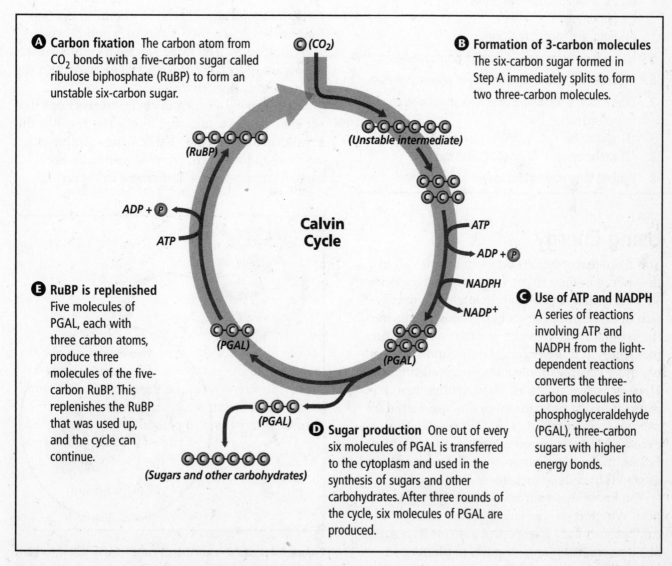

A **Carbon fixation** The carbon atom from CO_2 bonds with a five-carbon sugar called ribulose biphosphate (RuBP) to form an unstable six-carbon sugar.

B **Formation of 3-carbon molecules** The six-carbon sugar formed in Step A immediately splits to form two three-carbon molecules.

C **Use of ATP and NADPH** A series of reactions involving ATP and NADPH from the light-dependent reactions converts the three-carbon molecules into phosphoglyceraldehyde (PGAL), three-carbon sugars with higher energy bonds.

D **Sugar production** One out of every six molecules of PGAL is transferred to the cytoplasm and used in the synthesis of sugars and other carbohydrates. After three rounds of the cycle, six molecules of PGAL are produced.

E **RuBP is replenished** Five molecules of PGAL, each with three carbon atoms, produce three molecules of the five-carbon RuBP. This replenishes the RuBP that was used up, and the cycle can continue.

Figure 3.3 During the Calvin cycle, sugars form from carbon dioxide.

The remaining molecule of PGAL can be used by an organism to make other sugars, complex carbohydrates, and other organic compounds.

Quick Review

1 Write a word equation to represent the process of photosynthesis. Use the terms *carbon dioxide*, *glucose*, *oxygen*, and *water*.

2 Explain how the term *dynamic equilibrium* relates to biochemical processes.

3 Which of the following is the primary source of the energy needed for life?
(1) the Sun   (3) the moon
(2) the Earth   (4) water

4 Which of the following reactions takes place in the stroma of the chloroplast?
(1) carbon fixation
(2) light-independent reactions
(3) photolysis
(4) light-dependent reactions

5 Name the raw materials used in photosynthesis.

6 Describe the role of chlorophyll in photosynthesis.

7 Which of the following uses carbon dioxide to form sugars?
(1) photolysis   (3) chlorophyll
(2) Krebs cycle   (4) Calvin cycle

8 Explain why some plant leaves appear green.

Using Energy

You have learned that some organisms can use the energy in light to convert inorganic molecules, such as carbon dioxide and water, into energy-rich organic compounds like glucose. Cells in these organisms then can use the energy in the molecules of these organic compounds to assemble more complex molecules, such as proteins, DNA, starches, and fats. Photosynthetic organisms often can produce more glucose than they can use to maintain their life processes. This excess glucose is stored in cells of the organism. For example, some plants store the excess glucose as starch in cells of their roots.

You know that your body needs energy to function. Where does this energy come from? You can't absorb light energy and convert it to sugars, but you can eat plants or parts of plants and access the transformed light energy in that way.

When you eat and digest this food, the plant's complex molecules are broken down into simple molecules that can be used by your body cells.

✓ **CHECK FOR UNDERSTANDING** Explain how animals are able to access light energy without chloroplasts.

All cells, including those in your body, can undergo chemical reactions that release energy from organic compounds, such as food. In prokaryotic cells—cells that lack organelles—these reactions occur in the cell's cytoplasm. However, in eukaryotic cells—cells that have organelles—the process begins in the cell's cytoplasm and can continue in mitochondria, like the one in Figure 3.4. Two energy-releasing processes that can occur in most cells are cellular respiration and fermentation.

Cellular Respiration

Cellular respiration is the biochemical process that breaks down food molecules and produces ATP molecules. The three stages of cellular respiration are glycolysis, the citric acid cycle, and the electron transport chain.

Glycolysis is a series of chemical reactions that occurs in the cytoplasm of a cell. The result is the breakdown of glucose, a six-carbon compound, into two molecules of pyruvic acid, a three-carbon compound, as illustrated in Figure 3.5.

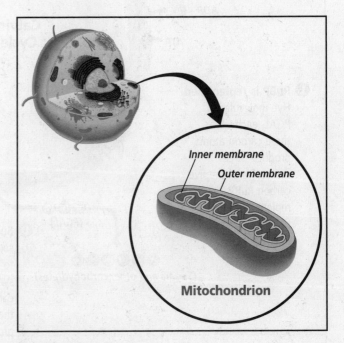

Figure 3.4 Cellular respiration is completed in mitochondria of eukaryotic cells.

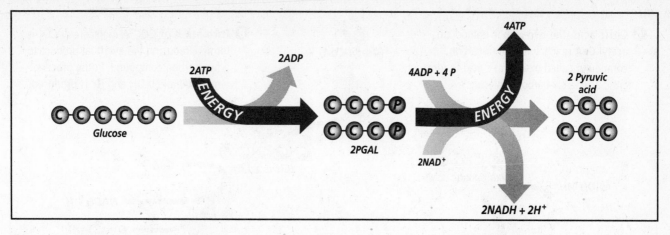

Figure 3.5 Glycolysis results in the breakdown of one molecule of glucose into two molecules of pyruvic acid.

Glycolysis produces four ATP molecules for each molecule of glucose that is broken down. This stage of cellular respiration is **anaerobic**—it does not require the presence of oxygen. Following glycolysis, the pyruvic acid molecules move into mitochondria where cellular respiration is completed. This process uses two ATP molecules.

The final two stages of cellular respiration are **aerobic** processes—they require the presence of oxygen. Before these stages begin, pyruvic acid undergoes a series of reactions. These reactions produce a molecule of carbon dioxide that combines with another molecule to form acetyl-CoA, as shown in Figure 3.6.

The next stage of cellular respiration is the **citric acid cycle,** also called the Krebs cycle. It is a series of chemical reactions that breaks down a molecule of acetyl-CoA to form an ATP molecule and carbon dioxide. Figure 3.7 on page 30 illustrates the reactions in the citric acid cycle.

Each cycle produces one ATP molecule and two carbon dioxide molecules. Because glycolysis produces two molecules of pyruvic acid from one glucose molecule, each glucose molecule is processed through the citric acid cycle twice. This means that each glucose molecule yields two ATP molecules during this stage of cellular respiration. The citric acid cycle uses two electron carriers to pass energized electrons on to the electron transport chain in the inner membrane of a mitochondrion.

The electron transport chain is the last stage in cellular respiration. It is similar to the electron transport chain found in the thylakoid membrane of chloroplasts and is used during photosynthesis. Once the energized electrons are in the inner membrane of a mitochondrion, they pass from protein to protein and slowly release energy at each step. Some of that energy is used to form ATP molecules.

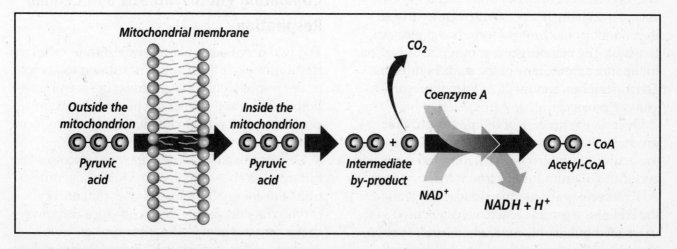

Figure 3.6 After glycolysis, but before the citric acid cycle begins, pyruvic acid undergoes a series of reactions inside a mitochondrion that forms acetyl-CoA.

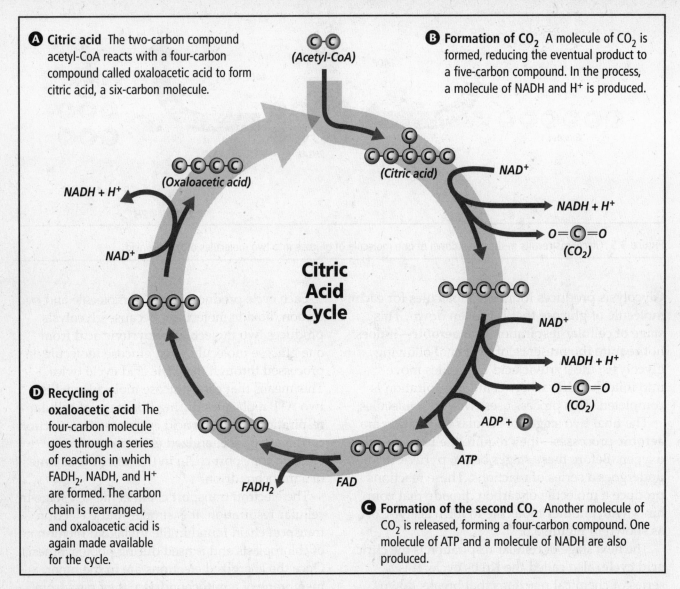

A Citric acid The two-carbon compound acetyl-CoA reacts with a four-carbon compound called oxaloacetic acid to form citric acid, a six-carbon molecule.

B Formation of CO_2 A molecule of CO_2 is formed, reducing the eventual product to a five-carbon compound. In the process, a molecule of NADH and H^+ is produced.

(Acetyl-CoA)

(Citric acid)

(Oxaloacetic acid)

NADH + H^+

NAD^+

NAD^+

NADH + H^+

$O=C=O$
(CO_2)

Citric Acid Cycle

NAD^+

NADH + H^+

$O=C=O$
(CO_2)

ADP + P

ATP

D Recycling of oxaloacetic acid The four-carbon molecule goes through a series of reactions in which $FADH_2$, NADH, and H^+ are formed. The carbon chain is rearranged, and oxaloacetic acid is again made available for the cycle.

$FADH_2$

FAD

C Formation of the second CO_2 Another molecule of CO_2 is released, forming a four-carbon compound. One molecule of ATP and a molecule of NADH are also produced.

Figure 3.7 Acetyl-CoA is broken down during the citric acid cycle, and ATP and carbon dioxide form.

Oxygen is the final electron acceptor at the end of the chain. It reacts with four hydrogen ions and four electrons to form two molecules of water. The aerobic process of ATP production in the inner membrane of the mitochondrion generates 32 molecules of ATP from each glucose molecule.

Overall, the process of cellular respiration produces 38 ATP molecules from each glucose molecule: 4 from glycolysis, 2 from the citric acid cycle, and 32 from the electron transport chain. ATP molecules are produced most efficiently at the end of the process when oxygen is used in the inner membrane of the mitochondrion. Carbon dioxide and water are the waste products of cellular respiration.

Comparing Photosynthesis and Cellular Respiration

The two processes—photosynthesis and cellular respiration—produce and break down food molecules respectively and are similar in several ways. Both use electron transport chains and electron carriers and a cycle of chemical reactions to form ATP molecules.

Despite these similarities, the two processes are different, as shown in Figure 3.8. Photosynthesis traps the energy in light and uses that energy, carbon dioxide, and water to produce carbohydrates and oxygen. Cellular respiration uses oxygen, and carbohydrates are broken down into carbon dioxide and water with a release of energy.

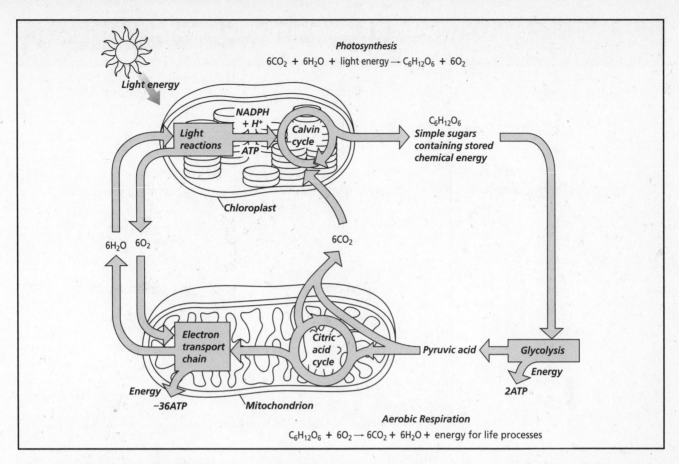

Photosynthesis
$$6CO_2 + 6H_2O + \text{light energy} \rightarrow C_6H_{12}O_6 + 6O_2$$

Light energy

NADPH + H⁺

Light reactions

Calvin cycle

ATP

Chloroplast

$C_6H_{12}O_6$
Simple sugars containing stored chemical energy

$6H_2O$ $6O_2$

$6CO_2$

Electron transport chain

Citric acid cycle

Pyruvic acid

Glycolysis

Energy

2ATP

Energy
~36ATP

Mitochondrion

Aerobic Respiration
$$C_6H_{12}O_6 + 6O_2 \rightarrow 6CO_2 + 6H_2O + \text{energy for life processes}$$

Figure 3.8 The products of photosynthesis are used during cellular respiration, and the products of cellular respiration are the raw materials used for photosynthesis.

Table 3.1 • Comparison of Photosynthesis and Cellular Respiration	
Photosynthesis	**Cellular Respiration**
Food is synthesized.	Food is broken down.
Light energy is transformed and stored in the chemical bonds of glucose molecules.	Energy is transformed from the chemical bonds of glucose molecules for cellular use.
Carbon dioxide and water are the required materials for photosynthesis.	Sugars and oxygen are the required materials for cellular respiration.
Glucose and oxygen are produced.	ATP molecules are produced and carbon dioxide and water are waste products.
Light is required.	Light is not required.
This process occurs only in the presence of chlorophyll and takes place in choloroplasts.	This process occurs in all living cells. In most organisms, this process is completed in mitochondria.

Photosynthesis only occurs if a cell contains chlorophyll, but cellular respiration takes place in all living cells. Table 3.1 compares the two processes.

Fermentation

What happens when cells that normally undergo cellular respiration are not supplied with enough oxygen? This is what happens when, for example, you run long distances. Your cells lack sufficient oxygen for a short period of time. Instead of cellular respiration continuing in mitochondria, an anaerobic process called fermentation follows glycolysis. This process allows the cells to continue to produce ATP until oxygen becomes available. As you will see, these anaerobic processes do not produce ATP as effectively as the aerobic process.

Lactic acid fermentation is one of the processes that can supply energy when oxygen for aerobic respiration is scarce. This process reverses the reactions that produce pyruvic acid. Two molecules of pyruvic acid use NADH to form two molecules of lactic acid.

Table 3.2 • Comparison of Fermentation to Cellular Respiration		
Lactic Acid	Alcoholic	Cellular Respiration
glucose	glucose	glucose
↓	↓	↓
glycolysis (pyruvic acid)	glycolysis (pyruvic acid)	glycolysis (pyruvic acid)
↓	↓	↓
	carbon dioxide	carbon dioxide
	+	+
lactic acid	alcohol	water
+	+	+
2 ATP	2 ATP	36 ATP

NAD^+ is released by this reaction and is used in glycolysis to form two ATP molecules for each glucose molecule. Strenuous exercise produces lactic acid in muscle cells. Muscle fatigue is a result of lactic acid building up in muscle cells. Lactic acid is transferred from the muscle cells to the liver where it is converted back to pyruvic acid.

Alcoholic fermentation is another anaerobic process. Yeast cells and some bacteria use this type of fermentation to convert pyruvic acid into carbon dioxide and ethyl alcohol. Like lactic acid fermentation, alcoholic fermentation produces two molecules of ATP for each molecule of glucose. If you have ever baked bread, you have seen alcoholic fermentation at work. The yeast cells in bread dough use alcoholic fermentation when they break down the sugars in the dough and produce alcohol and carbon dioxide bubbles. These bubbles raise the dough. During baking, the yeast are killed and the alcohol evaporates but the bubble pockets remain to lighten the bread. Table 3.2 compares these two anaerobic processes with cellular respiration.

✓ CHECK FOR UNDERSTANDING Why is fermentation a less effective energy source than cellular respiration?

Enzymes: Controlling Reactions

The chemical reactions in photosynthesis and cellular respiration—and in nearly all metabolic processes—are made possible by a large set of biological catalysts called enzymes. An **enzyme** is a protein that changes the rate of chemical reactions. During a reaction, the enzyme is neither changed nor used up and can perform the same function over and over.

The rate of enzyme activity can be influenced by several factors. Changes in the shape of an enzyme molecule, pH, or temperature can speed up or slow down the rate at which enzymes work.

Enzymes and other molecules, such as hormones, receptor molecules, and antibodies, have specific shapes that influence how they function and how they interact with other molecules. Each type of enzyme has a unique physical structure. An area on the surface of the enzyme, called an active site, fits the shape of reacting molecules, called substrates. Together, the substrates are like a key that fits into a "lock"—the active site. Figure 3.9 illustrates how an enzyme and substrates act like a lock and key to facilitate chemical reactions. If the shape of the enzyme changes, it cannot function properly.

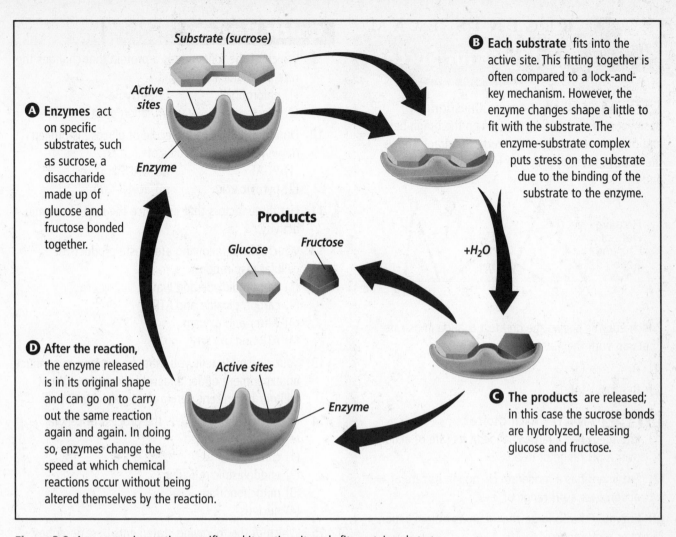

Figure 3.9 An enzyme is reaction specific and its active site only fits certain substrates.

An enzyme's activity rate will increase as temperature increases until the temperature reaches a specific point. The maximum enzyme activity occurs at this optimum temperature. For human enzymes, the optimum temperature for enzyme activity is about 37°C—normal body temperature, as shown in Figure 3.10. For some unicellular organisms that live in hotsprings, the optimal temperature for enzyme activity is about 72°C. At temperatures above the optimum point, the activity rate drops quickly because the enzyme begins to change shape or break apart. That is why cooked meats and other foods are safer to eat than raw foods. The heat of cooking affects the enzymes of any disease-causing organisms that might be present. If their enzymes cannot function properly, the disease-causing organisms die.

The **pH** of a solution is a measure of how acidic or basic it is. Substances with a pH below 7 are acidic and those with a pH above 7 are basic. Substances with a pH near 7 are called neutral. Most body fluids and cells have a pH near 7.

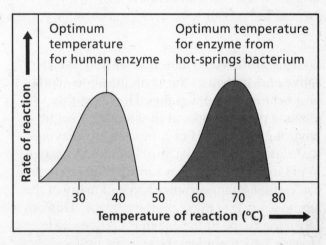

Figure 3.10 Each enzyme functions best at its optimum temperature.

Strategies for Success

Quick Review

STEP 1 READ the Regents Question . . .

Base your answer to the question on the graph below and on your knowledge of biology. The graph shows the relative rates of action of four enzymes, A, B, C, and D.

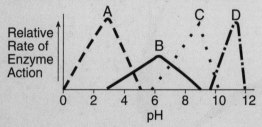

Which enzyme shows the greatest change in its rate of action with the *least* change of pH?

(1) A   (3) C

(2) B   (4) D

STEP 2 ANALYZE each choice . . .

(1) Enzyme A has a large change in its rate of action over a pH range of 0–5.

(2) Enzyme B has a moderate change in its rate of action over a pH range of 3–9.

(3) Enzyme C has a large change in its rate of action over a pH range of 6–10.

(4) Enzyme D has a large change in its rate of action over a pH range of 10–12.

STEP 3 CHOOSE the best answer . . .

After considering all of the options, the correct answer is number 4 because rate of action for D is as great as that of A and C but its pH change is less.

So most human enzymes, such as amylase in saliva and trypsin in the small intestine, work best near neutral pH ranges. However, the enzyme pepsin works in the stomach's acidic environment at a pH of 2. Lipases are enzymes that function well in basic pH ranges. A change in pH in the environment surrounding an enzyme can cause a change in the charge of many of the amino acids that make up the enzyme. This can cause the shape of the enzyme's active site to change, which renders the enzyme useless.

9 Which of the following is a protein that changes the rate of chemical reactions?
(1) chlorophyll   (3) enzyme
(2) reactant   (4) chloroplast

10 During glycolysis, a molecule of glucose is broken down into two molecules of
(1) PGAL   (3) $NADP^+$
(2) pyruvic acid   (4) acetyl-CoA

11 List three factors that influence the rate of enzyme activity.

12 Which of the following are waste products of cellular respiration?
(1) carbon dioxide and water
(2) carbon dioxide and ATP
(3) water and oxygen
(4) ATP and oxygen

13 Your classmate tells you that she is going to conduct an experiment under anaerobic conditions. What will *not* be present during the experiment?

14 In which cell organelle is the process of cellular respiration concluded?
(1) chloroplast
(2) endoplasmic reticulum
(3) mitochondrion
(4) nucleus

15 Which of the following statements best describes the process of cellular respiration?
(1) Cellular respiration circulates nutrients to cells.
(2) Cellular respiration uses carbon dioxide and water to synthesize glucose.
(3) Cellular respiration splits water molecules.
(4) Cellular respiration converts chemical energy into a usable form.

16 Which type of fermentation results in muscle fatigue?

17 How many molecules of ATP are produced through cellular respiration?
(1) 38   (3) 4
(2) 36   (4) 2

Content Questions for Regents Exam Practice

Part A

1 A characteristic of hormones and enzymes that allows them to work effectively with other organic molecules is their

(1) specific shape

(2) small size

(3) concentration of carbon and hydrogen atoms

(4) high-energy bonds

2 ATP is a compound that is synthesized when

(1) chemical bonds between carbon atoms are formed during photosynthesis

(2) energy stored in chemical bonds is released during cellular respiration

(3) energy stored in nitrogen is released, forming amino acids

(4) digestive enzymes break amino acids into smaller parts

3 The diagram below illustrates a biochemical process that occurs in organisms.

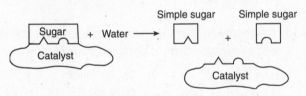

The substance labeled "catalyst" also is known as

(1) a hormone

(2) an enzyme

(3) an antibody

(4) an inorganic compound

4 To remain healthy, organisms must be able to obtain materials, change the materials, move the materials around, and get rid of waste. These activities directly require

(1) energy from ATP

(2) the replication of DNA

(3) nutrients from inorganic sources

(4) manipulation of altered genes

5 The diagram below represents part of the process of cellular respiration.

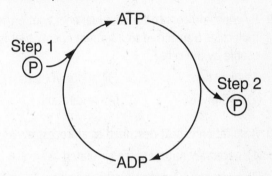

Energy is released and made available for metabolic activities at

(1) step 1, only

(2) step 2, only

(3) both step 1 and step 2

(4) neither step 1 nor step 2

6 Two test tubes were filled with a solution of bromthymol blue. A student exhaled through a straw into each tube, and the bromthymol blue turned yellow. An aquatic green plant was placed into each tube, and the tubes were corked. One tube was placed in the dark, and one was placed in direct sunlight. The yellow solution in the tube in sunlight turned blue, while the one in the dark remained yellow. Which statement best explains why the solution in the tube placed in sunlight returned to a blue color?

(1) Oxygen was produced by photosynthesis.

(2) Oxygen was removed by respiration.

(3) Carbon dioxide was removed by photosynthesis.

(4) Carbon dioxide was produced by respiration.

7 Which statement about enzymes is *not* correct?

(1) Enzymes are composed of polypeptide chains.

(2) Enzymes form a temporary association with a reactant.

(3) Enzymes are destroyed when they are used and must be synthesized for each reaction.

(4) Enzymes are specific because of their shape and catalyze only certain reactions.

8 The energy found in ATP molecules synthesized in animal cells comes directly from

(1) sunlight

(2) organic molecules

(3) minerals

(4) inorganic molecules

9 By which process is the potential energy of organic molecules transferred to a form of energy that is usable by the cells?

(1) digestion   (3) photosynthesis

(2) hydrolysis   (4) respiration

10 Respiration is best described as a process by which

(1) necessary nutrients are circulated

(2) hydrogen is used to synthesize glucose

(3) metabolic wastes are absorbed

(4) chemical energy is converted into a usable form

11 Which substances are necessary for the synthesis of most materials in an organism?

(1) hormones   (3) antibodies

(2) carbohydrates   (4) enzymes

12 The formation of lactic acid in human muscle cells is most closely associated with

(1) muscle fatigue

(2) protein synthesis

(3) an increase in alcohol consumption

(4) an increase in glucose production

13 In the material cycle shown below, which processes are represented by letters A and B?

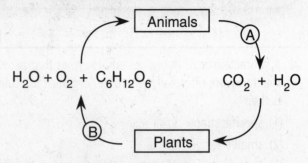

(1) A—excretion, B—respiration

(2) A—transpiration, B—excretion

(3) A—photosynthesis, B—transpiration

(4) A—respiration, B—photosynthesis

14 The equation below represents a summary of a biological process.

carbon dioxide + water → glucose + water + oxygen

This process is completed in

(1) mitochondria

(2) ribosomes

(3) cell membranes

(4) chloroplasts

15 The energy an organism requires to transport materials and eliminate wastes is obtained directly from

(1) DNA   (3) hormones

(2) starch   (4) ATP

Part B

16 A small piece of black paper was folded in half and used to cover part of the top and bottom portions of a leaf on a living geranium plant. After the plant was kept in sunlight for several days, the paper was removed. The leaf was then boiled in alcohol to remove the chlorophyll and placed in Lugol's iodine solution, which turns blue-black in the presence of starch. Only the part of the leaf that had *not* been covered turned blue-black. This investigation was most likely testing the hypothesis that

(1) light is necessary for photosynthesis to occur

(2) alcohol plus chlorophyll forms Lugol's iodine solution

(3) green plants use carbon dioxide in photosynthesis

(4) plants use alcohol in the production of chlorophyll

Base your answers to questions 17 through 19 on the information and data table below and on your knowledge of biology.

In an investigation, three seeds of the same species were allowed to germinate and grow in three different locations. Each seedling was grown in the same amount and type of soil, and each received the same amount of water during a 6-day period. At the end of the investigation, the height of each seedling and the color of its leaves were recorded. The results are shown in the data table.

Data Table		
Location	Height (cm)	Leaf Color
Sunny windowsill	7	green
Indirect sunlight	9	green
Closed closet	11	whitish yellow

17 Which hypothesis was most likely being tested in this investigation?

(1) A plant grown in the dark will not be green.

(2) The type of soil a plant is grown in influences how tall it will be.

(3) Plants need water to grow.

(4) Plants grown in red light are taller than plants grown in green light.

18 State *two* ways this investigation could be modified to lead to a more reliable conclusion.

19 Which statement correctly explains why chlorophyll production *decreased* in the seedlings kept in the closet?

(1) Lack of sunlight altered the expression of the gene for chlorophyll production.

(2) The enzymes involved in chlorophyll production mutate in cooler temperatures.

(3) Chloroplasts migrate to the center of the cell when light is not available.

(4) Chlorophyll is converted to another pigment when light is not present.

20 In the demonstration shown below, which process performed by the peas when they start to grow causes the drop of liquid to move to the left?

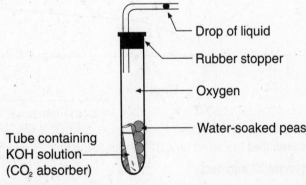

Tube containing KOH solution (CO₂ absorber)

Drop of liquid
Rubber stopper
Oxygen
Water-soaked peas

(1) protein synthesis   (3) digestion

(2) photosynthesis   (4) cellular respiration

21 Explain how carbohydrates provide energy for life functions.

22 One type of anaerobic respiration results in the production of

(1) water and oxygen   (3) nitrogen gas and ammonia

(2) pyruvic acid and glycerol   (4) alcohol and carbon dioxide

Base your answers to questions 23 and 24 on the information below and on your knowledge of biology.

A small green plant was placed in a flask as shown below. A sensor that measures the CO_2 content of the air in the flask was inserted, and then the flask was sealed with a rubber stopper. The other end of the sensor was connected to a computer to monitor and record CO_2 levels in the flask over a period of time.

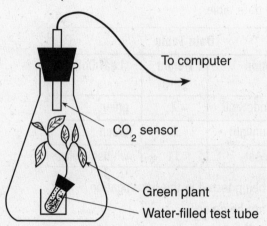

To computer

CO_2 sensor

Green plant

Water-filled test tube

For part of the time the flask was placed in bright light and for part of the time it was placed in total darkness. The graph below shows data that were recorded by the sensor over a period of time.

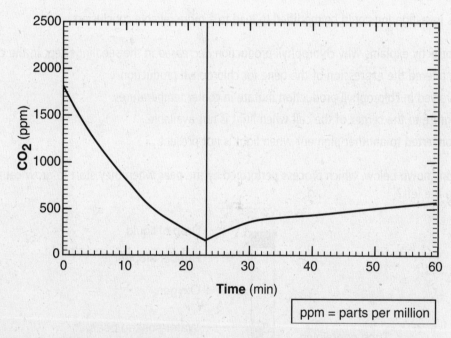

Time (min)

ppm = parts per million

23 Which condition most likely produced the effect on CO_2 level over the first 23 minutes?

(1) The light was on for the entire 23 minutes.

(2) The light was off for the entire 23 minutes.

(3) The light was off at the start and turned on after 10 minutes.

(4) The light could have been either on or off because it would have had no effect on the CO_2 level.

24 Which process most likely caused the change in CO_2 level in the flask over the last 37 minutes?

(1) photosynthesis   (3) active transport

(2) cellular respiration   (4) circulation

25 The effect of pH on a certain enzyme is shown in the graph below.

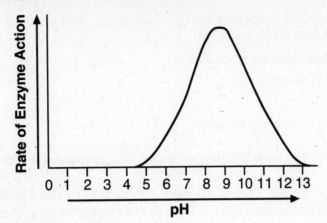

At what pH would the enzyme be most effective?

(1) above 10   (3) between 5 and 7

(2) between 8 and 10   (4) below 5

Base the answers to questions 26 and 27 on the information below and on your knowledge of biology.

A student completed a series of experiments and found that a protein-digesting enzyme (intestinal protease) functions best when the pH is 8.0 and the temperature is 37°C. During an experiment, the student used some of the procedures listed below.

Procedures
  A Adding more protease
  B Adding more protein
  C Decreasing the pH to 6.0
  D Increasing the temperature to 45°C
  E Decreasing the amount of light

26 Which procedure would have the *least* effect on the rate of protein digestion?

(1) *A*   (3) *C*

(2) *E*   (4) *D*

27 Which two procedures would most likely cause a *decrease* in the rate of protein digestion?

(1) *A* and *D*   (3) *C* and *D*

(2) *B* and *C*   (4) *A* and *E*

28 To collect data about the rate of photosynthesis in a certain type of algae when it is exposed to different colors of light, a student could measure the change in the

(1) temperature of the water surrounding the algae

(2) number of ribosomes in the algae cells

(3) color of algae cells

(4) number of gas bubbles given off by the algae

Base your answer to question 29 on the information below and on your knowledge of biology.

An investigation was performed to determine the effects of enzyme *X* on three different disaccharides (double sugars) at 37°C. Three test tubes were set up as shown in the diagram below.

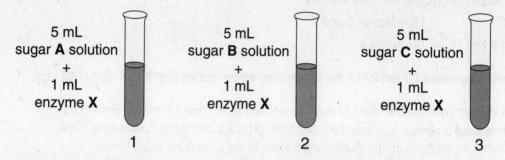

5 mL
sugar **A** solution
+
1 mL
enzyme **X**
1

5 mL
sugar **B** solution
+
1 mL
enzyme **X**
2

5 mL
sugar **C** solution
+
1 mL
enzyme **X**
3

At the end of 5 minutes, the solution in each test tube was tested for the presence of disaccharides (double sugars) and monosaccharides (simple sugars). The results of these tests are shown in the table below.

	Test Tube 1	Test Tube 2	Test Tube 3
Monosaccharide	not present	not present	present
Disaccharide	present	present	not present

29 What can be concluded about the activity of enzyme *X* from the data table? _____

_____

30 A process that occurs in the human body is shown in the diagram below.

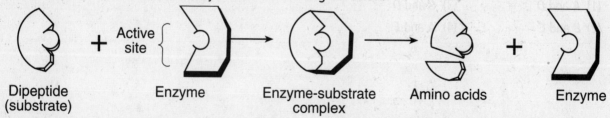

Dipeptide
(substrate)

Active
site

Enzyme

Enzyme-substrate
complex

Amino acids

Enzyme

What would happen if a temperature change caused the shape of the active site to be altered? _____

_____

Part D

Answer all questions in this part.

Directions (31–34): Base your answers on the information and diagram below and on your knowledge of biology.

When Charles Darwin visited the Galapagos Islands in 1835, he collected over 30 specimens of finches from three islands. The finches were very similar in structure except for their bills. The diagram below shows the head of two of the fourteen different finches found on the islands.

Geospiza magnirostris

Certhidea olivacea

31 Explain how the beak of the *C. olivacea* is better suited for probing for insects than the beak of the *G. magnirostris*. _____

_____

32 The *G. magnirostris* uses its beak to crush large dry seeds. Identify a tool that can be used in the laboratory to simulate the crushing nature of the beak and explain why this tool is a good choice.

_____

33 Which tool is best for simulating the movements of the beak of the *C. olivacea*?
   (1) small forceps
   (2) pliers
   (3) scalpel
   (4) test-tube holder

34 Explain why the Galapagos Island finches diversified in their beak structure and their food sources. _____

_____

_____

Directions (35–38): Base your answers on the information below and on your knowledge of biology.

During the 1970s and 1980s, Peter and Rosemary Grant and a number of their students studied the medium ground finch on the Galápagos Island of Daphne Major. The medium ground finch, *Geospiza fortis,* prefers to eat small, tender seeds. During wet years, these seeds are produced in abundance. During drier years, the birds must eat larger, drier seeds, which are harder to crush. The research teams carefully measured the depth of the beak at the base to see how the beak shape varied. The beak depth changed in a predictable manner. The graph below shows some of the results of their study.

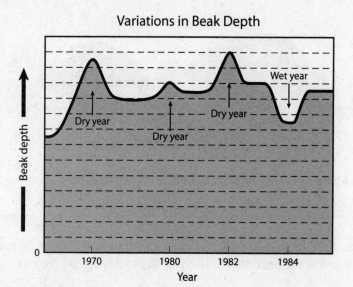

35 Explain why the average beak depth increased during the dry years. _____

_____

36 Explain why there is a dip in the graph in 1984. _____

_____

37 Three conditions existed in this population that demonstrated natural selection. Which condition does NOT belong in this list?

(1) Variation existed in the population.

(2) Variations were inherited.

(3) Variations led to differences in survival and reproductive success.

(4) Variations were controlled by the research team.

38 Which factor within a species increases the likelihood that some members of a species will survive when environmental conditions change altering available energy sources?

(1) variation

(2) disjunction

(3) polyploidy

(4) migration

antibodies	hormone	receptor
antigens	negative feedback system	response
dynamic equilibrium	osmosis	retrovirus
guard cells	pathogen	stimulus
homeostasis	phagocyte	vaccine

How are a human and an automobile alike? How do they differ? A human and an automobile both are made of complex, interacting systems. All of a human's systems must interact in order for survival, but if a car's heater fails, it does not affect the engine's performance. Each requires fuel in order to function and releases heat when the fuel is used. The human and the automobile function properly only when certain other conditions met. A human has internal mechanisms to maintain these conditions, but the automobile's owner must maintain these conditions for the car.

Homeostasis

All livings things, from unicellular bacteria to multicellular animals, have systems that allow for the regulation of their internal environments to maintain conditions suitable for survival. These biological systems can differ in complexity depending on the level of development of the organism. However, all systems share common functions that respond to the challenges of the environment that surrounds the organism. This regulation is referred to as **homeostasis.** The word homeostasis means "steady state."

Because there is a constant monitoring and adjusting of the internal environment of cells and the organism as a whole, homeostasis is often referred to as a **dynamic equilibrium.** In humans, homeostasis includes the ability to regulate and maintain the necessary amount of water and ions in its cells, the right amount of glucose in the blood, and a proper internal body temperature. For example, as you exercise, your internal body temperature begins to rise. How does your body respond to maintain body temperature within a normal range? A series of internal actions is triggered to bring body temperature back to normal range and restore homeostasis, as shown in Figure 4.1. If homeostasis cannot be maintained, disease or death can result.

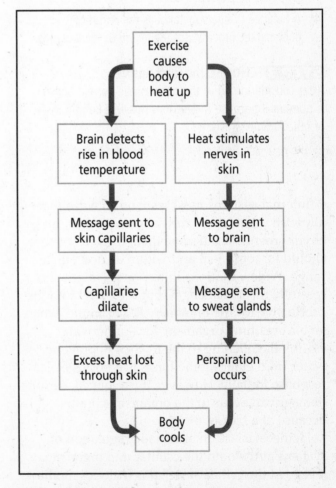

Figure 4.1 Human body temperature is maintained with through a series of actions and reactions.

STEP 1 READ the Regents Question . . .
What usually results when an organism fails to maintain homeostasis?

(1) Growth rates within organs become equal.

(2) The organism becomes ill or may die.

(3) A constant sugar supply for the cells is produced.

(4) The water balance in the tissues of the organism stabilizes.

STEP 2 ANALYZE each choice . . .

(1) For the organism to continue to perform life functions, such as growth, it must be in a state of dynamic equilibrium.

(2) When an organism cannot maintain homeostasis, it cannot continue to support life functions effectively. This can lead to illness or death.

(3) Sugar supply is not related directly to failed homeostasis.

(4) A balance of any substance is the result of homeostatic process, not the failure of homeostasis.

STEP 3 CHOOSE the best answer . . .
After considering all of the options, the correct answer is number 2 because it describes possible conditions of failed homeostasis.

Internal systems must respond in ways that allow an organism to thrive continually in an environment. At the same time, these responses should be consistent and within an acceptable range. Wide variations in responses might successfully meet challenges, but they might not be productive for the organism. For example, when an air-breathing organism goes underwater, closing the opening to the trachea to prevent water from entering the lungs is a positive response initially. However, if prolonged, serious damage can occur to the organism's brain because of a lack of oxygen.

Homeostasis is an automatic regulation of systems at the both the cellular and organismal levels. At the cellular level, this includes monitoring the concentration of materials within a cell to ensure that the cell can maintain its functions.

Water and ions must be exchanged with the external cellular environment in order to maintain homeostasis within the cell, as shown in Figure 4.2. Through the processes of diffusion, osmosis, and active transport, a dynamic equilibrium will be reached for the cell. Although there is a continuous movement of materials into and out of the cell, its internal environment remains in a steady state.

Osmosis is the diffusion of water through the cell membrane. Controlling the amount of water passing through the cell membrane is important in both one-celled organisms and multicellular organisms. If too much water enters a cell, the cell could expand and possibly burst. If there is too little water in a cell, the cell will shrink. In either case, proper functioning can be impaired and cell death can result.

At the organismal level, often an organism automatically responds to changes in the environment and reestablishes its previous state. For example, when you eat and your stomach fills, blood flow increases to the digestive track, digestive "juices" are excreted, and muscle contractions start that continue the digestive process. These responses occur automatically—you do not consciously direct them. When the stimulus of food is gone, these responses stop and the body returns to its previous state.

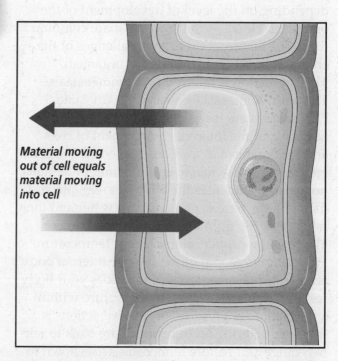

Material moving out of cell equals material moving into cell

Figure 4.2 When the movement of materials into and out of a cell are balanced, the cell is in dynamic equilibrium.

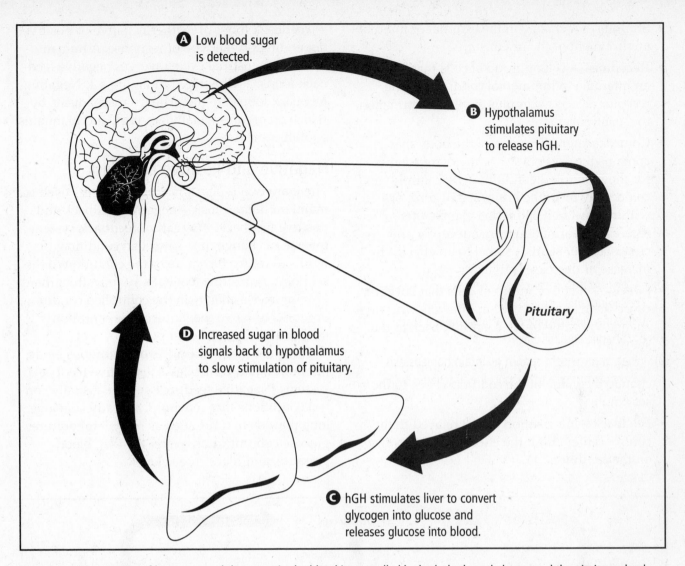

A Low blood sugar is detected.

B Hypothalamus stimulates pituitary to release hGH.

Pituitary

D Increased sugar in blood signals back to hypothalamus to slow stimulation of pituitary.

C hGH stimulates liver to convert glycogen into glucose and releases glucose into blood.

Figure 4.3 The amount of human growth hormone in the blood is controlled by both the hypothalamus and the pituitary gland.

Feedback Mechanisms

An automobile's warning lights report on such things as oil pressure, fuel level, and electric supply. Some cars also are equipped to produce a sound to indicate if lights are on, if the keys are in the ignition, or if someone other than an owner is attempting to enter the vehicle. The car's owner might respond to these stimuli by adjusting the oil pressure, filling the tank with fuel, checking the battery, turning off the lights, or removing the keys from the ignition.

Just as the car's owner might respond to his or her car's warning system to maintain the car in proper operating condition, an organism's feedback mechanisms allow it to maintain the dynamic equilibrium needed for the organism to function normally. Feedback includes all reactions to stimuli (singular, *stimulus*). **Stimuli** can be anything from an organism's external or internal

environment that will cause it to respond. The **response,** or reaction, to a change in an organism's internal or external environment can be by cells within the organism or by the organism itself. For example, when bone cells receive a signal that blood calcium levels are low, they might release calcium into the blood in response. An organism can respond through behavior as well. Beetles that live in the Namib Desert in Africa collect water droplets condensed from fog. In an environment where the availability of water is unpredictable, this behavior helps the beetles maintain homeostasis and insures their survival.

Feedback Loops

An organism's response to stimuli begins a process called a feedback loop. A feedback loop consists of several components, as illustrated in Figure 4.3 and listed on the following page.

- Stimulus—A change in the external or internal environment of the organism.
- **Receptor**—A cell or group of cells that monitor an internal environmental condition. If the receptor detects a stimulus, it relays information to a control center.
- Control center—The area of the body that contains the "set point," or the correct value for the monitored condition. The control center may be in the brain, spinal cord, or within cells of an endocrine gland. After receiving information from a receptor, the control center sends a signal to an effector to increase or decrease activity.
- Effector—A cell or group of cells that effect or cause the response to occur. Effectors work to change the value of the condition back to the set point.
- Response—The action of the effectors to change the value of the condition back to the set point.
- Feedback—Information that is relayed to the control center about the effect of the response on the condition.

Feedback loops are either negative or positive, depending on the type of response. A human female's menstrual cycle involves negative feedback loops, as illustrated in Figure 4.4. Negative feedback loops are the primary mechanisms by which an organism stabilizes itself and maintains equilibrium.

Negative and Positive Feedback

There are two types of feedback systems used to maintain homeostasis—negative feedback and positive feedback. A **negative feedback system** reverses a change in a controlled condition, or works to return the value of the condition to the set point. A positive feedback system strengthens or reinforces a change in the controlled condition, or works to move the value of the condition farther away from the set point.

There are many examples of conditions being monitored and controlled by negative feedback systems. Negative feedback systems usually control conditions that remain in a steady state over long periods of time, such as body temperature, glucose concentration, water content, blood pressure, and blood sugar levels.

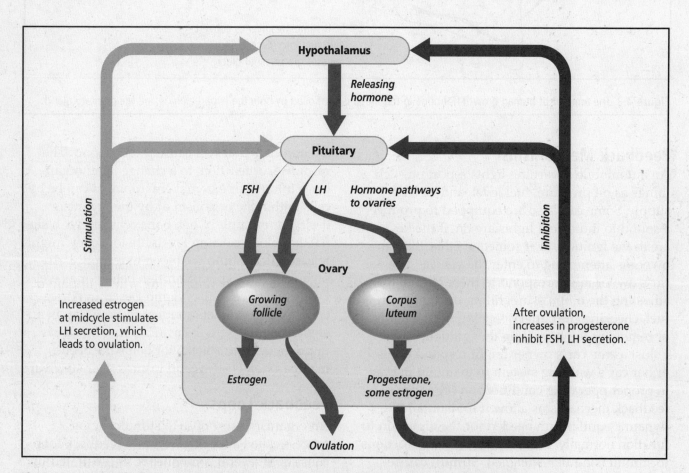

Figure 4.4 Internal feedback controls the levels of hormones during a human female's menstrual cycle.

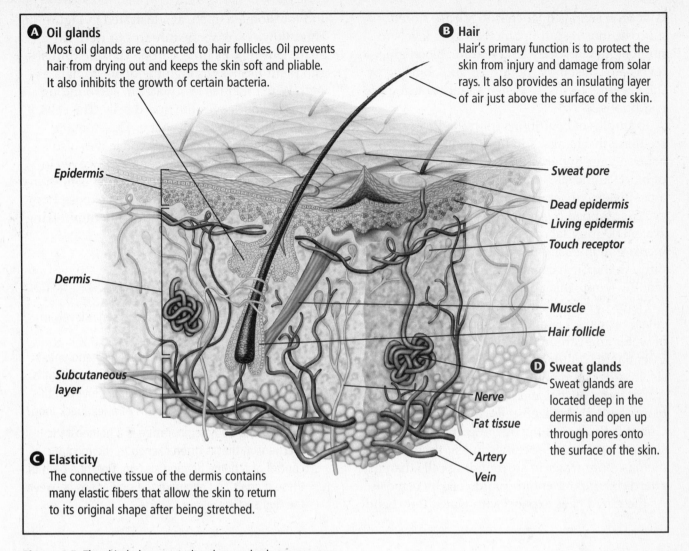

A Oil glands
Most oil glands are connected to hair follicles. Oil prevents hair from drying out and keeps the skin soft and pliable. It also inhibits the growth of certain bacteria.

B Hair
Hair's primary function is to protect the skin from injury and damage from solar rays. It also provides an insulating layer of air just above the surface of the skin.

Epidermis

Dermis

Subcutaneous layer

Sweat pore

Dead epidermis

Living epidermis

Touch receptor

Muscle

Hair follicle

D Sweat glands
Sweat glands are located deep in the dermis and open up through pores onto the surface of the skin.

Nerve

Fat tissue

Artery

Vein

C Elasticity
The connective tissue of the dermis contains many elastic fibers that allow the skin to return to its original shape after being stretched.

Figure 4.5 The skin helps to regulate human body temperature.

✓ **CHECK FOR UNDERSTANDING** What is the difference between positive and negative feedback? Which is found more frequently in humans?

As previously mentioned, body temperature in humans is maintained within an acceptable range by several mechanisms. When the body's temperature increases, the glands in the dermis layer of the skin, as shown in Figure 4.5, produce sweat and the body begins to perspire. Perspiration on the skin has a cooling effect because as the moisture evaporates, heat energy is lost and the body's normal temperature is maintained. Another response that is triggered by a rise in body temperature also occurs within the dermis of the skin. Small blood vessels in the dermis dilate, increasing blood flow near the skin's surface. Body heat is lost by radiation through the skin. When body temperature returns to normal, the feedback loop stops.

If body temperature begins to drop, the blood vessels in the skin constrict, and body heat is conserved. Shivering occurs as the body attempts to release heat through muscle contraction. In either case, if body temperature is not maintained within the normal range, functioning will be impaired.

Another condition controlled by negative feedback systems is blood glucose level. When blood glucose levels are high, the pancreas releases the hormone insulin. A **hormone** is a chemical produced in one part of the body and transported to another part, where it causes a physiological change. Insulin signals the liver and muscle cells to take in glucose, lowering blood glucose levels. When the glucose level in blood becomes too low, as it might for a runner during a marathon, the pancreas releases another hormone called glucagon.

Glucagon signals liver cells to release stored glucose, thus restoring blood glucose levels to normal. As with body temperature, blood glucose levels are constantly monitored and adjusted by the negative feedback systems that control these conditions.

Examples of conditions controlled by positive feedback mechanisms in humans include labor contractions, hyperventilation, and the clotting of blood at the site of a wound. The response of a positive feedback system continues until the cycle is stopped by some action from outside the system. During labor, contractions continue to increase in intensity until the baby is pushed through the birth canal. It is the birth of the baby that interrupts this positive feedback cycle.

Plants have mechanisms that maintain homeostasis as well. Examples include the regulation of water and carbon dioxide in plants, both essential for cellular processes and photosynthesis. In order to maintain the necessary amount of water and reduce water loss to the environment, plants have specialized cells called guard cells. **Guard cells** control the opening and closing of stomata, which are openings in leaf tissue. When there is more water in surrounding cells than in guard cells, water enters guard cells by osmosis. As the guard cells expand with water, they bend,

and the stomata open, as illustrated in Figure 4.6. This allows excess moisture to exit from the plant. During this time, carbon dioxide diffuses into plant tissues through the open stomata as well. When there is less water in surrounding tissues, water leaves the guard cells. The cells return to their previous shape. The stomata close, reducing water loss. Some leaves also have specialized cells that can cause leaves to curl in response to dry environmental conditions. This reduces the leaf's surface area exposed to drying effects of sunlight and wind, minimizing water loss.

Quick Review

1 How does insulin affect the blood sugar levels in the body?

2 A man turns on a faucet and puts his hand under the stream of water. The water is very hot. What is the man's response to this stimulus? How can this response be explained in terms of a feedback loop?

3 Maintaining body temperature is a homeostatic mechanism that is often likened to thermostatic control of a home heating system. Describe both of these models and compare the similarities between the two systems.

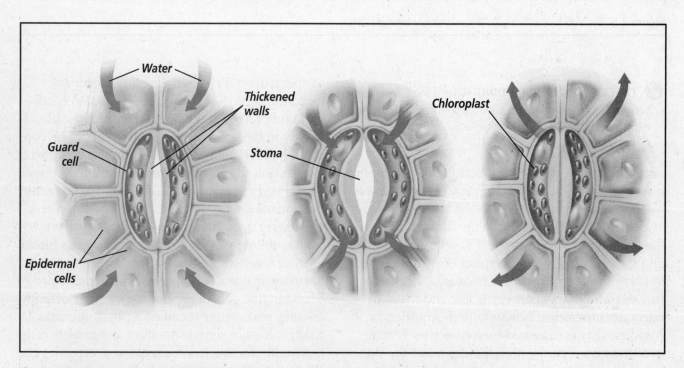

Figure 4.6 When a pair of guard cells fills with water, they bend apart and form a stoma. When water leaves the guard cells, they come together and close the stoma.

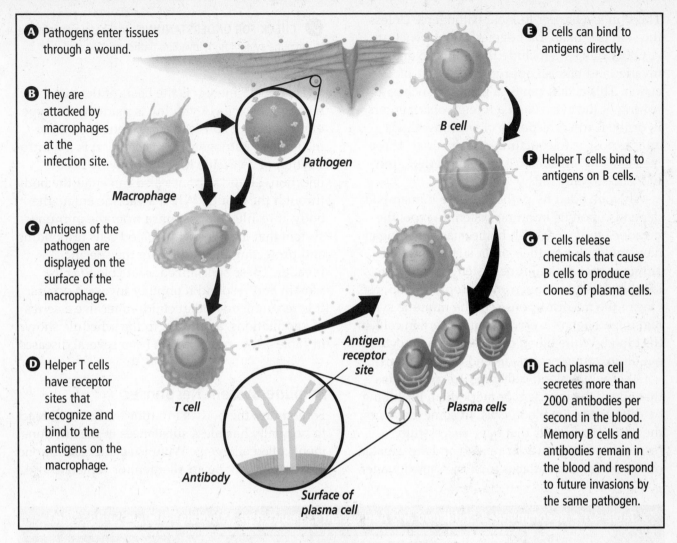

A Pathogens enter tissues through a wound.

B They are attacked by macrophages at the infection site.

C Antigens of the pathogen are displayed on the surface of the macrophage.

D Helper T cells have receptor sites that recognize and bind to the antigens on the macrophage.

E B cells can bind to antigens directly.

F Helper T cells bind to antigens on B cells.

G T cells release chemicals that cause B cells to produce clones of plasma cells.

H Each plasma cell secretes more than 2000 antibodies per second in the blood. Memory B cells and antibodies remain in the blood and respond to future invasions by the same pathogen.

Pathogen

Macrophage

B cell

T cell

Antigen receptor site

Plasma cells

Antibody

Surface of plasma cell

Figure 4.7 Antibody immunity involves several types of cells of your immune system.

4 Organisms undergo constant chemical changes as they maintain internal balance known as
   (1) interdependence   (3) synthesis
   (2) homeostasis   (4) recombination

5 Swimmers are cautioned not to go into the water immediately after eating, but to wait an hour, to avoid cramping. Considering the body's reaction to eating, what homeostasis mechanisms could be the basis of this advice? Explain your answer.

6 Body functions are sustained by homeostasis. Name at least three (3). Choose one of these and describe what might occur if a dynamic balance could not be maintained.

7 A feedback system that works to return the value of a condition back to the set point is called
   (1) positive   (3) generic
   (2) neutral   (4) negative

Immune System and Disease

When an organism is unable to maintain homeostasis, this indicates that the organism is afflicted by disease. Disease can result from abnormal cells, nutrition deficiencies, inherited disorders, styles of living, and invading organisms, called **pathogens.**

Pathogens and the Immune System

Pathogens are common in every environment. They are in the air, food, soil, and water, as well as on fabrics and surfaces that surround us. Viruses, bacteria, fungi, and animal parasites can infect plants and humans and interrupt normal life functions.

The human body has defenses against pathogens, as shown in Figure 4.7. It has various mechanisms that prevent pathogens from entering the body.

The skin is a barrier to most pathogens. Unless the skin is broken, pathogens cannot penetrate it. Other defenses include the ability to detect an invader and take an appropriate course of action. This action can be a reaction, such as tearing of the eyes when a foreign object enters it, or the learned response of washing hands after exposure to contaminated material. These mechanisms are effective, but not perfect, and will occasionally fail.

When invaded by pathogens, the human body depends upon its immune system to repel the invaders and reestablish homeostasis. Pathogens have molecules on their outer surfaces called **antigens** that the immune system usually can identify and then launch an appropriate response. One of the major responses of the immune system to pathogens is carried out by certain cells in the blood. White blood cells called **phagocytes** engulf invading organisms and destroy them.

Other white blood cells produce **antibodies** that attack the invaders or mark them for killing by different white blood cells. In some instances, the white blood cells that have successfully responded to the invader remain and are capable of deterring future attacks from the same invader.

✅ **CHECK FOR UNDERSTANDING** In what ways does the immune system fight invading pathogens?

This phenomenon is the basis of the development of vaccines. A **vaccine** is made of one type of pathogen. It consists of weakened, dead, or incomplete pathogens. A vaccination is the introduction of a vaccine into the body by needle injection. Liquid vaccines also can enter the body through the mouth. When a vaccine enters the body, it results in a response from the immune system that includes white blood cells responding and protecting the body from the specific invader. These specialized white blood cells remain and respond if another invasion occurs. It is recommended that children receive a series of vaccinations, according to the schedule shown in Table 4.1, to protect them from several diseases.

Immune System Responses

Sometimes, the body's immune system will react to normally harmless substances in the environment called allergens. What is an allergen for one person may not be an allergen for someone else.

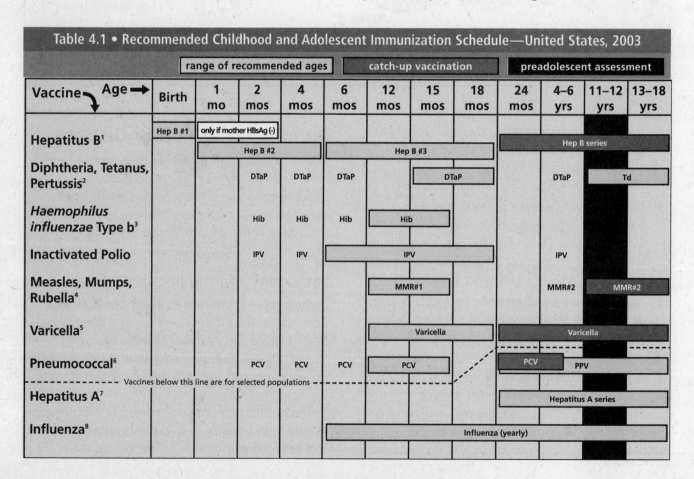

Table 4.1 • Recommended Childhood and Adolescent Immunization Schedule—United States, 2003

Vaccine \ Age →	Birth	1 mo	2 mos	4 mos	6 mos	12 mos	15 mos	18 mos	24 mos	4–6 yrs	11–12 yrs	13–18 yrs
Hepatitus B[1]	Hep B #1	only if mother HBsAg (-)	Hep B #2			Hep B #3				Hep B series		
Diphtheria, Tetanus, Pertussis[2]			DTaP	DTaP	DTaP		DTaP			DTaP	Td	
Haemophilus influenzae **Type b[3]**			Hib	Hib	Hib	Hib						
Inactivated Polio			IPV	IPV		IPV				IPV		
Measles, Mumps, Rubella[4]						MMR#1				MMR#2	MMR#2	
Varicella[5]						Varicella				Varicella		
Pneumococcal[6]			PCV	PCV	PCV	PCV			PCV	PPV		
Hepatitus A[7]										Hepatitus A series		
Influenza[8]					Influenza (yearly)							

range of recommended ages   catch-up vaccination   preadolescent assessment

Vaccines below this line are for selected populations

These reactions, called allergies, often appear suddenly. Allergens can include animal dander, mold, mildew, pollen, certain foods, cleaning solutions, contact with certain plants, such as poison ivy, insect bites, and natural and man-made fabrics.

The immune system responds to an allergen by releasing histamines to counteract what it perceives as a threat to the body. The histamines cause reactions in the body that vary from mild— watery eyes, sneezing, or skin rashes—to severe, such as swelling of the tongue and throat, which can constrict breathing. Antihistamine-containing medicines can alleviate some symptoms.

Although some allergies are more common than others, tolerances to them vary from individual to individual. Some individuals have extreme reactions to stimuli that others find minimally discomforting. The sting of a bee can cause extreme reactions in some people. If an antihistamine injection is not received immediately, the histamines produced by the body can cause the throat to close, preventing breathing and resulting in death. Some individuals respond adversely to materials common in daily life, such as peanuts and latex. Sensitive individuals can carry injectable antihistamine with them. Many schools, camps, hospitals, emergency and paramedic units stock preloaded injectable antihistamines that can be used in emergencies. Although it is highly unusual for a first allergic episode to be fatal, it is not impossible.

Transplant Rejection

A person's immune system also will respond to a transplanted organ because it carries different antigens on its cells than those found in the organ recipient's cells. The organ recipient's immune system will recognize these as foreign invaders and launch an attack to destroy them. To counteract this response, organ recipients often receive drug therapy to suppress the immune system's reaction. This will reduce the immune system's reaction to any invader and increase the chances of a successful transplant. It also increases the possibility of infection for the organ recipient because it weakens his or her immune system's response to all foreign invaders. An individual who receives an organ transplant will be more susceptible to pathogens from which he or she was previously immune.

Diseases of the Immune System

The effectiveness of the body's immune system to respond to invading pathogens or foreign material can be impaired by ways other than the body's reactions. Some viruses directly attack the immune system, creating damage that renders it ineffective against previously defended pathogens and diseases.

Acquired Immunodeficiency Syndrome (AIDS) is a disease caused by a retrovirus called the human immunodeficiency virus (HIV). A **retrovirus** can make DNA from RNA. The retroviral DNA is integrated into the chromosomes of the cell that the virus invades. Individuals acquire HIV through contaminated blood or body fluid contact. HIV usually is transmitted from one individual to another when they share hypodermic needles or when someone has sex with another person who carries the virus. HIV, as shown in Figure 4.8, attacks cells of the immune system that are essential to fighting diseases. The body becomes defenseless against a variety of diseases that previously posed no threat. Individuals with AIDS often succumb to diseases that a person with a healthy immune system would recover from easily.

✓ CHECK FOR UNDERSTANDING How is HIV transmitted from person to person?

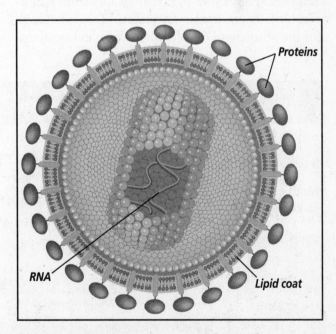

Figure 4.8 HIV is retrovirus covered with knoblike attachment proteins.

White blood cells usually differentiate between the surface molecules of cells that belong to the organism and those that do not. Occasionally, however, an organism's immune system will fail to make this distinction accurately, and it will begin to attack itself. This condition is called an auto-immune disease. This is the cause of one type of diabetes. The immune system fails to recognize the pancreas cells that produce insulin as part of the organism, then attacks and destroys them. Other autoimmune diseases include multiple sclerosis, rheumatoid arthritis, and Graves' disease.

Immune System and Other Diseases

Disease also can be the result of inheritance, poor nutrition, toxic substances, and organ malfunction. Some diseases result from certain personal behaviors. Some effects show up right away; others may not show up for years.

Often called the silent killer, high blood pressure (hypertension) can go undetected for years. Not only does it increase the likelihood of a stroke, it can badly damage the tissue of the kidneys. Research has shown that certain groups in the population are more prone to high blood pressure than others are. The tendency to develop high blood pressure is thought to be inherited. Individuals diagnosed with high blood pressure often are put on a low-salt diet that contributes to bringing the disease under control.

Poor nutrition can result in diseases, as listed in Table 4.2. For example, rickets results from a deficient intake of vitamin D. Vitamin D is necessary for the absorption of calcium by human intestines.

If vitamin D is lacking and not enough calcium can be absorbed, bones—especially those of children—soften and become deformed. Another disease associated with a vitamin deficiency is scurvy, which results from a lack of vitamin C.

Poor nutrition often is associated with under-weight individuals. However, poor nutrition can result in obesity when individuals choose foods that are high in calories and have little nutritional value. Morbid obesity puts a strain on all the body's systems and increases the incidence of disease, particularly in the circulatory system. Lack of exercise also can contribute to obesity and, directly and indirectly, to failure of other body systems.

Other personal habits, such as smoking, can cause diseases. Cigarette smoking has been linked to cancers of various organs of the respiratory system and emphysema. Illegal drug use, alcohol abuse, and indiscriminant sexual activity can result in diseases.

Cancer

The immune system also protects the body against some cancer cells, but not all of them. Many forms of cancer can attack different parts of the body. Some early warning signs of cancer are listed in Table 4.3.

Cancer can be caused by mutations in cells that result in uncontrolled cell division of cancerous cells. Research has shown that a predisposition for some types of cancers can be inherited, such as some types of breast cancer in women. Other cancers may be attributable to exposure to chemicals or other substances, such as asbestos.

Table 4.2 • Vitamin Deficiency		
Vitamin	Possible Deficiency Symptoms	Disease
A	blindness	
B_1	mental confusion: muscle weakness; impaired growth	beri-beri
B_2	dermatitis around nose and lips; eyes sensitive to light	
B_6	skin disorder; anemia; kidney stones; nausea	
B_{12}	anemia; numbness, tingling in fingers and toes	
C	bleeding gums; slow healing wounds; bruising; increased infections	scurvy
D	soft bones; dental cavities	rickets
E	neurological effects	
Folacin	anemia; smooth tongue; diarrhea	
K	bruising; clotting defects	
Niacin	skin disorders; diarrhea; mental confusion	pellagra

Table 4.3 • Some Early Warning Signs of Cancer (from the National Cancer Institute)
Changes in bowel or bladder habits
A sore that does not heal
Unusual bleeding or discharge
Thickening or lump in the breast or elsewhere
Chronic indigestion or difficulty swallowing
Obvious change in a wart or mole
Nagging cough or hoarseness

Exposure to asbestos has been linked to lung cancer. For many years, asbestos was used as a common insulating and building material. Legislation has been enacted that requires school districts in New York and other states to seek out and remove asbestos in school buildings.

Research also has shown that some personal behaviors, such as prolonged and repeated unprotected exposure to the ultraviolet rays in sunlight, have been associated with cancers. Research continues to determine links between cancer and diet, lifestyle, use of alcohol, tobacco, and drugs.

Research and Disease

Biological research has provided a great deal of data that can be studied by doctors and scientists to find cures for diseases not only in humans, but in other animals and in plants. Analyzing this data has led to new and more effective ways of diagnosing and treating diseases. The development of a polio vaccine and the obliteration of smallpox are two of the major contributions that have had widespread application and success.

Modern medicines and procedures assist in preventing and curing diseases, and repairing damage to tissues. For example, aspirin therapy has been found effective in preventing heart attacks. Surgical procedures allow treatment of impaired body functions, such as the implantation of pacemakers to maintain regular heartbeats, and repair of diseased tissue, such as implanting artificial knees, hips, and elbows. Microsurgery—surgery that involves the use of miniaturized surgical instruments and other tools—allows repair or removal of diseased or damaged tissues with minimal harm to surrounding healthy tissues.

Similar research efforts have improved crop productions by developing disease-resistant and higher-yielding plant species. Rice is a food staple in many developing countries. Growing higher-yielding rice species provides a basis of better nutrition in those countries, improving the health of those countries' populations.

Quick Review

8 What triggers an immune system's response to a pathogen?

9 Allergies are usually harmless reactions to environmental stimuli. What common items can elicit an allergic reaction?

10 Which statement best describes an immune response?
(1) It always produces antibiotics.
(2) It usually involves the recognition and destruction of pathogens.
(3) It stimulates asexual reproduction and resistance in pathogens.
(4) It releases red blood cells that destroy parasites.

11 The immune system can cause a transplant to be rejected. Explain why this happens.

12 Disease can
(1) be inherited
(2) be caused by toxic materials
(3) be the result of poor nutrition
(4) be all of the above

13 People with AIDS are unable to fight multiple infections because the virus that causes AIDS
(1) weakens their immune systems
(2) produces antibodies in their blood
(3) attacks muscle tissue
(4) kills pathogens

14 The uncontrolled division of certain body cells, which then invade the surrounding tissues and interfere with the normal functioning of the body, is known as
(1) cancer
(2) regeneration
(3) diffusion
(4) oogenesis

15 When people who are allergic to pollen come in contact with it, their eyes begin to water and itch due to the release of
(1) antigens from red blood cells
(2) enzymes from platelets
(3) histamines from body cells
(4) hormones from the pituitary gland

Part A

1 Certain microbes, foreign tissues, and some cancerous cells can cause immune responses in the human body because all three contain
   (1) antigens   (3) fats
   (2) enzymes   (4) cytoplasm

2 The blood of newborn babies is tested to determine the presence of a certain substance. This substance indicates the genetic disorder PKU, which may result in mental retardation. Babies born with this disorder are put on a special diet so that mental retardation will not develop. In this situation, modification of the baby's diet is an example of how biological research can be used to
   (1) change faulty genes   (3) stimulate immunity
   (2) cure a disorder   (4) control a disorder

3 Microbes that enter the body, causing disease, are known as
   (1) pathogens   (3) enzymes
   (2) antibodies   (4) hosts

4 Which statement describes the best procedure to determine if a vaccine for a disease in a certain bird species is effective?
   (1) Vaccinate 100 birds and expose all 100 to the disease.
   (2) Vaccinate 100 birds and expose only 50 of them to the disease.
   (3) Vaccinate 50 birds, do not vaccinate 50 other birds, and expose all 100 to the disease.
   (4) Vaccinate 50 birds, do not vaccinate 50 other birds, and expose only the vaccinated birds to the disease.

5 Which disease damages the human immune system, leaving the body open to certain infectious agents?
   (1) flu   (3) chicken pox
   (2) AIDS   (4) pneumonia

6 A characteristic shared by all enzymes, hormones, and antibodies is that their function is determined by the
   (1) shape of their molecules
   (2) DNA they contain
   (3) inorganic molecules they contain
   (4) organelles present in their structure

7 Which activity is *not* a response of human white blood cells to pathogens?
   (1) engulfing and destroying bacteria
   (2) producing antibodies
   (3) identifying invaders for destruction
   (4) removing carbon dioxide

8 In some individuals, the immune system attacks substances such as grass pollen that are usually harmless, resulting in
   (1) an allergic reaction
   (2) a form of cancer
   (3) an insulin imbalance
   (4) a mutation

9 The diagram below shows the interaction between blood sugar levels and pancreatic activity.

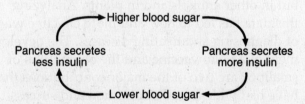

This process is an example of
   (1) a feedback mechanism maintaining homeostasis
   (2) an immune system responding to prevent disease
   (3) the digestion of sugar by insulin
   (4) the hormonal regulation of gamete production

10 In desert environments, organisms that cannot maintain a constant internal body temperature, such as snakes and lizards, rarely go out during the hot, sunny daylight hours. They stay in the shade, under rocks, or in burrows during the day. Explain how this behavior helps maintain homeostasis in these organisms.

11 The list below includes three ways of controlling viral diseases in humans.

- Administering a vaccine containing a dead or weakened virus that stimulates the body to form antibodies against the virus

- Using chemotherapy (chemical agents) to kill viruses, similar to the way in which sulfa drugs or antibiotics act against bacteria

- Relying on the action of interferon, which is produced in cells and protects the body against pathogenic viruses

Based on this information, which activity would contribute to the greatest protection against viruses?

(1) producing a vaccine that is effective against interferon

(2) developing a method to stimulate the production of interferon in cells

(3) using interferon to treat a number of diseases caused by bacteria

(4) synthesizing a sulfa drug that prevents the destruction of bacteria by viruses

12 Which graph of blood sugar level over a 12-hour period best illustrates the concept of dynamic equilibrium in the body?

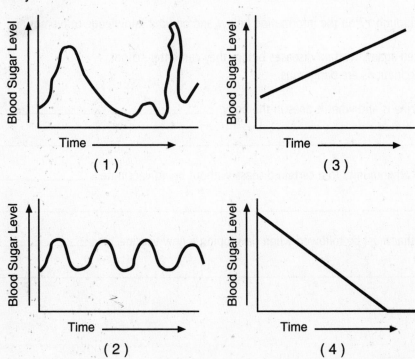

Part C

Base your answers to the questions 13 and 14 on the information in the newspaper article below and on your knowledge of biology.

Patients to Test Tumor Fighter

Boston—Endostatin, the highly publicized experimental cancer drug that wiped out tumors in mice and raised the hopes of cancer patients, will be tested on patients this year.

"I think it's exciting, but . . . you always have the risk that something will fail in testing," said Dr. Judah Folkman, the Harvard University researcher whose assistant, Michael O'Reilly, discovered endostatin.

Endostatin and a sister protein, angiostatin, destroy the tumors' ability to sprout new blood vessels. This makes cancer fall dormant in lab animals, but no one knows if that will happen in humans. —The Associated Press

13 Explain why it is necessary to test these experimental drugs on human volunteers as well as on test animals.

_____

14 State *one* reason that mice are often used by scientists for testing experimental drugs that may be used by humans.

_____

Base your answers to the questions 15 through 17 on the information below and on your knowledge of biology.

Children must be vaccinated against certain diseases before they can enter school. Some parents feel that vaccinations are dangerous.

15 Explain to these parents what a vaccine is and what it does in the body. _____

_____

16 State *one* way a child could develop an immunity to a certain disease without being vaccinated. _____

_____

17 Identify *one* part of a research plan that must be followed when developing a new vaccine. _____

_____

Part D

Answer all questions in this part.

Directions (18–20): Base your answers on the information and diagram below and on your knowledge of biology. The diagram represents the blood of a patient undergoing dialysis. The blood of the patient is separated from the dialysis fluid by a selectively permeable membrane.

The primary function of the human kidney is to maintain homeostasis in the human body. The kidneys filter water, salt, and waste products from the blood. If the kidneys fail, these substances build to toxic levels and the person will die. The blood can be filtered artificially through a process called dialysis or hemodialysis. Dialysis uses the same principles as those in the Diffusion Through a Membrane laboratory activity. During dialysis, the blood is separated from the dialysis fluid by a selectively permeable membrane. Dissolved waste products in the blood, such as urea and salts, can freely pass through the membrane. However, red and white blood cells, platelets, and proteins are too large to pass through the membrane.

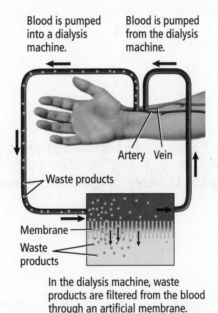

Blood is pumped into a dialysis machine.

Blood is pumped from the dialysis machine.

Artery   Vein

Waste products

Membrane

Waste products

In the dialysis machine, waste products are filtered from the blood through an artificial membrane.

18 Explain what concentration levels must be in place on both sides of the membrane so that urea and salts will pass through the membrane into the dialysis fluid.

_____

19 During dialysis, substances such as sugars, amino acids, and some salts can pass through the membrane. What conditions must exist in the dialysis fluid to keep these nutrients from passing from the blood, through the membrane, to the dialysis fluid.

_____

20 During dialysis, water from the dialysis fluid passes through the membrane into the blood. Explain what could happen to the cells in the blood and what must be done to maintain homeostasis in the cells.

_____

Directions (21): Base your answers on the information and diagram below and on your knowledge of biology. The diagram represents substances crossing a plasma membrane in a cell.

21 What characteristic of the plasma membrane is illustrated in this drawing?

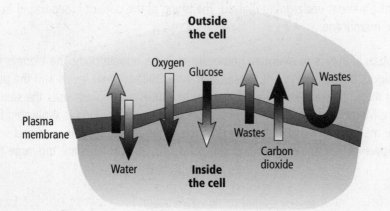

(1) selective permeability

(2) phospholipid bilayer

(3) fluid mosaic construction

(4) impermeability to water

Directions (22–23): Base your answers on the information below and on your knowledge of biology.

22 Which movement of substances through a cell membrane against a concentration gradient requires energy?

(1) osmosis

(2) diffusion

(3) active transport

(4) facilitated diffusion

23 Which statement best describes what happens to an animal cell that is bathed in distilled water?

(1) Water flows out of the cell and the cell shrivels.

(2) There is no change in the animal cell.

(3) The cell fills with water and swells.

(4) The cell begins to divide.

Reproduction and Heredity

amino acid
asexual reproduction
cloning
development
diploid
DNA
fertilization

gametes
gene
haploid
homologous chromosomes
meiosis
messenger RNA
mitosis

mutation
sexual reproduction
species
transcription
transfer RNA
zygote

In biological terms, life's purpose is to maintain homeostasis long enough for a species to reproduce. An individual organism does not have to reproduce to survive, but for a species to survive, some of its members must reproduce. **Species** are groups of organisms capable of interbreeding naturally and producing fertile offspring. Species survive or transcend only if they consistently produce enough offspring to replace organisms that die due to disease, predation, aging, or accidents. The genetic information of individual organisms is transferred to new generations by reproduction.

Reproduction Basics

When an organism reproduces, cell structures called chromosomes carry genetic information to the next generation. Chromosomes are made of segments called **genes.** Each gene segment contains coded information that directs the production of protein. Therefore, genes control the types of proteins an organism makes. Proteins produced by an organism determine its traits.

The body cells of an organism are **diploid;** they contain pairs of chromosomes, or 2*n*. The two chromosomes in each pair are called **homologous chromosomes** because they carry genes for the same traits. The sequence of genes on homologous chromosomes is the same. The alternate form of each gene on homologous chromosomes is called an allele. Figure 5.1 shows a pair of homologous chromosomes and alleles found in garden peas.

Types of Reproduction

There are two types of reproduction that pass genetic information to future generations—asexual reproduction and sexual reproduction. Some organisms reproduce asexually. In **asexual reproduction,** one parent produces offspring.

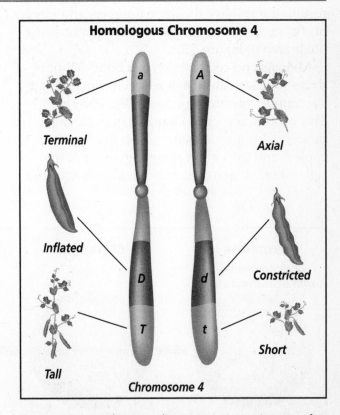

Homologous Chromosome 4

Terminal

Axial

Inflated

Constricted

Tall

Short

Chromosome 4

Figure 5.1 In garden peas, chromosome 4 contains genes for flower position, pod shape, and plant height. On a plant, flowers only are located along the stem—axial—or flowers only are clustered at the tip of stems—terminal. Pod shape is either inflated or constricted; and plant height is either tall or short.

The offspring are genetically identical to each other and the parent because all the genetic information comes from one parent. Other organisms reproduce sexually. In **sexual reproduction,** two parents produce offspring that have a combination of genes usually with half the genetic information contributed by each parent. The genetic information is in each parent's specialized sex cells called **gametes** or eggs in females and sperm in males.

Cell Division

All types of reproduction are by cell division that includes the division of the nucleus either by mitosis or meiosis. During cell division, chromosomes of a cell are copied and distributed to new cells known as daughter cells.

Mitosis and cell division of a body cell produce two daughter cells, each with a complete set of chromosomes. Mitosis and cell division produce new diploid cells for growth, repair, reproduction, and development. During mitosis, chromosomes in a parent cell's nucleus are copied, and then are equally distributed to two new cells. The resulting cells have the same numbers and kinds of chromosomes as the parent cell. Mitosis is illustrated in Figure 5.2.

Meiosis and cell division of a body cell produces four sex cells. Each new cell contains half the number of chromosomes as the body cell. This condition is called **haploid** or *n*. During meiosis, chromosomes from a body cell are copied, and then align along the center of the cell as homologous pairs. In the first meiotic cell

division, pairs of chromosomes move apart, and in the second division, copied chromosomes separate from each other. These two divisions distribute the chromosomes into four haploid gametes each with one chromosome from each homologous pair, therefore, one allele for each trait. These gametes are not genetically identical. The process of meiosis is illustrated in Figure 5.3.

✔ CHECK FOR UNDERSTANDING Compare and contrast mitosis and meiosis.

Asexual Reproduction

In asexual reproduction, one parent passes copies of all of its chromosomes to each of its offspring. The offspring are genetically identical to each other and to the parent unless a gene **mutation**—a change in genetic code—occurs. In some organisms, asexual reproduction is merely an extension of growth. A group of new cells produced by mitosis and cell division separates from the parent to form offspring. Asexual reproduction can be a type of **cloning**—the production of identical genetic copies of an organism. Table 5.1 on page 57 shows types of asexual reproduction.

Asexually reproducing organisms may create offspring rapidly and in large numbers. In an unchanging environment, asexual reproduction is advantageous because successful parents will produce successful offspring. But, if organisms are not well adapted to a changing environment, asexual reproduction may not provide new varieties of organisms that can survive and reproduce.

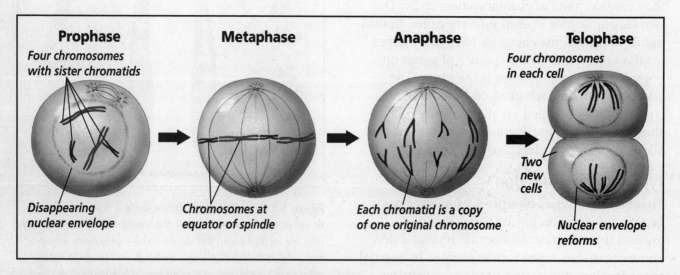

Figure 5.2 Mitosis and cell division produce genetically identical cells.

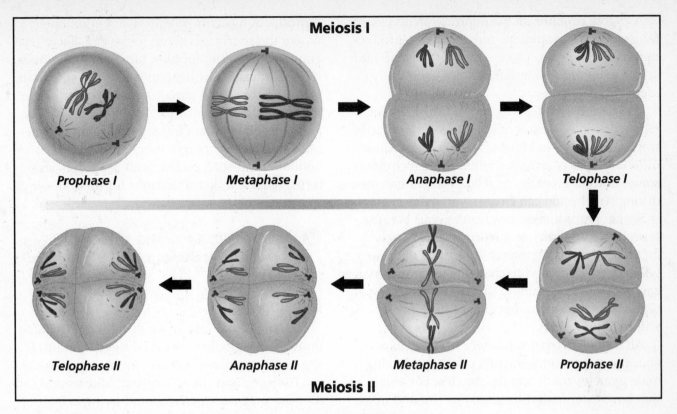

Meiosis I

Prophase I   Metaphase I   Anaphase I   Telophase I

Telophase II   Anaphase II   Metaphase II   Prophase II

Meiosis II

Figure 5.3 Meiosis and cell division reduce the chromosome number by half.

✓ **CHECK FOR UNDERSTANDING** Suppose a bacterium reproduced for 16 generations and formed a colony of thousands of cells. When a scientist examined the colony, she noted that all of the cells had identical characteristics. Explain why this is possible.

Sexual Reproduction

Cells produced by meiosis usually do not grow into new organisms. To produce an offspring, two haploid gametes must fuse during the process of fertilization to form a fertilized egg called a **zygote. Fertilization** results in a cell with the diploid ($2n$) chromosome number like that of body cells. The zygote then undergoes cell divisions and development to form a new organism.

Sexual reproduction usually involves two parents. Each offspring inherits chromosomes from both of its parents when their gametes fuse. Simply stated, the offspring will receive half of its chromosomes from its father's sperm and half of its chromosomes from its mother's egg. At fertilization, the full complement of chromosomes is restored with the formation of the zygote.

Table 5.1 • Some Types of Asexual Reproduction	
Type	**Example**
Binary fission A one-celled organism divides evenly to form two one-celled offspring.	Paramecium
Budding A cell or group of cells pinches off from the parent to form a new individual.	Hydra *Bud*
Spore formation Parent produces reproductive cell with a hard outer coat. This cell forms a new organism without the fusion of gametes.	Moss
Regeneration (animals) A new organism is produced through the replacement or regrowth of body parts.	Planarian
Vegetative propagation (plants) A new plant is produced from existing roots, stems, or leaves.	Strawberry

A zygote contains all the information necessary for growth, development, and eventual reproduction of an offspring. The zygote will develop into an offspring that is similar, but not genetically identical to its parents.

The variety of offspring produced by sexual reproduction is a result of both meiosis and fertilization as shown in Figure 5.4. Meiosis produces different types of gametes with different chromosomes and different genes. The fusion of gametes during fertilization can create a variety of zygotes.

Sexual reproduction is advantageous because it produces a variety of offspring. This variety increases the chance that at least a few offspring will be better adapted to changing environmental conditions. The variability that results from sexual reproduction reduces that chance that species will become extinct.

All organisms that reproduce sexually experience the same environmental problem—having male gametes reach female gametes. For animals that have external fertilization, like fish and frogs, reproduction occurs in watery environments where the sperm can swim to the egg. Terrestrial animals, including reptiles, birds, and mammals, rely on internal fertilization where the sperm are introduced into the female's moist reproductive tract. Seed plants produce male gametes in tiny pollen grains that are transported to the female reproductive organ(s) of the plant by wind or animals. Non-seed plants, such as mosses and ferns, require moist conditions for the transfer of sperm to eggs.

✓ CHECK FOR UNDERSTANDING Sexual reproduction produces a variety of offspring. Why is this an advantage?

Development

The changes that take place throughout the lifetime of an organism are called **development.** It is a highly regulated process involving mitosis, cell division, and differentiation. Mitosis and cell division increase the number of living cells.

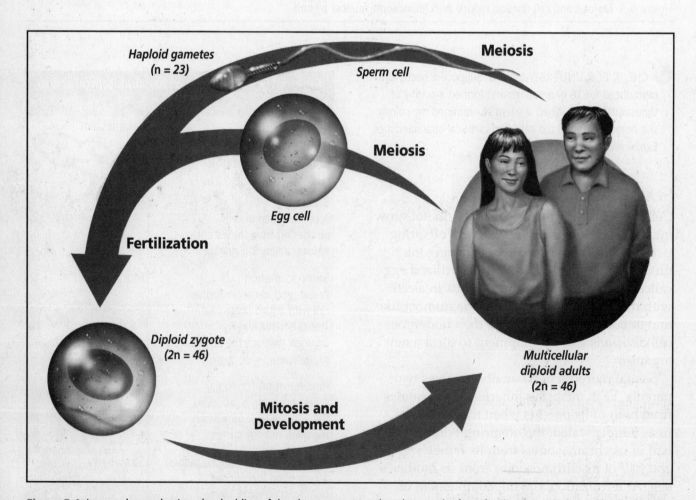

Figure 5.4 In sexual reproduction, the doubling of the chromosome number that results from fertilization is balanced by the halving of the chromosome number that results from meiosis.

In the process diagrammed below, which event does NOT occur between stages 2 and 11?

(1) a decrease in cell size

(2) DNA replication

(3) mitotic cell division

(4) fertilization

Early Embryonic Development of a Mouse

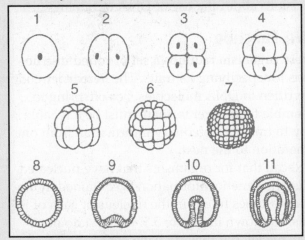

(1) Stage 1 represents a fertilized egg. Stage 11 represents the layers in an embryonic cell that will become tissues, organs, and organ systems. As a fertilized egg begins to develop, it undergoes mitotic cell divisions rapidly. In the early stages, each daughter cell formed is smaller than the parent cell as shown in the diagram.

(2) Before each cell division can occur, DNA is replicated to ensure that newly formed daughter cells contain all the genetic information necessary to maintain homeostasis.

(3) Mitotic cell divisions result in growth and development. This is represented in stages 2 through 11.

(4) Stage 1 is the zygote. The sex cells fused to make a zygote. Fertilization is not shown in the diagram.

After considering all the options, the correct answer is number 4 because fertilization is not shown.

Differentiation is the process by which these new cells specialize and become different from one another. Differentiation produces different kinds of cells, tissues, and organs that perform specific functions.

The early stages of development in many animals are similar. First, the zygote undergoes rapid mitotic cell divisions to produce a ball or disk of cells. As mitotic cell divisions continue, the ball pinches in and forms three embryonic layers, as shown in figure number eleven of the diagram in Regents Exam Strategies for Success. Then these layers differentiate to form the specialized tissues, organs, and systems of a developing embryo.

Differentiation

The many body cells in an individual can be different from one another, even though they all are descended from a one diploid cell—the fertilized egg—and have identical genetic instructions. This is because different parts of these instructions are used in different types of cells and are influenced by the cell's environment and history. Differentiation occurs in different types of cells when certain genes are expressed or turned on and others are not expressed or turned off.

For development to occur, an embryo must have a watery environment, an adequate food supply, and protection. For some aquatic animals, external development outside of the mother is possible. Some terrestrial animals, such as birds, have external development in an egg that provides protection, moisture, and nutrients. Most mammals, such as humans, have internal development in which the embryo is protected and nourished inside the mother's body.

The environment can affect reproduction and development. An example of this happened when DDT, a pesticide, spilled into a lake in Florida. Years later, biologists discovered that alligator hatchlings were abnormal in the environment surrounding the lake. One abnormality was that the males had poorly developed reproductive organs. Further research showed that chemicals from the pesticide had interfered with the natural development of alligator reproductive organs. There is much concern today of the environmental impact of chemicals on human reproduction and development.

1 After mitosis, the number of chromosomes in a newly formed cell is
   (1) double the number of the parent cell
   (2) half the number of the parent cell
   (3) equal to the number of the parent cell
   (4) double the number of both parent cells

2 If a cell with 36 chromosomes undergoes mitosis, each new cell will have
   (1) 36 chromosomes   (3) 18 chromosomes
   (2) 2 chromosomes   (4) 9 chromosomes

3 What are homologous chromosomes?

4 Mitosis and meiosis have many things in common. Which of the following statements is NOT common to both processes?
   (1) DNA is duplicated before the process begins.
   (2) Daughter cells come from one parent cell.
   (3) Prophase, metaphase, anaphase, and telophase occur.
   (4) Identical daughter cells are produced.

5 When you get a paper cut, your skin cells help to repair the injury. They do this by using the process of _____.

6 _____ includes two cell divisions and results in four daughter cells.

DNA, Reproduction, and Traits

The year 2003 marked the fiftieth anniversary of the discovery of the DNA molecule's structure. Today, **DNA**—deoxyribonucleic acid—is the topic of many TV news programs and newspaper and magazine articles. Understanding the structure of the DNA molecule is important because the coded instructions that specify the characteristics of all organisms are carried in each organism's DNA.

Coded information in DNA does two things. First, during the lifetime of all organisms, the DNA code controls the production of proteins that determine the structure and function of an organism. Second, during reproduction, the DNA code is replicated or copied and passed to the new generation. Investigations into the chemical and structural properties of the DNA molecule have helped scientists understand how genetic information is encoded in genes and replicated during reproduction.

Over the years, collaborations by many scientists have led to a greater understanding of this genetic code. Understanding the genetic information in DNA has revolutionized biology, medicine, and industry. Scientists have translated parts of the code and used this information to detect genetic diseases, to design medicines, and to study the evolutionary history of life. They also have learned how to engineer new kinds of plants and animals by changing the code or transferring DNA from one organism to another. Concerns and questions about the ethical, legal, and social implications also are products of the DNA revolution. Understanding these concerns and questions, in the light of genetics and DNA information, helps all of us make informed decisions about the use of DNA technology.

DNA Function

Every organism requires a set of coded instructions for specifying its traits. The hereditary code is written in DNA molecules. For offspring to resemble their parents, there must be a reliable way to transfer hereditary information from one generation to the next.

Recall that for organisms that have nucleated cells, the genetic information is contained in the chromosomes found in the nucleus of each of its cells, as shown in Figure 5.5. Bacteria do not have nuclei, but they do have genes and DNA. Chromosomes contain thousands of genes, and genes are segments of DNA molecules.

DNA Structure

Each chromosome is a long, spiral, ladderlike molecule of DNA called a double helix. Figure 5.6 shows a small section of a DNA molecule. DNA is made of subunits called nucleotides. Each nucleotide consists of a sugar-phosphate molecule bonded to one of four nitrogenous bases—adenine, cytosine, guanine, or thymine. In DNA, the nitrogenous bases of nucleotides only bond as either adenine—thymine (A–T) or cytosine—guanine (C–G). A and T are called complementary bases, as are C and G. These are the rungs of the ladder. Sugar-phosphate molecules make up the supporting uprights of the ladder.

✓ CHECK FOR UNDERSTANDING What is the complementary base sequence to the portion of a DNA strand with this sequence of bases—A-T-C-G-T-A?

Just as the sequence of letters in the English alphabet are arranged into words and sentences

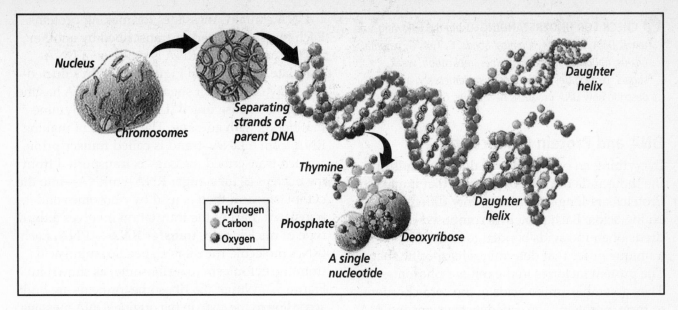

Figure 5.5 When separated, each strand of the DNA double helix acts as a template for synthesizing a new strand. Replication produces two helices, each a copy of the parent DNA.

that have meaning, so is the sequence of DNA bases. The alphabet of bases—A, C, G, and T—is arranged into three-letter words each of which can be translated into the code for an **amino acid,** the building block of proteins. A long sentence composed of these three-letter words is a gene that specifies the order of amino acids in one protein molecule. A chromosome is like a chapter of many protein sentences. These proteins control cellular chemistry and contribute to cell structure and functions that specify our traits such as eye color and blood type. During reproduction, an organism's chromosome chapters are replicated and transferred to its offspring.

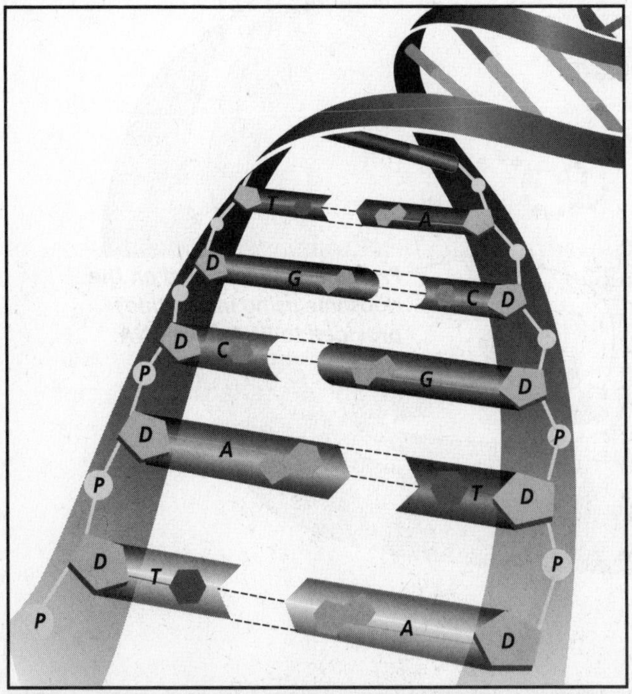

DNA Replication

Accurate replication of the sequence of DNA bases contained in genes must occur during reproduction. DNA is replicated when chromosomes are copied during both mitotic and meiotic cell divisions.

DNA replication occurs in a series of steps. Many enzyme molecules act as helpers in the process of replication. First, with the help of an enzyme, the weak bonds between paired nucleotides break. The A nucleotides pull away from their complementary Ts, and the Cs pull away from their complementary Gs. This process—often referred to as "unzipping"—forms two strands of DNA. Next, the separated strands act as templates or patterns for two new DNA molecules. The unpaired nitrogenous bases attract other free nucleotides. Once again, A bonds with T, and C bonds with G. Finally, the sugar-phosphate molecules of the newly attached nucleotides link together to form the sides of the ladder. Replication results in two DNA ladders that are identical to each other and to the original.

Figure 5.6 The structure of DNA resembles a twisted ladder.

☑ **CHECK FOR UNDERSTANDING** Using the following terms, *DNA, template, chemical bonds, C, T, A, G, parental, unzips, daughter strands, enzymes, replication, weak, sugars, phosphates, molecules, complementary,* and *bases,* describe how DNA produces new copies of itself.

DNA and Protein Production

Everything an organism is or does depends on the thousands of types of proteins that it makes. Proteins are long chains of twenty different amino acids. Each protein is composed of hundreds of amino acids bonded together in a unique order that determines its specific shape. The protein factories in the cell are ribosomes. They assemble amino acids in the correct order to form a protein. The coded instructions in DNA contain directions on how to arrange and fold the amino acids to make all of a cell's proteins. Therefore, if genes code for proteins, and proteins make us what we are, then how are proteins made from DNA?

DNA contains messages for making proteins. Each message is read or transcribed by another nucleic acid—RNA. RNA is made on a DNA template, as shown in Figure 5.7. RNA's nucleotides have a different sugar base and RNA has the nitrogenous base uracil (U) instead of thymine that bonds with adenine. The process of making RNA from a DNA strand is called **transcription.**

Each transcribed message is transported from the nucleus as **messenger RNA**—mRNA—into the cytoplasm, and then is read by ribosomes and translated. Part of the translation involves a third type of nucleic acid, **transfer RNA**—tRNA. Each tRNA molecule transfers a specific amino acid from the cytoplasm to a ribosome, as shown in Figure 5.7. Within the ribosome, proteins are built according to the code in the original DNA message.

Proteins and Traits

Different kinds of molecules carry out the work of the cell. Most of these molecules are proteins that the cell makes or synthesizes. Many proteins

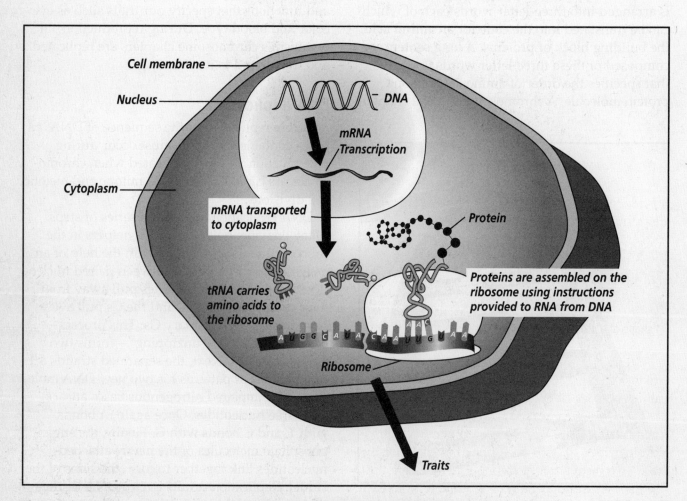

Figure 5.7 Protein production involves DNA, mRNA, tRNA, amino acids, and ribosomes.

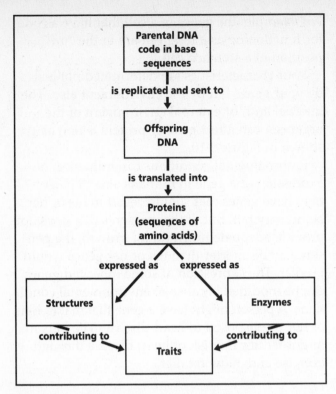

Figure 5.8 This concept map illustrates the relationship among DNA, proteins, and traits.

STEP 1 READ the Regents Question . . .

The diagram below represents a process that occurs within a cell in a human organ.

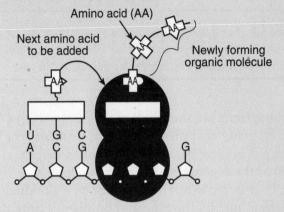

This process is known as

(1) digestion by enzymes
(3) energy production

(2) protein synthesis
(4) replication of DNA

STEP 2 ANALYZE each choice . . .

(1) Digestion is a breaking-down process not a building-up (synthesis) process.

(2) Protein *synthesis* indicates a building process. The term amino acid is an indication of protein synthesis. Proteins are made of amino acids.

(3) An energy diagram would most likely contain a graphic of ATP. Nothing in the diagram indicates that energy is released.

(4) DNA does not contain uracil (U). DNA is double stranded.

STEP 3 CHOOSE the best answer . . .

After considering all the options, the correct answer is number 2 because amino acids are the building blocks of proteins.

are enzymes that make specific cellular chemical reactions possible. Other types of proteins are used in building cell structures.

Offspring resemble their parents because they inherit similar genes that code for the production of similar proteins, which form similar structures and perform similar functions. Each type of protein has a different amino acid sequence, which determines the protein's three-dimensional shape. The shape of each type of protein, in turn, determines its function. Protein function results in the traits of an organism. Figure 5.8 illustrates the relationship between DNA and traits of an organism and its offspring.

✓ CHECK FOR UNDERSTANDING What determines the shape of a protein molecule?

A gene and the protein it produces might control just one trait. For example, some thumbs naturally bend back at the joint, as shown in Figure 5.9 on page 64. This is called hitchhiker's thumb and is a dominant trait. A person showing this trait inherited at least one dominant allele for this trait. To have a straight thumb, the recessive trait, a person must inherit a recessive allele from each parent. This means that the parents must have

inherited their alleles from their parents, who inherit them from their parents, and so on. Because a straight thumb is a recessive trait, a human can inherit the trait without it being shown, unlike a dominant trait. By observing and recording traits in several generations and throughout the extended family, we can discover some of the genes that individuals inherit.

DNA, Reproduction, and Traits • 71

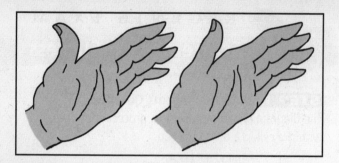

Figure 5.9 If an individual inherited two recessive alleles (bb), thumbs are straight. When an individual inherits at least one dominant allele (BB or Bb), hitchhiker's thumbs are present.

Some traits are the result of the interaction of several genes that produce several proteins. For example, several genes control human height. Each of these genes makes a protein that is involved in growth. The height of an individual is determined by the type and number of growth proteins that are coded for in his or her genes.

Some genes produce a protein that affects more than one chemical reaction or cell structure. This can result in one gene affecting many traits. For example, the gene that produces the protein fibrillin affects many body functions and structures. One abnormal fibrillin gene can produce weak tendons, ligaments, and other connective tissues in the body, including the make up of the arteries. This one defective gene has a "domino effect" on many body processes and structures.

Gene Expression

Genes are like light switches; they can be turned off or turned on by a variety of mechanisms that are dependent on the environment and history.

For example, the genes in a cell that have a code for functioning as a lung cell are in the "off" position in a stomach cell.

Your characteristics are determined not just by your genes but by the environment also. The internal and/or external environment of the organism can affect gene or protein action as shown in Figure 5.10.

Environmental conditions can influence the expression of a gene in humans also. A person may have genes that should result in his or her being very tall. But, if that person's diet does not provide adequate nutrition for growth, the person may be shorter than his or her genes would predict. The expression of some inherited genes can be modified because of environmental conditions. A person might have a gene that makes him or her predisposed to heart disease. The person might reduce the risk of heart disease through exercise and a low fat diet.

Mutations

DNA is usually replicated accurately, but mistakes can occur. The result of a change in the DNA base sequence is called a gene mutation. Gene mutations can result from an addition of one or more bases, a deletion, a substitution, or a mismatch in a DNA molecule, as shown in Figure 5.11 on page 65. Any cell containing these errors will pass them to daughter cells. If the cell is a reproductive cell, the mutation can be inherited.

When a gene mutation occurs, the DNA message has a new meaning. Now, the code for making a protein might cause the cell to produce a different protein having a different shape and

Figure 5.10 An experiment on a Himalayan hare indicates how the environment affects gene expression. Without harming the hare, an ice pack was applied to a region of shaved hair on the hare's back. It resulted in the growth of black hair instead of white hair.

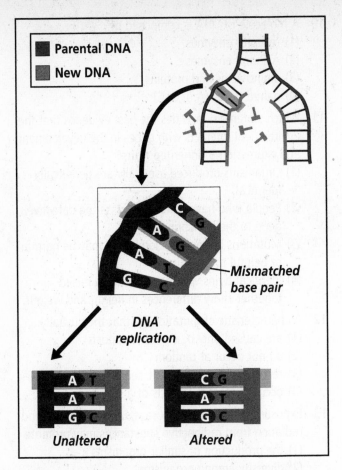

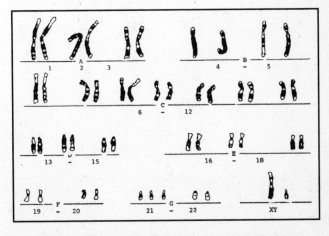

Figure 5.11 A mismatched base pair might occur during replication of DNA. In daughter cells, corresponding positions of replicated DNA will have different base pairs.

of having a child with Down syndrome increase for older mothers—those over 40 years of age.

Some mutations occur spontaneously—they have no identifiable cause. Other mutations are known to be caused by environmental factors, such as chemicals or radiation, particularly X rays or UV (ultraviolet) rays. Mutations can have a range of effects on organisms from none to serious, such as cancer or inherited diseases. Mutations occur naturally, but we can decrease the chances for mutations by avoiding environmental hazards such as cigarette smoke, radiation, and high voltage electric fields, all known to trigger mutations.

Mutations usually are harmful, but sometimes, the alteration may be beneficial because it allows for variations in offspring that increase their chances for survival. These rare mutations can provide the variation in a species that help it evolve.

Human Genome Project

Mapping, sequencing, and identifying genes; storing and analyzing data; and addressing the ethical, legal, and social issues that may arise from availability of personal genetic information are some of the goals of the U.S. Human Genome Project (HGP). The ultimate goal of the HGP is to obtain the DNA sequence of the 3 billion bases—A–T and C–G—present in human DNA. In the months and years ahead, there will be great strides made in understanding chromosomes, genes, and the proteins produced from the code of life, DNA.

function. This can lead to a change in the traits of offspring, just as a typographical error in an English composition can change, "He is here." to "He is there." In DNA, a mistake in the base sequence results in a mutation that can alter an organism.

Mutation also can occur during meiotic cell division when DNA is distributed to daughter cells. This type of mutation is called a chromosomal mutation. Offspring may inherit too many chromosomes or too few chromosomes. One example of this is Down syndrome. A person with Down syndrome has an extra chromosome 21, as shown in Figure 5.12. An individual with this chromosomal condition has distinctive facial features such as flat face, slanted eyes, and protruding tongue. Various body systems are weakened and intelligence varies greatly. Some individuals are mentally impaired while others may attend college. The odds of having a child with Down syndrome are about 1 in 700 live births. The odds

Figure 5.12 This karyotype reveals that the individual has three copies of chromosome 21 and will exhibit traits of Down syndrome.

7 Which statement best describes the relationship between the number of genes and the number of chromosomes in human skin cells?
(1) There are more genes than chromosomes in skin cells.
(2) There are more chromosomes than genes in skin cells.
(3) There are equal numbers of genes and chromosomes in skin cells.
(4) There are many genes and no chromosomes in skin cells.

8 The diagram below represents the organization of genetic information within a cell nucleus.

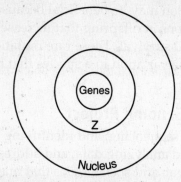

The circle labeled Z most likely represents
(1) amino acids   (3) vacuoles
(2) chromosomes   (4) molecular bases

9 New inheritable characteristics would *least* likely to result from
(1) mutations that occur in muscle cells and skin cells
(2) mutations that occur in male gametes
(3) mutations that occur in female gametes
(4) the sorting and recombination of existing genes during meiosis and fertilization

10 A molecule of DNA is composed of
(1) receptor enzymes
(2) ATP and enzymes
(3) amino acids and proteins
(4) paired bases (A, T, G, C)

11 Which statement provides the best evidence that the environment interacts with genes in the development and expression of inherited traits?
(1) Organisms produced asexually are genetically identical.
(2) People who have cancer can pass the defective gene to their offspring.
(3) Mutations happen randomly and may be harmful or helpful to organisms.
(4) Identical twins who have not been raised together show differences in height and weight.

12 A characteristic of mutations is that they usually
(1) are caused only by events in mitosis
(2) do not occur at random
(3) result in different genetic sequences
(4) occur to meet the needs of a species

13 Exposure to cosmic rays, X rays, ultraviolet rays, and radiation from radioactive substances may promote
(1) the production of similar organisms
(2) diversity among organisms
(3) an increase in the population size
(4) a change from sexual to asexual reproduction

14 When a person's teeth are being x-rayed, other body parts of this person are covered with a protective lead blanket to prevent
(1) loss of hair
(2) increase in cell size
(3) changes in DNA molecules
(4) changes in glucose structure

Part A

1 Which statement best explains the significance of meiosis in helping to maintain continuation of a species?

(1) Meiosis produces eggs and sperm that are alike.

(2) Meiosis provides for chromosomal variation in the gametes produced by an organism.

(3) Equal numbers of eggs and sperm are produced by meiosis.

(4) The gametes produced by meiosis ensure the continuation of any particular species by asexual reproduction.

2 Which diagram best represents part of the process of sperm formation in an organism that has a normal chromosome number of eight?

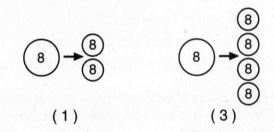

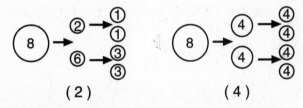

3 Which statement best explains the significance of meiosis in the process of evolution within a species?

(1) The gametes produced by meiosis ensure the continuation of any particular species by asexual reproduction.

(2) Equal numbers of eggs and sperm are produced by meiosis.

(3) Meiosis produces eggs and sperm that are alike.

(4) Meiosis provides for variation in the gametes produced by an organism.

4 Which phrases best identify characteristics of asexual reproduction?

(1) one parent, union of gametes, offspring similar to but not genetically identical to the parent

(2) one parent, no union of gametes, offspring genetically identical to parent

(3) two parents, union of gametes, offspring similar to but not genetically identical to parents

(4) two parents, no union of gametes, offspring genetically identical to parents

5 Which characteristic of sexual reproduction has specifically favored the survival of animals that live on land?

(1) fusion of gametes in the outside environment

(2) male gametes that may be carried by the wind

(3) fertilization within the body of the female

(4) female gametes that develop within ovaries

6 The diagram below shows two different structures, 1 and 2, that are present in many single-celled organisms. Structure 1 contains protein A, but not protein B, and structure 2 contains protein B, but not protein A.

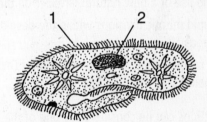

Which statement is correct concerning protein A and B?

(1) Proteins A and B have different functions and different amino acid chains.

(2) Proteins A and B have different functions but the same amino acid chains.

(3) Proteins A and B have the same function but a different series of bases (A, C, T, and G).

(4) Proteins A and B have the same function and the same sequence of bases (A, C, T, and G).

7 A certain mutant bacterial cell cannot produce substance *X*. The mutation was most likely the result of a change in the

(1) structure of the cell membrane

(2) ability of the DNA to replicate

(3) amino acid sequence of DNA

(4) gene that codes for a specific protein

8 During warm temperatures of summer, the arctic fox produces enzymes that cause its fur to become reddish brown. During the cold temperatures of winter, these enzymes do not function. As a result, the fox has a white coat that blends into the snowy background. This change in fur color shows that

(1) the genes of a fox are made of unstable DNA

(2) mutations can be caused by temperature extremes

(3) random alteration of DNA can occur on certain chromosomes

(4) the expression of certain genes is affected by temperature

9 Flower color in primrose plants is controlled by an individual gene. The sudden appearance of one white flowering primrose in a plant breeder's field of red primrose plants is most likely due to

(1) a change in the amount of glucose produced during photosynthesis

(2) the use of a new natural fertilizer on the field

(3) rapid mitotic divisions within the developing seeds

(4) a random change in the structure of DNA during meiosis

10 Mutations can be considered as one of the raw materials of evolution because they

(1) contribute to new variations in organisms

(2) are usually well-adapted to the environment in which they appear

(3) are usually beneficial to the organism in which they appear

(4) are usually harmful and cause species of organisms to become extinct

11 The presence of DNA is important for the cellular metabolic activities because DNA

(1) directs the production of enzymes

(2) is a structural component of cell membranes

(3) directly increases the solubility of nutrients

(4) is the major component of cytoplasm

12 Which event occurring in the life cycle of a bacterium most directly involves the replication of DNA?

(1) The bacterium copies its single chromosome.

(2) As the cell grows, the two copies of the chromosome separate.

(3) The cell divides as a partition separates it into equal halves.

(4) Each new cell receives one copy of the chromosome.

13 Heavy cigarette smoking and use of alcohol throughout pregnancy usually increase the likelihood of

(1) the birth of twins

(2) the birth of a male baby

(3) a baby being born with a viral infection

(4) a baby being born with medical problems

14 Which diagram illustrates fertilization that would most likely lead to the development of a normal human female?

15 Meiosis occurs in the development of sex cells. Mitosis occurs in most other cells. Identify *two* additional differences between these processes.

_____

_____

16 The chart below shows information about the relationship between the age of the mother and the occurrence of Down syndrome in the child.

Age of Mother	Occurrence of Down Syndrome per 1000 Births
25	0.8
30	1.0
35	3.0
40	10.0
45	30.0
50	80.0

State one conclusion that can be drawn from the chart concerning the relationship between the age of the mother and the chance of her having a child with Down syndrome.

_____

_____

17 Using *one* specific example, identify *one* action taken by a mother that could have a negative effect on the embryonic development of her baby.

_____

_____

18 Hemoglobin is a complex protein molecule found in red blood cells. Hemoglobin with the normal sequence of amino acids is able to carry oxygen to body cells effectively. In the disorder known as sickle cell anemia, one amino acid is substituted for another in the hemoglobin. One characteristic of this disease is poor distribution of oxygen to the body cells. Explain how the change in amino acid sequence of this protein could cause the results described.

_____

_____

19 To help them understand inherited genetic diseases, scientists study the structure and function of both DNA and protein molecules.

a Use your understanding of biology to complete the following chart that compares DNA and protein molecules.

	DNA molecules	Protein molecules
Building blocks or subunits		
One function		

b Describe the relationship between DNA molecules and protein molecules.

_____

Base your answers to questions 20 through 23 on the passage below and on your knowledge of biology.

The Mystery of Deformed Frogs

Deformities, such as legs protruding from stomachs, no legs at all, eyes on backs, and suction cup fingers growing from sides, are turning up with alarming frequency in North American frogs. Clusters of deformed frogs have been found in California, Oregon, Colorado, Idaho, Mississippi, Montana, Ohio, Vermont, and Quebec.

Scientists in Montreal have been studying frogs in more than 100 ponds in the St. Lawrence River Valley for the past 4 years. Normally, less than 1% of frogs are deformed, but in ponds where pesticides are used on surrounding land, as many as 69% of the frogs were deformed. A molecular biologist from the University of California believes that the deformities may be linked to a new generation of chemicals that mimic growth hormones. The same kinds of deformities found in the ponds have been replicated in laboratory experiments.

Some scientists have associated the deformities with a by-product of retinoid, which is found in acne medications and skin rejuvenation creams. Retinoids inside a growing animal can cause deformities. For this reason, pregnant women are warned not to use skin medications that contain retinoids. Recent laboratory experiments have determined that a pesticide can mimic a retinoid.

A developmental biologist from Hartwick College in Oneonta, New York, questioned whether a chemical could be the culprit because there were no deformed fish or other deformed animals found in ponds where deformed frogs were captured. He believes parasites are the cause. When examining a three-legged frog from Vermont, the biologist found tiny parasitic flatworms packed into the joint where a leg was missing. In a laboratory experiment, he demonstrated that the invasion of parasites in a tadpole caused the tadpole to sprout an extra leg as it developed. Scientists in Oregon have made similar observations.

20 Pregnant women are advised not to use skin medicines containing retinoids because retinoid by-products

   (1) may cause fetal deformities

   (2) may cause parasites to invade developing frogs

   (3) are the main ingredient in most pesticides

   (4) reduce abnormalities in maternal tissue

21 Which statement is most likely true, based on the information in the passage?

   (1) Only a few isolated incidents of frog deformities have been observed.

   (2) If frog parasites are controlled, all frog deformities will stop.

   (3) Deformities in frogs are of little significance.

   (4) Factors that affect frogs may also affect other organisms.

22 A possible reason for the absence of deformed fish in the ponds that contained deformed frogs is that

   (1) fish can swim away from chemicals introduced into the pond

   (2) fish cannot develop deformities

   (3) parasites that affect frogs usually do not affect fish

   (4) frogs and fish are not found in the same habitat

23 Describe how pesticides could cause deformities in frogs.

24 Although human muscle cells and nerve cells have the same genetic information, they perform different functions. Explain how this is possible.

_____

25 How would a baby's DNA sequence compare to the DNA sequence of its mother? _____

_____

26 A family has three daughters with the same parents. State whether the girls would look alike or be different, then state at least one scientific fact that helps to support your answer.

Base your answers to questions 27 and 28 on the diagram below, which provides information related to heredity, and on your knowledge of biology.

```
        ┌─────────────────────────┐
        │  Hereditary Information  │
        └─────────────────────────┘
                    │
                is stored in
                    │
                    ↓
               ┌─────────┐
               │  Genes  │
               └─────────┘
                    │
                are made of
                    │
                    ↓
                 ┌─────┐
                 │  A  │
                 └─────┘
                 ╱       ╲
              can      controls production of
              ╱               ╲
        ┌───────────┐       ┌─────┐
        │ Replicate │       │  B  │
        └───────────┘       └─────┘
```

27 The type of molecule in box *A* serves as a template. Explain what this means.

_____

28 Which molecules are represented by box *B*?

(1) bases

(2) proteins

(3) amino acids

(4) simple sugars

Part C

29 A team of behavioral scientists claimed that genes exert a strong influence on eating patterns. The research team asked 10 adult monozygotic twins and 10 adult dizygotic twins to keep a week-long diary of their meals and snacks, as well as how hungry they felt before and after each meal. Monozygotic twins develop when one developing zygote splits to form two embryos. Dizygotic twins develop from two different zygotes.

a If the scientists' hypothesis is correct, which type of twin would be expected to have the most similar eating patterns? Support your answers with a biological explanation.

_____

b Explain how the scientists' experiment could be revised to increase the reliability of their results. _____

_____

30 Proteins have many different functions in our bodies. By studying the detailed structures of protein molecules, scientists are better able to understand how proteins function normally and how some proteins with abnormal shapes can cause disease.

a Describe one function performed by a protein that your body produces. _____

_____

b Explain how the production of a protein with an abnormal shape could lead to disease. _____

_____

c State one example of an inherited disease that is caused by a change in the production of a protein.

_____

31 In studying a link between genes and enzymes, scientists found that two normal parents could produce an infant with a genetic disease that causes affected individuals to produce urine that turns black on exposure to air. The diagram below compares the cells of a normal infant with the cells of an infant with the genetic disease. The scientists analyzed normal infants and infants afflicted with the hereditary condition. Analysis supported the realization that genes can specify the activity of enzymes.

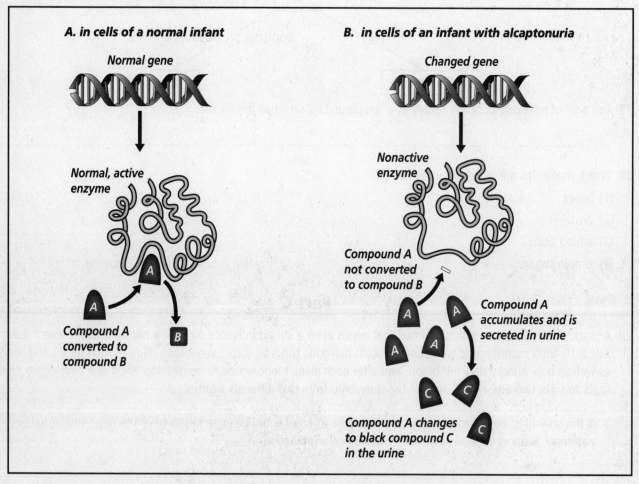

Explain how a changed gene could result in the "black urine" trait in an infant with the genetic disease. Include the following information in your explanation:

- one type of DNA alteration that could result in the genetic disorder.

- how a DNA alteration affects the protein produced by an infant with the genetic disorder.

- how it is possible for two normal parents to produce an infant with the genetic disorder.

_____

_____

Part D

Answer all questions in this part.

Directions (33–37): For those questions that are followed by four choices, circle the number of the choice that best answers the question. For all other questions in this part, follow the directions given in the question.

Chlorophyll from plant leaves can be separated using this chromatograph. A dot of chlorophyll extract is placed near one end of the filter paper or chromatograph paper. The strip is then placed in a solvent such as alcohol as shown below.

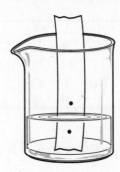

32 What is the purpose of chromatography? _____

_____

33 Explain how chromatography works. _____

_____

Directions (34–37): Use your knowledge of DNA and protein synthesis to answer the following questions.

34 Which composes a molecule of DNA?
   (1) amino acids and proteins
   (2) ATP and enzymes
   (3) paired nucleotides
   (4) receptor enzymes

35 Describe the functions of the following types of RNA.

a mRNA _____

_____

b rRNA _____

_____

c tRNA _____

_____

36 The diagram below shows a portion of a DNA molecule. The letters in the diagram represent four bases: adenine (A), thymine (T), guanine (G), and cytosine (C). Which sequence of bases do the question marks represent?

(1) C-A-C

(2) G-C-A

(3) G-A-C

(4) T-C-A

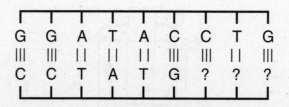

37 In most organisms, the start of translation is signaled by an AUG codon. What is the first amino acid in most proteins?

(1) isoleucine

(2) leucine

(3) methionine

(4) praline

6 Biotechnology

VOCABULARY

artificial selection
genetic engineering
hybrid
natural selection

pathogens
plasmid
recombinant DNA

restriction enzymes
transgenic organism
vectors

The term *biotechnology* refers to the application of biological sciences to our daily lives. It can include the use of living organisms and their products to improve the health of humans and other organisms. Biotechnology also can include applications of biological sciences to improve the environment or solve environmental problems.

Biotechnology Overview

Biotechnology is a part of our lives just as it was for our ancestors. Thousands of years ago, humans unknowingly applied biotechnology. They discovered how to make bread, beer, and wine. What they did not know was that these products were the result of yeast fermentation. Some people made cheese and yogurt from milk without understanding that these processes involved microbial action. They controlled the breeding of plant and animal populations by selecting and crossing varieties with desirable traits without knowing about DNA or genetics.

Natural selection is a mechanism by which populations change. Organisms best suited to an environment survive and reproduce in greater numbers. For example, plant species that produce small, lightweight seeds that are easily dispersed into new environments, as shown in Figure 6.1, have evolved in greater numbers than other plant species.

Artificial Selection

When humans began to grow crops, they recognized that seeds needed to be separated and planted. But, small seeds are difficult to harvest because they scatter and are even harder to handle for planting. Also, it takes greater amounts of small seeds than larger seeds to produce a nourishing meal. These farmers changed a biological system to meet their needs and found ways of using data and engineering techniques to solve problems. They had no manuals or laboratories but they altered natural conditions for their benefit.

Long ago, farmers noticed a new type of wheat growing. It had larger kernels than the kind of wheat that they grew. Today, it is known that the new wheat was a hybrid of emmer wheat and a type of wild oat grass. A **hybrid** is an offspring of parents that have different forms of a trait.

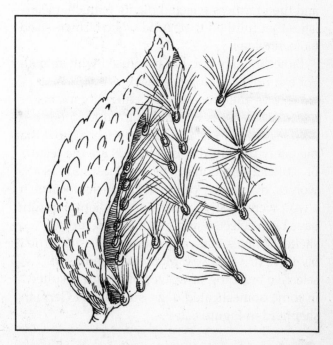

Figure 6.1 Milkweed seeds are lightweight and have thread-like structures that allow them to disperse easily into new environments.

Figure 6.2 The domesticated dog, German shepherd, resulted from centuries of artificial selection.

This hybrid wheat is known as bread wheat. The farmers knew that in order to grow more wheat, its seeds needed to be collected, separated, and planted. They observed the plants as they grew and then farmers selected plants with characteristics that fulfilled their needs. The farmers used biotechnology.

Biotechnology also has been used with animals. For example, the dog is a result of **artificial selection**—the process of breeding organisms with specific traits in order to produce offspring with identical traits. DNA comparisons show that the many present-day dog breeds are the result of artificial selection of wild canines, such as wolves, over many centuries. In ancient times, if a wolf were relatively tame or obedient, it might have been selected and given food scraps or shelter. Wolves that were more aggressive probably were driven away. Many generations of selective breeding of wolves over time resulted in some domesticated dogs, such as the German shepherd in Figure 6.2.

✓ **CHECK FOR UNDERSTANDING** Describe the process that farmers use to develop new plant and animal varieties.

Have you ever taken penicillin or another antibiotic for treatment of a bacterial infection or illness? Alexander Fleming was one of the first scientists to apply biotechnology. During his research, he discovered a mold, like the one shown in Figure 6.3, growing on one of his staphylococcus (a bacterium) cultures. He observed that no bacteria grew in the area surrounding the mold, *Penicillium*. Fleming discovered that the mold produced a substance that killed bacteria. He named the substance *penicillin*. Later, other scientists isolated, purified, and mass produced penicillin. Since Fleming's discovery of the penicillin-producing mold, many other organisms have been identified as sources of antibiotics. Fleming's observations of penicillin's effects on bacteria proved to be a true biotechnological find, and one of the most important discoveries in medical history.

Biotechnology Today

Today's biotechnology relies on the collaboration of many scientists—biologists, chemists, physicists, engineers, and computer technologists. It also involves the use of many recently developed techniques, as shown in Figure 6.4. Increasingly, scientists who work to understand life's processes are working with technologists who apply this understanding.

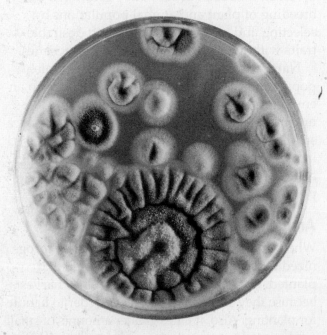

Figure 6.3 The antibiotic penicillin is derived from the mold *Penicillium notatum* shown here in its various stages of growth.

Biotechnology is advancing rapidly. There is much excitement over its benefits and potential uses. There also is a growing concern about the moral questions, current and possible ethical issues, and safety concerns that it presents. People should be aware of the processes, benefits, and risks of biotechnology. There must be extensive testing to ensure that biotechnology does not have unintended short- or long-term negative consequences. Laws are and will be legislated to govern biotechnology issues.

3   Over time, which of the following is a factor for natural selection?
    (1) learned skills
    (2) the size of an organism
    (3) ample food supply
    (4) large numbers of offspring
4   What is a hybrid?
5   Name an ancient use of biotechnology.
6   Why is Fleming's discovery of penicillin an example of biotechnology?

Quick Review

1   Define artificial selection and give one example of it.
2   The application of biological sciences to our daily lives is _____.

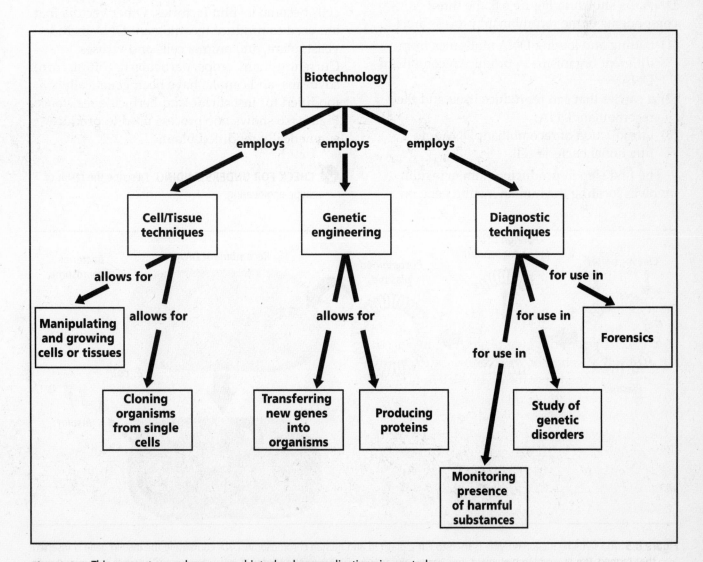

Figure 6.4 This concept map shows some biotechnology applications in use today.

Biotechnology Applications

Have you ever rearranged the paragraphs of a document by cutting and pasting them? In a similar way, **genetic engineering** involves cutting the DNA of one organism and transferring it to another organism.

Recombinant DNA

Each organism's DNA can be thought of as a unique document that consists of letters, words, and sentences. The actual editing is complex. It involves the manipulation of microscopic pieces of bacteria. Scientists can use this technique and bacteria "factories" to produce human insulin. These bacteria are known as **transgenic organisms** because they contain functional DNA from other organisms.

Connecting or recombining fragments of DNA from different sources produces **recombinant DNA.** As shown in Figure 6.5, the three components of the recombinant process are:

(1) cutting and joining DNA molecules from different organisms to produce recombinant DNA,

(2) a carrier that can reproduce itself and the recombinant DNA,

(3) introduction of recombinant DNA into a functional bacteria cell.

The first step in producing human insulin involves locating the human insulin gene on a chromosome. Then, the insulin gene is cut from the chromosome by a restriction enzyme. The **restriction enzyme** functions like scissors and cuts both strands of a DNA molecule at a specific nucleotide sequence. This produces an isolated human insulin gene.

Next, the same restriction enzyme is used to cut a **plasmid**—a small ring of bacterial DNA. If the isolated insulin genes are mixed with cut plasmids, some plasmids will attach to insulin genes. The resulting recombinant DNA has plasmids that contain human insulin and bacterial genes—the second component of the recombinant process. These bacterial plasmids are known as **vectors,** which are means for carrying DNA from one species into a new host species. Once inside the host cell, the plasmids can replicate. Finally, the bacteria with newly acquired plasmids reproduce, making millions of cells that produce the protein coded by the foreign DNA. The bacterial cells become insulin factories. Other vectors that are used to produce recombinant DNA include yeast, plant, and animal cells and viruses. Currently, many crops, particularly cotton, corn, soybeans, and canola, have been genetically modified for insecticide and herbicide resistance. Figure 6.6 shows one process used to produce a genetically modified plant.

✔ CHECK FOR UNDERSTANDING Describe the result of genetic engineering.

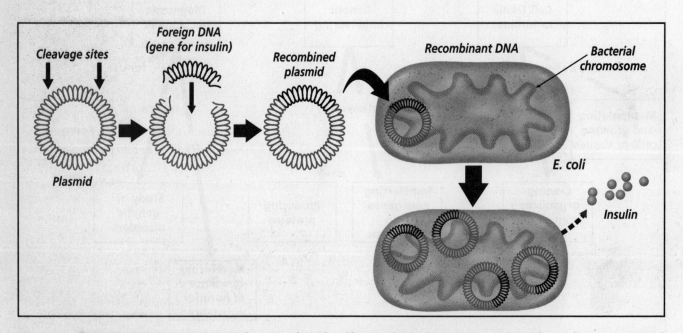

Figure 6.5 The same restriction enzyme is used to cut a plasmid and human chromosome. DNA containing the insulin gene is inserted into the plasmid. The recombinant plasmid then carries the foreign DNA into the bacterial cell, where it replicates independently of the bacterial chromosome. Each bacterial cell produces insulin, which can be used to treat patients with diabetes.

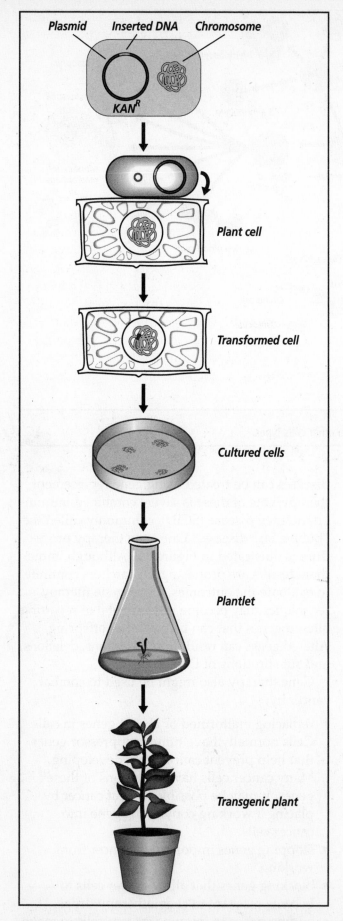

Figure 6.6 Genetic engineering is used to produce transgenic plants.

Labels in figure: Plasmid, Inserted DNA, Chromosome, KAN^R, Plant cell, Transformed cell, Cultured cells, Plantlet, Transgenic plant

Cell/Tissue Techniques

Stem cells are undifferentiated cells that have the potential to develop into different types of tissue. When you cut your finger, activated stem cells make new skin. Stem cells are in other tissues within the body, such as bone and bone marrow, as shown in Figure 6.7 on page 78. Other animals also have stem cells. For a lizard, they are the cells from which it can regenerate a new tail. Currently, mouse stem cells are the subject of much research.

In theory, stem cells could be the basis for replacements of almost any part of the human body. If stem cells could be isolated and controlled, they possibly could provide a means to cure diseases caused by cell breakdown, such as age-related macular degeneration of the eye. Stem cells also may be a way to repair tissues that cannot repair themselves, such as nerve tissue. Heart damage, spinal cord injuries, and diabetes are other conditions that might be treated or cured as a result of stem cell research.

Scientists are studying precisely how stem cells remain unspecialized and self-renewing for many years and identifying the cell signals that cause a stem cell to become specialized. One of the goals of stem cell research is to create replacement tissues and organs by treating stem cells with appropriate chemical signals.

Mammal Cloning

The first successfully cloned mammal was Dolly the sheep. Three sheep were used to clone Dolly. A body cell was taken from the mammary gland of a female sheep. An egg cell was taken from a different female sheep and its nucleus was removed. The body cell and egg cell were joined in the laboratory. The resulting zygote developed into an embryo in a test tube. Finally, the embryo was implanted in the uterus of a third female sheep, and about five months later on February 24, 1997, Dolly was born. Unfortunately, Dolly contracted a disease and died in 2003.

✅ **CHECK FOR UNDERSTANDING** Dolly was a clone of which of the three female sheep?

Other cloned mammals since Dolly include cats, cattle, and mice, but there have been many problems. Researchers hypothesize that cellular development and differentiation of an artificially fertilized body cell is not the same as that for a normal fertilized egg. Results of continuing research will support or refute this hypothesis.

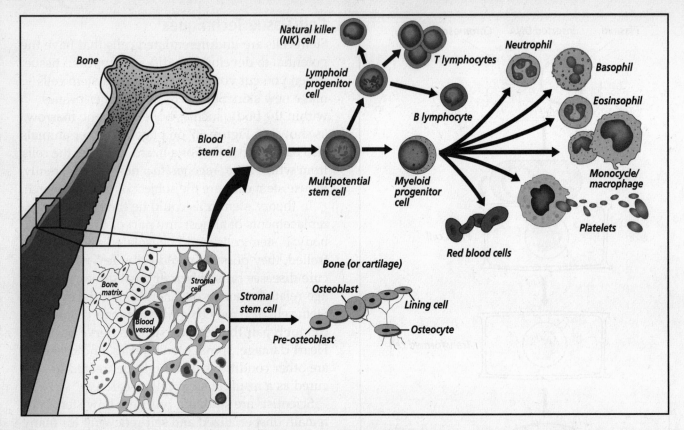

Figure 6.7 Stem cells in bones and bone marrow differentiate into other cells types.

Diagnostic Techniques

It is now possible to use the tools of DNA technology to detect many diseases and medical conditions more quickly and with greater accuracy. For example, detection tests are available that reveal the presence of **pathogens**—disease-producing agents—that cause AIDS and hepatitis. Biotechnology tools can detect certain cancers and eliminate the need for exploratory surgery. Many genetic diseases can be diagnosed using genetic technology.

Defective genes that no longer carry the correct code for the production of specific proteins may cause some human diseases. Recombinant DNA techniques are producing those missing necessary proteins.

Gene Therapy

Gene therapy is a biotechnology that holds promise for the treatment of some diseases. It involves inserting copies of a specific gene into cells to restore a missing function or to give the cells a new function. For diseases that are caused by missing or damaged genes, this is one possible way to replace a missing gene or repair a damaged one. However, only certain genetic diseases can be treated using gene replacement therapy. One of these is severe combined immunodeficiency disease (SCID), commonly called the "bubble boy disease." One gene therapy procedure is illustrated in Figure 6.8. Although immediate results are promising, researchers continue to evaluate the outcomes. Other gene therapy techniques may become instrumental in repairing altered genes that can be passed to offspring. Altered genes can result from insertions, deletions, and substitutions of DNA.

Gene therapy also might be used to combat cancer by:

- replacing malformed or absent genes in cells. Cells normally have tumor suppressor genes that help prevent cancer from developing. Many cancer cells have mutations of these genes. It may be possible to treat cancer by placing a working copy of the gene into cancer cells.
- stopping genes important to cancer from working.
- blocking genes that allow cancer cells to become resistant to chemotherapy drugs.
- adding genes to immune system cells to make them better able to detect cancer cells.

- adding genes to tumor cells so they are more easily detected and destroyed by the body's immune system.
- stopping genes that contribute to blood vessel formation around tumor cells. Tumors need a constant blood supply to grow. If this supply can be cut off, tumors may stop growing.

Organ Transplant

Organs and cells from other species, such as pigs, may be potential sources of donor organs and cells. However, when nonhuman tissue is placed in a human body, the blood flow to the area stops and cells of the immune system attack the foreign tissue. Genetic modification could be used to avoid this rejection. This technique deletes the pig gene that regulates the production of the enzyme, which is the main cause of rejection, or adds human genetic material to disguise pig cells as human cells.

DNA Fingerprinting

A biotechnology process called DNA fingerprinting is used to compare DNA sequences between individuals. It can be performed on DNA from any biological specimen and reveal or disprove genetic relationships. A technique known as polymerase chain reaction (PCR) is used to make large quantities of the DNA sample. In only three hours, over a million copies of a sample can be generated.

STEP 1 READ the Regents Question . . .
A small amount of DNA was taken from a frozen mammoth fossil. Genetic technology was used to copy and produce a large quantity of the DNA. In this technology, the original DNA sample was used to do which of the following?

(1) stimulate differentiation in other mammoth cells

(2) provide fragments to replace certain body chemicals

(3) act as a template for repeated replication

(4) trigger mitosis to obtain new base sequences

STEP 2 ANALYZE each choice . . .

(1) Because the mammoth's cells are dead, they cannot respond to any stimulus or differentiate.

(2) Body chemicals are not DNA.

(3) A template is a pattern used to make more of something. Polymerase chain reaction (PCR) uses a DNA template to make millions of copies.

(4) Dead mammoth cells are incapable of mitosis.

STEP 3 CHOOSE the best answer . . .
After considering all the options, the correct answer is number 3 because the amount of extracted DNA must be increased for testing.

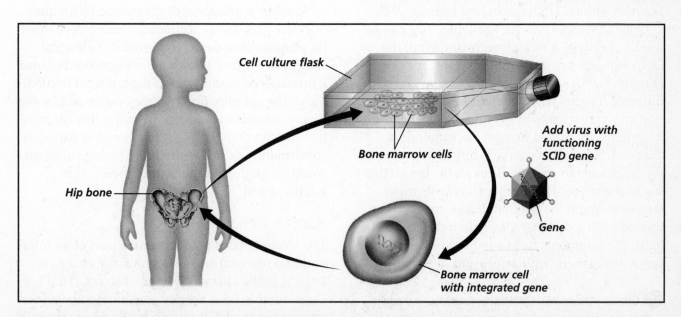

Cell culture flask

Add virus with functioning SCID gene

Bone marrow cells

Hip bone

Gene

Bone marrow cell with integrated gene

Figure 6.8 In SCID gene therapy, bone marrow cells are removed from a patient's hipbone and grown in a flask. Genetically engineered viruses containing a normal SCID gene are added. The bone marrow cells insert the normal gene into their DNA. When the modified cells are returned to the patient's bone marrow, the gene begins to function.

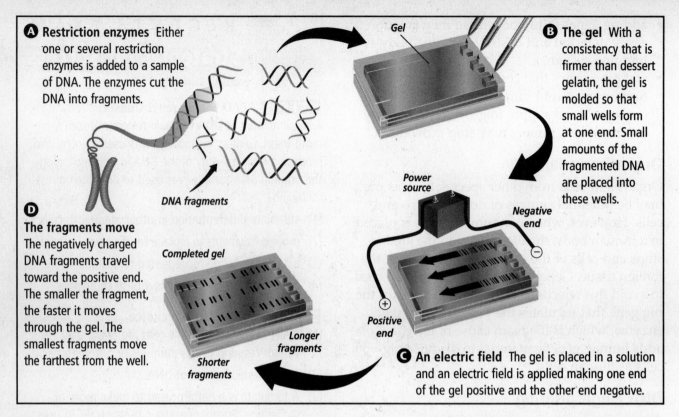

A Restriction enzymes Either one or several restriction enzymes is added to a sample of DNA. The enzymes cut the DNA into fragments.

Gel

B The gel With a consistency that is firmer than dessert gelatin, the gel is molded so that small wells form at one end. Small amounts of the fragmented DNA are placed into these wells.

DNA fragments

D The fragments move The negatively charged DNA fragments travel toward the positive end. The smaller the fragment, the faster it moves through the gel. The smallest fragments move the farthest from the well.

Completed gel

Longer fragments

Shorter fragments

Power source

Negative end

Positive end

C An electric field The gel is placed in a solution and an electric field is applied making one end of the gel positive and the other end negative.

Figure 6.9 After restriction enzymes cut DNA, scientists need to determine exactly what fragments have been formed. The DNA fragments are separated on a gel and many other techniques, such as DNA sequencing, are used to specifically identify each DNA fragment.

PCR uses heat to separate DNA strands that act as templates. Then primers—short, single-stranded sections of DNA—are added to start the process. In the presence of an enzyme, DNA replication begins when nucleotides are added. The procedure is essential to analyzing bacterial, plant, or animal DNA, including human DNA.

Once DNA samples are available, they can be used to produce a DNA fingerprint. First, the DNA samples are cut with restriction enzymes. Different DNA samples produce fragments of different lengths when cut with the same restriction enzymes as shown in Figure 6.9. Next, the fragments are placed in a gel electrophoresis chamber. An electric charge is applied that causes the fragments to migrate through the gel according to their size. The smaller fragments move farther through the gel than larger ones. When treated with a dye that glows under ultraviolet light, the fragments form a pattern of bands that can reveal genetic similarities and differences.

CHECK FOR UNDERSTANDING Parents who thought that their infant might have been mistakenly switched in the hospital's nursery requested a DNA test for the baby. To be their child, what should the test reveal?

Researchers are currently using DNA fingerprinting to study evolutionary relationships among organisms. The presence of similar bands indicates a common evolutionary history. The more similar the banding patterns, the closer the evolutionary relationship.

Another application of diagnostic techniques is a new gene-based technology being developed. Its purpose is to detect exposure to biological weapons within 24 hours after exposure because a human's cells will react to them almost immediately. The combination of genes expressed by the biological agent is unique. By using this diagnostic biotechnology within a few hours of exposure, confirmation of exposure to the biological agent could be made and the proper medication administered.

Human Genome Project

The United States government is part of an international research and biotechnology effort known as the Human Genome Project. (HGP). Considerable time, money, and energy have been invested in the HGP, and scientific breakthroughs resulting from an HGP finding are frequently reported in the popular press. The project began in 1990 with an expected completion date in 2005. Technological advances allowed completion of the human genetic sequence in 2003. Table 6.1 lists other goals of the project.

Data from the Human Genome Project will help scientists understand how the information coded in genes leads to the complex traits of an organism. Data also might lead to a better understanding of how gene mutations result in inherited diseases. Scientists can then apply this knowledge and develop new technologies to prevent, diagnose, treat, or cure diseases. It is difficult to predict what the impact of the HGP will have on biological sciences, clinical medicine, informatics, and technology.

Table 6.1 • Human Genome Project	
Goal	Status
Identify all of the approximately 30,000 genes in human DNA.	Ongoing
Determine the sequences of the 3 billion chemical base pairs that make up human DNA.	Completed
Store this information in databases.	Ongoing
Improve tools for data analysis.	Ongoing
Transfer related technologies to the private sector.	Ongoing
Address the ethical, legal, and societal issues (ELSI) that may arise from the project.	Ongoing

Quick Review

7 To determine the identity of their biological parents, adopted children sometimes request DNA tests. These tests involve comparing DNA samples from the child to DNA samples taken from the likely parents. Possible relationships may be determined from these tests because the
(1) base sequence of the father determines the base sequence of the offspring
(2) DNA of parents and their offspring are more similar than the DNA of nonfamily members
(3) position of genes on each chromosome is unique to each family
(4) mutation rate is the same in closely related individuals

8 The insertion of a human DNA fragment into a bacterial cell might make it possible for
(1) the bacterial cell to produce human protein
(2) the cloning of the human that donated the fragment
(3) humans to become immune to an infection by this type of bacteria
(4) the cloning of this type of bacteria

9 The nucleus is removed from a body cell of one organism and is placed in an egg cell that has had its nucleus removed. This process, which results in the production of organisms that are genetically alike, is known as
(1) cloning
(2) fertilization
(3) biological adaptation
(4) DNA production

10 The diagram below illustrates some key steps of a biotechnological procedure.

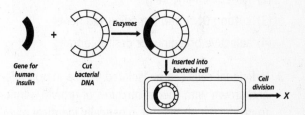

The letter X most likely represents
(1) bacterial cells that are unable to synthesize insulin
(2) human cells that are able to synthesize antibodies
(3) bacterial cells that are able to synthesize insulin
(4) human cells that are unable to resist antibiotics

11 A great deal of information can now be obtained about the future health of people by examining the genetic makeup of their cells. There are concerns that this information could be used to deny an individual health insurance or employment. These concerns best illustrate that
(1) scientific explanations depend upon evidence collected from a single source
(2) scientific inquiry involves the collection of information from a large number of sources
(3) acquiring too much knowledge in human genetics will discourage future research in that area
(4) while science provides knowledge, values are essential to making ethical decisions using this knowledge

Part A

1 "Dolly" is a sheep developed from an egg cell of her mother that had its nucleus replaced by a nucleus from a body cell of her mother. As a result of this technique, Dolly is

(1) no longer able to reproduce

(2) genetically identical to her mother

(3) able to have a longer life span

(4) unable to mate

2 Which process is a common practice that has been used by farmers for hundreds of years to develop new plant and animal varieties?

(1) cloning

(2) genetic engineering

(3) cutting DNA and removing segments

(4) selective breeding for desirable traits

3 Individual cells can be isolated from a mature plant and grown with special mixtures of growth hormones to produce a number of genetically identical plants. This process is known as

(1) cloning

(2) meiotic division

(3) recombinant DNA technology

(4) selective breeding

4 Which statement best describes the result of some of the processes involved in genetic engineering?

(1) They alter the arrangement of hereditary material.

(2) They provide energy for mitosis and meiosis.

(3) They are necessary for normal gamete formation.

(4) They reduce variation in organisms that reproduce asexually.

5 A woman has a gene that causes a visual disorder. To prevent the disorder from appearing in future generations, the defective gene would have to be repaired in the mother's

(1) nervous system   (3) eye

(2) reproductive cells   (4) uterus

6 Many diabetics use insulin made by certain bacteria. The ability of these bacteria to produce insulin was most likely the result of

(1) deleting many DNA segments from bacterial DNA

(2) genetic mapping of bacterial DNA to activate the gene for insulin production

(3) inserting a portion of human DNA into the ring-shaped DNA of bacteria

(4) using radiation to trigger mutations

7 When humans first domesticated dogs, there was relatively little diversity in the species. Today, there are many variations such as the German shepherd and the Dalmatian. This increase in diversity is most closely associated with

(1) cloning of selected body cells

(2) selective breeding

(3) mitotic cell division

(4) environmental influences on inherited cells

8 Scientists have cloned sheep but have not yet cloned a human. The best explanation for this situation is that

(1) the technology to clone humans has not been explored

(2) human reproduction is very different from that of other mammals

(3) there are many ethical problems involved in cloning humans

(4) cloning humans would take too long

Base your answers to questions 9 through 12 on the information below and on your knowledge of biology.

Organ Transplants of the Future

While most people take good health for granted, thousands of others desperately need to replace a failing organ with one that is healthy. Most healthy organs come from people who agreed to donate them upon their death, although it is possible to remove some tissue and organs (such as kidneys and bone marrow) from living donors. Unfortunately, organs for transplant are in short supply. As of 1992, over 22,000 Americans were waiting for a transplant.

Although increasingly common, transplants are risky procedures. During the operation, veins and arteries must be blocked to prevent blood loss. This deprives parts of the body of oxygen and nutrients and may result in permanent damage. In addition, the body may recognize the transplanted organ as foreign and mount an immune response in which specialized white blood cells (T-cells) attack the transplanted organ.

Drugs called immunosuppressants are given to transplant patients to prevent their immune system from rejecting the transplanted organ. However, these drugs weaken the ability of the body to fight disease and leave the patient less able to fight infection.

Scientists are exploring new technology for producing transplant tissues and organs. Unspecialized cells called stem cells are removed from the patient and then grown in a laboratory. Treating stem cells with the appropriate chemicals causes them to differentiate into various specialized tissues. In the future, scientists hope to develop chemical treatments that will cause stem cells to grow into complete organs needed for transplants. Transplants produced by this process would not be foreign material and, therefore, would not be rejected by the immune system of the patient.

9 Explain why a transplant might be dangerous to the health of a patient. _____

_____

10 State *one* reason that transplant patients might take an immunosuppressant drug. _____

_____

11 State *one* specific *disadvantage* of taking an immunosuppressant drug. _____

_____

12 Explain why doctors would consider using tissues or organs that have been grown from stem cells. _____

_____

13 Farmers or animal breeders sometimes use artificial insemination to produce new animals. In this process, sperm is collected and used later to fertilize eggs. Often the sperm samples are frozen and stored in a sperm bank until needed. The process involves placing the sperm into the female's body and allowing fertilization to occur in a normal manner.

State one benefit that using artificial insemination provides to farmers or animal breeders. _____

_____

14 For many years, humans have used a variety of techniques that have influenced the genetic makeup of organisms. These techniques have led to the production of new varieties of organisms that possess characteristics that are useful to humans. Identify *one* technique presently being used to alter the genetic makeup of an organism, and explain how humans can benefit from this change. Your answer must include at least:

- the name of the technique used to alter the genetic makeup
- a brief description of what is involved in the technique
- one specific example of how this technique has been used
- a statement of how humans have benefited from the production of this new variety of organism

_____

15 Give three examples of how the technology of genetic engineering allows humans to alter the genetic makeup of organisms.

_____

Base your answers to questions 16 and 17 on the passage below and on your knowledge of biology.

Plastics Produced by Plants

Plastics are generally thought of as materials made exclusively by human technology. However, some plants and bacteria naturally make small amounts of plastics. Furthermore, unlike synthetic plastics, plastics produced by plants and bacteria break down easily in the environment. Synthetic plastics, which are produced from petroleum, are the fastest growing type of waste in the United States. Researchers are learning how to greatly increase the amount of plastic made by plants. One day farmers may grow crops of plastic-producing plants in addition to wheat and corn crops.

A researcher at the Carnegie Institution of Washington was one of the first to attempt to use plants to make plastics. He knew that a common bacterium, known as *Alcaligenes eutrophus,* naturally produced a plastic called polyhydroxybutyrate (PHB), which resembles the type of plastic used to make garbage bags.

However, growing bacteria to produce plastic can be expensive. In order to determine if genetically engineered plants could make plastic, genes were isolated from *A. eutrophus* and inserted into plants. After a few tries, the researchers were able to produce healthy plastic-producing plants.

16 By what process were the plastic-producing plants developed? _____

17 Explain why the use of the plastic produced by these plants is better for the environment than plastic produced by human technology, and explain why this plastic would be a benefit to future generations.

_____

Answer all questions in this part.

Directions (18–25): For those questions that are followed by four choices, circle the number of the choice that best answers the question. For all other questions in this part, follow the directions given in the question.

Gel electrophoresis is a laboratory technique that can be used to separate mixtures of molecules. Use the diagram below, your knowledge of this process, and your knowledge of biology to answer the following questions.

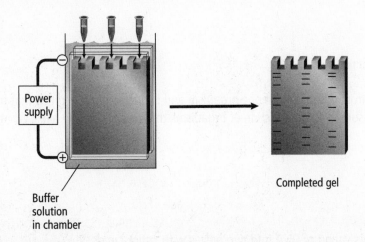

18 Which characteristic below is NOT used to separate molecules during gel electrophoresis?

(1) boiling point

(2) charge

(3) shape

(4) size

19 Which sample would you most likely place in the gel electrophoresis wells to analyze?

(1) acid

(2) carbohydrate

(3) DNA

(4) lipid

20 Explain why the gel electrophoresis instrument must have a power supply.

_____

21 State one fact about the fragments that moved the farthest in the electrophoresis chamber.

_____

Directions (22–25): Use your knowledge of DNA to answer the following questions.

22 Which can be used to transfer foreign pieces of DNA into organisms?

(1) carrier enzymes

(2) restriction enzymes

(3) test crosses

(4) vectors

23 Researchers inserted a gene for bioluminescence into mosquito larvae. What is this technology called?

(1) gel electrophoresis

(2) DNA sequencing

(3) genetic engineering

(4) polymerase chain reaction

24 The nucleus is removed from a body cell of one organism and is placed in an egg cell that has had its nucleus removed. This process results in the production of organisms that are genetically alike. What is this process called?

(1) adaptation

(2) cloning

(3) fertilization

(4) inbreeding

25 What was used to cut this strand of DNA into two pieces with "sticky ends"?

_____

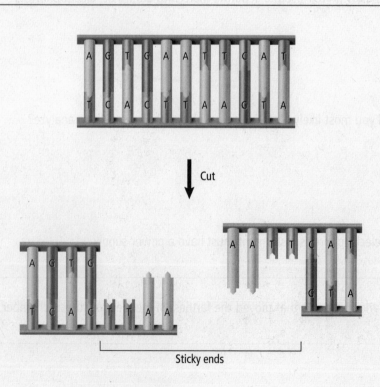

Sticky ends

7 Evolution

VOCABULARY

adaptation

artificial selection

endangered species

evolution

extinction

fossil

genetic recombination

homologous chromosomes

homologous structures

natural selection

niche

punctuated equilibrium

The central, unifying theme of biology is the theory that individual organisms and species change or evolve over an extended period of time. At present, there are over 1.5 million identified species of life on Earth. This diversity is the result of changes to organisms over time, which has allowed so many distinct life forms to evolve.

Species Change over Time

The concepts of different species evolving from a common ancestor over time and how a species changes make up the theory of evolution. These ideas were suggested by Charles Darwin during the latter part of the 19th century. Since his initial proposals, scientists have gathered evidence from many areas of science that support Darwin's original thoughts. Some of this evidence is the result of the work of geologists who have looked at fossils in Earth's crust. **Fossils** are physical evidence of organisms that lived long ago. Fossils can be found in rocks, amber, ice, or peat bogs, and at different levels of Earth's crust. Scientists use fossils to study the past.

The age of a fossil can be estimated by knowing the age of the material in which it is embedded. Fossils found at lower levels of Earth's crust can be dated to billions of years ago and those on the higher levels, perhaps, millions of years ago. A fossil record is a collection of fossils across the millennia and covers most of the time that life has existed on Earth. By studying fossil records, scientists can learn much about life as it existed long ago, extinct species, and how certain organisms evolved over time. Fossils found in the different horizontal layers of Earth's crust, as shown in Figure 7.1, can provide researchers with information about evolution.

✓ CHECK FOR UNDERSTANDING How do the fossils found in different layers of Earth's crust help to support the theory of evolution?

Biologists, biochemists, and geneticists also have added to the evidence in support of the theory of evolution. They have conducted studies that compare organisms. Their research has included the study of cell structure and function, and the processes of heredity.

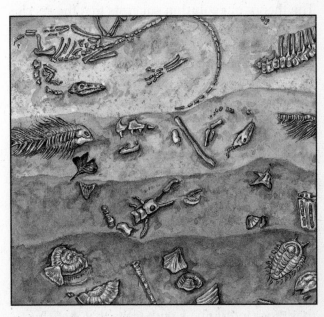

Figure 7.1 Rocks found with fossils in the layers of Earth's crust can be used to estimate the age of a fossil.

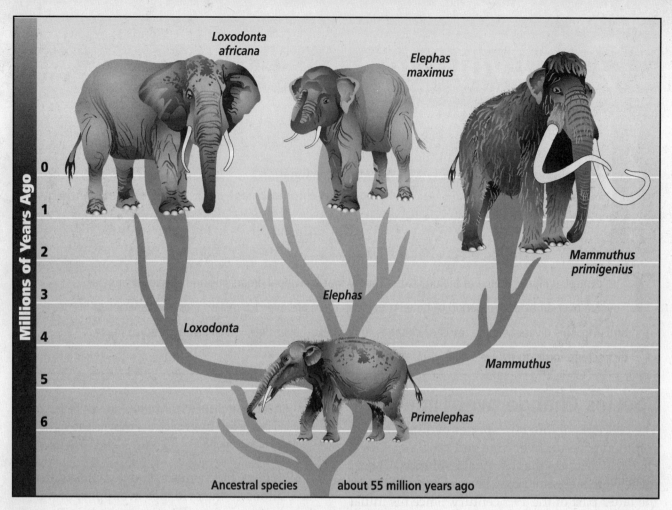

Millions of Years Ago

0
1
2
3
4
5
6

Loxodonta africana

Elephas maximus

Mammuthus primigenius

Elephas

Loxodonta

Mammuthus

Primelephas

Ancestral species   **about 55 million years ago**

Figure 7.2 Living and extinct elephant species evolved from a common ancestor.

Mechanisms of Evolution

The theory of **evolution** suggests that the species existing on Earth today developed from earlier species adapting to changing conditions. Evidence accumulated by many scientists over time indicates that life on Earth probably began billions of years ago as unicellular organisms. About 1.8 billion years ago, multicellular organisms appeared, amphibians appeared about 400 million years ago, and early reptiles appeared about 300 million years ago with dinosaurs appearing about 250 million years ago. The first mammals appeared about 225 million years ago.

Darwin hypothesized that evolution partly is due to the concept of natural selection. **Natural selection** occurs when organisms with favorable variations survive, reproduce, and pass their variations to the next generation. Darwin indicated that those individuals with traits that were best suited to meet the challenges of an environment would be more likely to survive and reproduce

than those without such traits. Those inherited traits that enabled the individuals to survive would be among all of the traits passed on to their offspring, increasing the offspring's chance of survival. Individuals not well suited to the pressures of an environment would die and/or fail to reproduce. This ensures survival of the fittest. Over time, those individuals of the species that survive and flourish show different characteristics than those of the original species and are recognized as new species. The fossil record of elephant evolution, as shown in Figure 7.2, is an example of how different species can develop from a common ancestor.

Rate of Evolution

The rate of evolution varies from species to species. The fossil record shows that some species have changed gradually over time. Most present-day organisms evolved over millions of years and are different from, but resemble, their ancestors.

However, some organisms, such as horseshoe crabs, alligators, ginkgo trees, and cockroaches, have changed little from their fossil relatives. The rate of evolution for some species is relatively rapid. Antibiotic-resistant strains of bacteria have evolved over just the past few decades. Fossil evidence also indicates that the evolution of some species occurred with sudden changes followed by long periods of little change, an idea known as **punctuated equilibrium.**

Mutation

Changes to an organism can be brought about by mutations as shown in the example in Figure 7.3. A mutation is any change or random error in a DNA sequence, the hereditary material of a cell. In unicellular organisms, all mutations to the cell's DNA are passed to offspring during reproduction. In multicellular organisms, only mutations in sex cells are passed to offspring. Mutations in body cells of an organism are not inheritable.

Traits acquired without a change in DNA are not passed to offspring. This means that if a person exercises and develops muscles, a lamb has its tail docked, or a plant is grown as a bonsai, the acquired trait only is seen in that particular organism and will not be inherited by its offspring.

Changes to DNA can be caused by many factors. Exposure to radiation can cause mutations. Sources of radiation include radon gas, X rays, ultraviolet light, and radioactive substances used in manufacturing, research, and medicine. Chemicals can cause changes in DNA. Although many, such as asbestos and dioxins, have been identified, the potential for hundreds more exists.

Mistakes during the DNA replication that precedes mitotic or meiotic cell division can be a source of mutations. Nucleotides can pair incorrectly, genes can be deleted, or gene sequences on a chromosome can change. If these changes occur in reproductive cells before they undergo meiosis to form sex cells, they can be passed to offspring.

✓ CHECK FOR UNDERSTANDING In recent years, some strains of bacteria have become resistant to anti-bacterial compounds. How could a mutation in some of these bacteria have contributed to this development?

Normal   *(Albino) Mutation*

Figure 7.3 Albinism is a relatively common mutation in which no pigmentation is present in the organism. A white rabbit with pink eyes is an albino.

Generally, mutations are harmful or neutral. Harmful mutations are usually so severe that it affects the individual's ability to survive and reproduce. Neutral mutations appear to be neither advantageous nor disadvantageous for an organism in its current environment.

There are a small percentage of mutations that are considered beneficial. Mosquitoes were initially susceptible to the pesticide DDT, and many were killed off. A few survived, however, that were resistant to the pesticide. When these mosquitoes bred, they passed this resistance on to their offspring. Able to withstand the pesticide, these mosquitoes continue to survive, thrive, and multiply, having an adaptive advantage due to the earlier mutation. Although this mutation may not be considered beneficial to humans and other species, it is considered beneficial to the mosquito since the species continues to thrive and reproduce.

Genetic Variation

In addition to mutations, changes that affect the offspring can occur during meiosis and fertilization. **Homologous chromosomes** are paired chromosomes with genes for the same traits arranged in the same order. When cells begin meiosis, the duplicated homologous chromosomes line up and exchange parts. As genes are sorted and recombined during these processes, new combinations are created that are different from the parent. This is called **genetic recombination** and results from reassortment or crossing over during meiosis, as shown in Figure 7.4. There are a limitless number of genetic combinations possible. Successful combinations will continue because they will be passed to offspring.

Those that are not successful eventually will be eliminated because individuals that carry them will not survive in sufficient numbers to reproduce effectively.

Evolutionary Changes and Genetic Variations

Whether changes in the genes are caused by a mutation or by new combinations of genes during meiosis and fertilization, the results of genetic variation occur in the structure, function, and/or behavior in individuals of a species. Variations can result in adaptations. An **adaptation** is the evolution of a structure, behavior, or internal process that enables an organism to respond to environmental factors and to live to produce offspring.

Structural Variations

Structural changes represent the evolution of the species. The structure of the present-day horse is the culmination of evolutionary changes from its ancestor of 60 million years ago. Studying the anatomy or structure of organisms also gives scientists a clue as to common traits among different species.

Investigating bone structure among reptiles, birds, and humans and other mammals, such as whales and bats, discloses a similar structure among these species. As shown in Figure 7.5, all have a large long bone, joined to two long bones that are joined to a splay of five jointed bones. These limbs also serve similar functions in each organism. When structures of different species show such similarity in structure and function, they are called **homologous structures.**

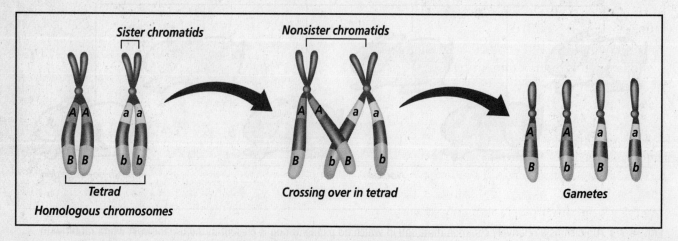

Figure 7.4 Crossing over can occur during meiosis and often is the source of gene variation.

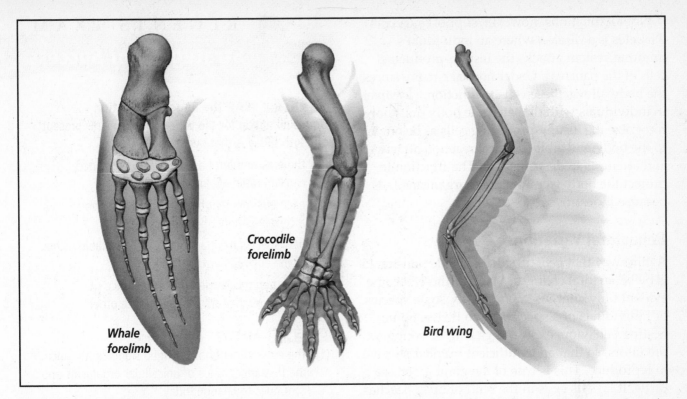

Figure 7.5 The forelimbs of a whale, crocodile, and bird are homologous structures. The bones, although modified, are similar and the forelimbs have similar functions—forms of locomotion.

Crocodile forelimb

Whale forelimb

Bird wing

They provide evidence of evolution from a common ancestor. Homologous structures have common evolutionary origins and can be similar in arrangement, in function, or both. Using this information, scientists have grouped and sorted organisms into groups they believed to have similar characteristics and therefore, a common ancestor.

✓ **CHECK FOR UNDERSTANDING** How does genetic variation affect changes in a species? Give an example of structural similarities that can be found in different present-day species.

Functional Variations

Another way in which evolutionary changes are demonstrated is by functional variations. Changes in an organism's functions are the result of a change in the DNA, because DNA controls the production of proteins that regulate cellular functions. These functions can support survival.

Skunks have a potent defense that they use against potential enemies. The skunk's noxious spray has insured its survival for eons. Bees are capable of making poisonous venom that they can inject into animals that threaten them. In some instances, this results in the death of individual

bees, but the hive of bees and the species survives. In the sea, squids and octopuses can produce a dark, inklike substance that clouds the water enabling them to escape predators. As shown in Figure 7.6, this functional adaptation improves the octopus species' chances of survival.

Figure 7.6 An octopus's cloud of ink confuses a predator long enough for the octopus to escape.

Not all functions, however, support survival. Diabetes is a disease where an individual's immune system attacks the insulin-producing cells of the pancreas. Under normal circumstances, the body allows these cells to function. However, in individuals with diabetes, the body does not recognize the insulin-producing cells as belonging to the body and a biochemical reaction attacks and attempts to destroy them. The function to protect the body from invading organisms fails because it destroys its own cells.

Behavioral Variations

A third way that genetic variation is demonstrated is by behavioral changes. Many of these become evident only after researching why some species or individuals of a species fail to thrive. Some nesting behaviors expose eggs and/or young to predators, so that an insufficient number survive to reproduce. This is true of the giant green sea turtle. It lays its eggs in the sand of open beaches with little or no protection from hungry predators. Those that hatch have a perilous trip to the water. Even in the sea, the hatchlings are prey for crabs, fish, and sea birds. In addition, humans have hunted turtles for food and for their shells. Humans also have influenced survival numbers by collecting eggs and killing adult turtles. Recently, many countries have banned turtle hunting and well-organized groups have assisted officials in protecting eggs and hatchlings to insure that more turtles survive.

Mating behaviors of species also can affect their ability to survive. In some, fights among suitors or elaborate mating rituals determine the successful mate. The most appealing and/or successful behaviors have a greater probability of securing a mate and of producing offspring with the same traits.

CHECK FOR UNDERSTANDING Name one behavior that is the result of genetic variation.

Others species demonstrate behaviors that expose them to danger, which can result in extinction. **Extinction** is the disappearance of a species when the last of its members dies. Such was the case of the now-extinct dodo bird that once inhabited Mauritius, one of the Mascarene Islands east of Madagascar in the Indian Ocean. This large flightless bird became extinct mostly

Strategies for Success

STEP 1 READ the Regents Question . . .
One explanation for the variety of organisms present on Earth today is that over time

(1) the environment has remained unchanged, causing rapid evolution.

(2) each environment has changed to support a certain variety of organism.

(3) new species have adapted to fill available niches in the environment.

(4) evolution has caused the appearance of organisms that are similar to each other.

STEP 2 ANALYZE each choice . . .

(1) The environment has changed significantly since the first appearance of unicellular organisms and continues to change today.

(2) Although the environment does change, it does not change to meet the needs of the organism. In order to survive and thrive, organisms must adapt to a changing environment.

(3) Those species with greater variations usually have better chances of adapting to fill available niches.

(4) Evolution cannot cause anything; rather, a variety of species from common ancestors is the result of evolution.

STEP 3 CHOOSE the best answer . . .
After considering all the options, the correct answer is number 3 because species that survive in a changing environment are those that are able to adapt.

because of what happened when humans invaded this previously uninhabited island.

Sailing ships visited Mauritius looking for food to replenish their food stores. Sailors found the slow-moving dodos easy prey. Their meat was not particularly tasty, but it was free and readily available. In addition, the female dodo laid only one egg in an unprotected nest on the ground. Pigs and monkeys introduced to the islands by sailors easily found dodo nests and devoured their contents. By the late 1600s, dodos were gone from Mauritius.

1 The first life-forms to appear on Earth were likely
   (1) simple unicellular organisms
   (2) simple multicellular organisms
   (3) complex unicellular organisms
   (4) complex multicellular organisms

2 Which statement is best supported by fossil records?
   (1) Many organisms that lived in the past are now extinct.
   (2) Organisms that live in the same habitat have the same environmental needs.
   (3) The struggle for existence between organisms results in changes in populations.
   (4) Structures such as leg bones and wing bones can originate from the same type of tissue found in embryos.

3 A doctor prescribes an antibiotic for a patient with a bacterial infection, and within ten days, the patient has recovered. Several months later, the patient returns with the same bacterial infection, the doctor prescribes the same medication, but this time the patient does not respond and a different antibiotic must be prescribed. What could be the reason that the antibiotic did not work the second time?

4 The rate of evolution varies for different species. How would changes in the environment affect this rate?

5 What are some environmental factors that cause changes to DNA? Name at least one that can be controlled to some extent by humans. Name at least one cause that cannot be controlled by humans.

6 How does the study of fossils represent the evolution of species over geological time?

7 What are the ways that genetic variation can occur in a species?

8 In what three areas can genetic variation cause changes in a species?

9 Genetic variation can be the result of meiosis. How do the gametes produced provide variation for offspring?

10 A tame, domesticated duck is attacked by an aggressive dog and loses part of its wing. As a result, it is unable to fly, but survives as a protected pet. When the eggs she lays hatch, all the ducklings have normal wings and eventually fly. Explain this using the concepts of the theory of natural selection.

11 Grasshoppers vary in color from a sandy shade to a deep green. In summers when there is a great deal of consistent rainfall, there are more green grasshoppers than those of the lighter, sandy shade. During arid summers, there are more sandy colored grasshoppers than green ones. What could be the causes of this?

Patterns of Evolution

Evolution can occur over time as described by Darwin's concept of natural selection. In addition to Darwin's initial proposals, scientists have determined several factors that affect the selection and survival of those species best adapted to the environment and able to survive and reproduce. Those factors are:

- the species overproduces
- the species demonstrates a wide variety in its offspring due to mutation and recombination of genes
- individuals with successful variations will pass them to offspring
- a finite supply of resources

Overproduction

Successful species have the potential to produce offspring in such numbers that if they were all to avoid predators and disease and reach adulthood, they would overpopulate the world. However, in nature, only individuals with traits that ensure their survival live to reproductive age. Populations of successfully adapted species remain relatively stable, regardless of how many offspring are produced. For example, some species of fish produce millions of eggs, to have only a few hundred survive to adulthood.

✓ CHECK FOR UNDERSTANDING Successful species have the potential to overproduce. Why is this important for the survival of the species?

Species Variation

Within any species, there exists a wide variety of physical characteristics due to genetic variation. These variations include but are not limited to height, weight, color, shape, form, certain abilities, and adaptability. Under similar circumstances, some individuals will meet the challenges of an environment in particular ways, while others will use alternative solutions.

In nature, organisms produce more offspring than can survive. Fishes sometimes can lay millions of eggs.

In any population, individuals have variations. Fishes may differ in color, size, and speed.

Individuals with certain useful variations survive in their environment, passing those variations to the next generation.

Over time, offspring with certain variations make up most of the population and may look entirely different from their ancestors.

Figure 7.7 Darwin proposed the idea of natural selection to explain how species, such as the fish shown here, change over time.

Humans have influenced species variation by selectively breeding organisms. The process of breeding organisms with specific traits in order to produce offspring with identical traits is **artificial selection.** Pedigree dogs have been bred for centuries for the traits that distinguish them from other breeds. Those individuals exhibiting the desired traits are selected and bred with other equally desirable individuals. In a similar manner, plants also have been selectively bred for disease resistance, size, abundance of fruit, color, hardiness, etc. In some cases, artificial selection is used in an attempt to save an endangered species.

Finite Resources

All species in an environment use the resources of that environment. Most of these resources are limited, and individuals within a species must compete with one another for those resources. Although random events, such as being in the right place and the right time, do affect the success of some members, in general, those with beneficial adaptive characteristics will be successful and survive to reproduce. Therefore, those advantageous characteristics are passed to their offspring. In the next generation, those individuals who demonstrate successful adaptations will survive and reproduce, and the percent of these individuals will increase in each successive generation, as shown in Figure 7.7.

Several species may exist in the same habitat and appear to be competing for the same resources. Although different species share the same habitat, the manner in which each species adapts to that environment differs. Each species holds a **niche**—the role or position a species has in its environment and includes all interactions with living and nonliving elements as an animal meets its needs for survival and reproduction. The turkey vulture and the horned owl often share the same habitat, however, they have adapted differently. The vulture feeds on carrion and is active during daylight hours. The owl captures and feeds on living animals and is active at night. Each has its own niche and can coexist until competition for finite resources forces change.

✓ **CHECK FOR UNDERSTANDING** One of the factors that affects the adaptation of a species to the environment is a finite supply of resources. Explain how this occurs.

Species Decline

When a species is unable to respond successfully to the pressures of the environment, its populations will start to dwindle. Eventually, it will reach a point where the number of surviving individuals cannot sustain reproduction. When this occurs, the species is said to be endangered. An **endangered species** is one in which the number of individuals falls so low that extinction is possible.

Governments and organizations have taken steps to protect endangered species and create opportunities for the population to increase. These efforts have been successful in saving and increasing the populations of bald eagles, peregrine falcons, and other species.

A concern of many people today is the needless slaughter of animals, such as elephants, for commercial purposes. In some instances, the desire to protect an endangered species conflicts with the needs of other species, and with political and/or commercial interest. Those forces complicate the problem.

The bald eagle came close to extinction because, among other things, the widely used pesticide DDT affected the shells of the eggs of the eagle. This resulted in a drastic decline in the number of eaglets surviving each year. The banning of DDT and efforts of conservation groups have contributed to the increase in bald eagle populations.

Breeding captive animals for future release can be successful for some endangered species, such as the peregrine falcon. Attempts to breed the giant panda have been less successful. Restoring habitats and providing viable alternatives are additional methods that have been successful.

Extinction of species is not a recent phenomenon. Fossil evidence indicates that most of the species that have lived on Earth are now extinct. The dinosaurs became extinct millions of years ago after having roamed Earth for eons. Although there is much speculation as to how this came about, most agree that a radical change in the environment with which the animals were ill equipped to deal, signaled their demise.

Quick Review

12 What can occur if a species is too successful and overproduces?

13 There is variation among individuals of the same species that occurs normally. Why is this important to the survival of the species?

14 Thousands of years ago, a large flock of hawks was driven from its normal migratory route by a severe storm. The birds scattered and found shelter on two distant islands, shown on the map below. The environment of island A is very similar to the hawk's original nesting region. The environment of island B is very different from that of island A. The hawks have survived on these two islands with no contact between the populations. Which statement accurately predicts the present-day conditions of these two hawk populations?

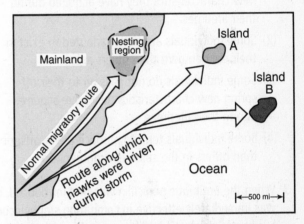

(1) The hawks that landed on island B have evolved more than those on island A.
(2) The hawks that landed on island A have evolved more than those on island B.
(3) The populations on islands A and B have undergone identical mutations.
(4) The hawks on island A have given rise to many new species.

Part A

1 Which ecosystem has a better chance of surviving when environmental conditions change over a long period of time?

(1) one with a great deal of genetic diversity

(2) one with plants and animals but no bacteria

(3) one with animals and bacteria but no plants

(4) one with little or no genetic diversity

2 According to the theory of natural selection, why are some individuals more likely than others to survive and reproduce?

(1) Some individuals pass on to their offspring new characteristics they have acquired during their lifetimes.

(2) Some individuals are better adapted to exist in their environment than others are.

(3) Some individuals do not pass on to their offspring new characteristics they have acquired during their lifetimes.

(4) Some individuals tend to produce fewer offspring than others in the same environment do.

3 When the antibiotic penicillin was first introduced, it was immediately effective in combating staphylococcus bacterial infections. After a number of years, there were outbreaks of staphylococcal infections that did not respond to treatment with penicillin. The best explanation for this situation is that

(1) members of the original population of bacteria that were penicillin resistant survived and reproduced, creating a more resistant population

(2) the bacteria that survived exposure to penicillin learned to avoid it

(3) the bacteria that caused the new outbreaks were from populations that had never been exposed to penicillin

(4) during each generation, the bacteria modified their own DNA to increase their ability to resist penicillin and passed this ability on to their descendants

4 Which statement about the rates of evolution for different species is in agreement with the theory of evolution?

(1) They are identical, since the species live on the same planet.

(2) They are identical, since each species is at risk of becoming extinct.

(3) They are different, since each species has different adaptations that function within a changing environment.

(4) They are different, since each species has access to unlimited resources within its environment.

5 Which concept is not a part of the theory of evolution?

(1) Present-day species developed from earlier species.

(2) Some species die out when environmental changes occur.

(3) Complex organisms develop from simple organisms over time.

(4) Change occurs according to the needs of an individual organism to survive.

6 Even though the environment changes, a population that occupies a given geographic area will most likely continue to be found in this area if the

(1) variations in the population decrease over time

(2) members of the population decrease in number

(3) members of the population exceed the carrying capacity

(4) population passes on those genes that result in favorable adaptations

7 State what could happen to a species in a changing environment if the members of that species do not express any genetic variations.

_____

8 A European species of rabbit was released on a ranch in Victoria, Australia. The species thrived and reproduced rapidly. The rabbits overgrazed the land, reducing the food supply for the sheep. The _Myxoma sp._ virus was used to kill the rabbits. The first time this virus was applied, it killed 99.8 percent of the rabbits. When the rabbits became a problem again the virus was applied a second time. This time, only 90 percent of the rabbits were killed. When the rabbits became a problem a third time, the virus was applied once again, and only 50 percent of the rabbits were killed. Today, this virus has little or no effect on this species of rabbit. Explain what happened to the species of rabbit as a result of the use of this virus. You must _include_ and _circle_ the following terms in your answer.

- gene
- adaptive value _or_ adaptation _or_ adapted
- variation
- survival of the fittest

_____

Base your answers to questions 9 and 10 on the information and graph below and on your knowledge of biology.

A small community that is heavily infested with mosquitoes was sprayed weekly with the insecticide DDT for several months. Daily counts providing information on mosquito population size are represented in the graph below.

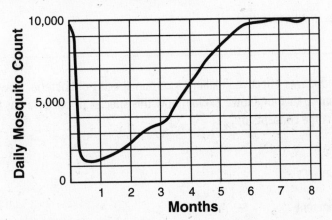

9 Which statement best explains why some mosquitoes survived the first spraying?

(1) The weather in early summer was probably cool.

(2) Most of the mosquitoes were of reproductive age.

(3) Environmental factors varied slightly as the summer progressed.

(4) Natural variation existed within the population.

10 What is the most probable reason for the decreased effectiveness of the DDT?

(1) DDT caused mutations in the mosquitoes, which resulted in immunity.

(2) DDT was only sprayed once.

(3) Mosquitoes resistant to DDT lived and produced offspring.

(4) DDT chemically reacted with the DNA of the mosquitoes.

11 When Charles Darwin was developing his theory of evolution he considered variations in a population important. However, he could not explain how the variations occurred. Name *two* processes that can result in variation in a population. Explain how these processes actually cause variation.

_____

12 According to the interpretation of the fossil record by many scientists, during which time interval shown on the time line below did multicellular organisms appear on Earth?

_____

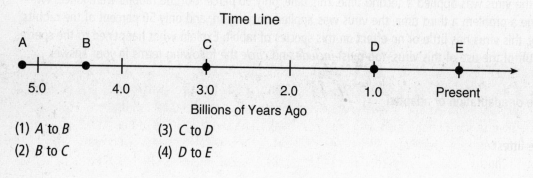

Time Line

A   B   C   D   E

5.0   4.0   3.0   2.0   1.0   Present

Billions of Years Ago

(1) *A* to *B*   (3) *C* to *D*

(2) *B* to *C*   (4) *D* to *E*

Part C

13 Some people claim that certain carnivores should be destroyed because they kill beneficial animals. Explain why these carnivores should be protected. Your answer must include information concerning:

- prey population growth
- extinction
- importance of carnivores in an ecosystem

_____

14 In the past, a specific antibiotic was effective in killing a certain species of bacteria. Now, most members of this bacterial species are resistant to this antibiotic. Explain how this species of bacteria has become resistant. Your answer must include at least the concepts of:

- overproduction
- variation
- natural selection
- adaptation to the environment

_____

Base your answers to questions 15 through 17 on the diagram at right and on your knowledge of biology. The diagram shows an interpretation of relationships based on evolutionary theory. The letters represent different species.

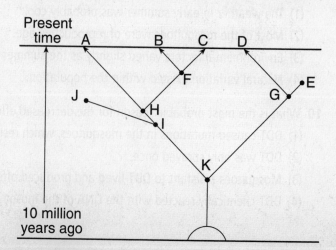

15 Explain why species B and C are more closely related than species A and C are.

_____

16 The diagram indicates that a common ancestor for species *C* and *E* is species

(1) *F*

(3) *H*

(2) *G*

(4) *K*

17 Which species are *least* likely to be vital parts of a present-day ecosystem?

(1) *A* and *E*

(3) *E* and *J*

(2) *C* and *D*

(4) *B* and *F*

Part D

Answer all questions in this part.

Directions (18–21): Base your answers on the information and diagram below and your knowledge of biology.

Many biologists believe that the Galápagos Island finches are descendents of a similar species found on the mainland in South America. When the ancestral birds arrived on islands, they began to occupy diverse ecological niches. As a result, the ancestral finches split into diverse populations each with their own beak characteristics. Some of the finches evolved into separate species. Today, the 14 species of finches are divided into four groups: the ground finches, the tree finches, the warbler finches, and the vegetarian finches. A representative from each group is shown below.

Ground finch   Tree finch   Vegetarian finch   Warbler finch

18 When Charles Darwin was developing his theory of evolution, he considered variations in a population important. However, he could not explain how the variations occurred. Which two processes could cause variations?

(1) symbiosis and metamorphosis

(2) commensalism and mutualism

(3) crossing over and mutations

(4) phagocytosis and pinocytosis

19 In order for evolution to occur, what must happen in a population?

(1) genetic drift

(2) geographic isolation

(3) natural selection

(4) reproductive isolation

20 Scientists can estimate more accurately at what point various groups of organisms diverged evolutionarily from one another by using which source of information?

(1) fossil record

(2) DNA evidence

(3) migration patterns

(4) genetic equilibrium

21 According to the theory of natural selection, why are some individuals more likely than others to survive and reproduce?

(1) They pass on to their offspring new characteristics they acquired during their lifetimes.

(2) They are better adapted to exist in their environment than others.

(3) They do not pass on to their offspring new characteristics they have acquired during their lifetimes.

(4) They tend to produce fewer offspring than do others in the same environment.

Directions (22–23): Base your answers on the information and diagram below and your knowledge of biology.

Nearly one-third of the world's population of fruit flies, *Drosophila*, exists on the Hawaiian Islands. These flies are believed to have evolved from a small group of colonizers. These flies have adapted to an assortment of ecological niches that include predators, parasites, and herbivores. Another group of flies found on the Hawaiian Islands, *Scaptomyza,* has also adapted well. There are as many as 300 species of *Scaptomyza* on the islands. Upon closer inspection of the approximately 800 species of the two genera, biologists believe that the flies evolved from a single common ancestor. The evolution of *Drosophila* in the Hawaiian Islands is very similar to the evolution of the finches in the Galapagos Islands.

22 Biologists believe that the great diversity of these flies is due to the geological formation of the islands. New islands continually form and are colonized by the flies from the other islands. Explain why this process results in such a variety of new species.

_____

23 Which term best describes the pattern of evolution exhibited by the finches on the Galápagos Islands and the *Drosophila* flies on the Hawaiian Islands?

(1) adaptive radiation

(2) coevolution

(3) convergent evolution

(4) rapid speciation

alveoli
amylase
aorta
atria
autonomic nervous
   system (ANS)
cardiac muscle
cartilage
central nervous
   system (CNS)
cerebellum
cerebrum
development
diaphragm
endocrine glands

epididymis
epiglottis
fetus
follicle
hemoglobin
homeostasis
hormone
joint
ligament
lymph
medulla oblongata
menstrual cycle
negative feedback
   system
nephron

neuron
neurotransmitter
ovary
oviduct
ovulation
pepsin
peripheral nervous
   system (PNS)
peristalsis
pharynx
placenta
reflex
semen
seminal vesicles
skeletal muscle

smooth muscle
somatic nervous
   system
synapse
tendons
trachea
umbilical cord
ureter
urethra
uterus
vas deferens
ventricles
villus
zygote

Human Body—Structure and Function

The human body is a complex organism composed of cells, tissues, organs, and organ systems. Human organ systems interact to perform life functions that maintain **homeostasis**—the process of regulation of an organism's internal environment. These interactions include all metabolic processes such as taking in and digesting food, distributing nutrients and oxygen throughout the body, responding to changes in the environment, and eliminating wastes. A disruption to any body system may cause an imbalance in homeostasis.

Organs and organ systems provide all cells with their basic needs. Different kinds of cells exist in the body and are grouped in ways to help them function together.

Digestive System

The human digestive system consists of a one-way alimentary canal, or gastrointestinal tract, as shown in Figure 8.1. It also includes accessory organs such as the tongue, liver, gallbladder, and pancreas.

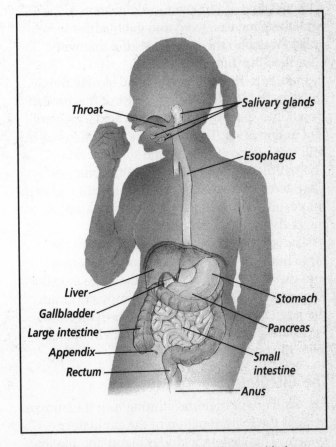

Figure 8.1 The human digestive system begins with the mouth and ends with the anus.

Mechanical and chemical digestion begin in the mouth. Chewing breaks food into smaller pieces. Salivary glands secrete saliva that moistens food. It contains the enzyme **amylase** that chemically helps to break down starch. The tongue moves food to the back of the mouth where it is swallowed and enters the esophagus. Food moves by **peristalsis**—a series of involuntary smooth muscle contractions—to the stomach.

The stomach is a muscular organ where digestion continues. Peristalsis churns and mashes food, and glands in the stomach lining secrete gastric juices, such as pepsin and hydrochloric acid. **Pepsin** helps begin the chemical digestion of proteins. Hydrochloric acid provides the proper pH for pepsin to work effectively.

✓ **CHECK FOR UNDERSTANDING** How does the action of hydrochloric acid effect digestion in the stomach?

From the stomach, partially digested food enters the small intestine—a muscular, convoluted tube about 6 m long and about 2.5 cm in diameter. Glands lining the intestine secrete enzymes that aid in chemical digestion. In addition, the pancreas, liver, and gallbladder secrete substances into the small intestine that help complete the digestion process.

Liquid, partially digested food slowly moves through the small intestine. Most of it is broken down into glucose (sugar), fatty acids, glycerol, and amino acids. Tiny fingerlike projections called villi (singular, *villus*) line the small intestine. Each villus contains a network of capillaries. Digested food molecules move into villi and then into capillaries, and eventually reach all parts of the body by the circulatory system.

Undigested foods and water pass into the large intestine or colon. Water and salts move into capillaries in the walls of the large intestine. Remaining wastes, called feces, move through the large intestine by peristalsis to the rectum. Feces are stored in the rectum and eliminated from the body through the anus.

The Circulatory System

The delivery of materials throughout the human body is the main function of the circulatory system. This system includes blood and blood vessels, lymph and lymph vessels, and the heart.

Blood is a tissue composed of plasma, red blood cells, white blood cells, and platelets. Plasma is approximately 90 percent water. It transports blood cells, wastes, nutrients, antibodies, enzymes, and hormones.

Red blood cells are round, disk-shaped cells that are produced and mature in the marrow of some long bones. Red blood cells contain **hemoglobin**—an iron-containing molecule that carries oxygen to the body's cells. A red blood cell loses its nucleus as it matures.

White blood cells fight infections and are produced in the bone marrow and lymph tissue. They are larger than red blood cells and contain one or more nuclei. There are several types of white blood cells, such as phagocytes and lymphocytes.

Platelets are small, non-nucleated fragments of cytoplasm surrounded by a cell membrane. Platelets are involved in the clotting of blood.

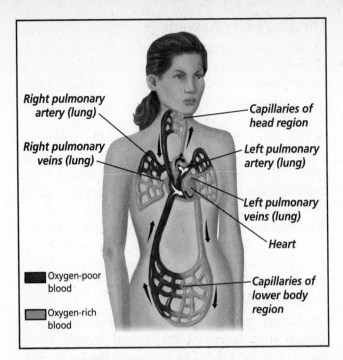

Right pulmonary
artery (lung)

Right pulmonary
veins (lung)

Capillaries of
head region

Left pulmonary
artery (lung)

Left pulmonary
veins (lung)

Heart

■ Oxygen-poor
blood

■ Oxygen-rich
blood

Capillaries of
lower body
region

Figure 8.2 In the circulatory system, oxygen-poor blood and oxygen-rich blood do not mix.

✓ CHECK FOR UNDERSTANDING What is the function of plasma, red blood cells, white blood cells, and platelets?

The blood vessels—arteries, veins, and capillaries—transport blood throughout the body. Arteries carry blood away from the heart to all parts of the body. The thick, muscular artery walls are elastic and expand when the heart contracts and contract when the heart relaxes. This rhythmic expanding and contracting of arteries is your pulse.

Capillaries are microscopic and have walls only one cell thick. They connect arteries to veins and are where the exchange of nutrients and gases occurs between the blood and the surrounding body cells.

Veins carry blood from body cells back to the heart. They are thin-walled and carry blood that is under a lower force than in arteries. The contraction of skeletal muscles helps move the blood in veins. Veins have one-way valves that prevent the backflow of blood.

Lymph forms from a portion of plasma that diffuses out of capillaries and helps transport dissolved materials between capillaries and body cells. Excess intercellular fluid enters lymph

vessels by diffusion. Once inside, this fluid is called lymph. Lymph vessels merge, forming larger vessels, until all lymph flows into two large lymph ducts that empty into veins near the heart. Fluid returns to blood plasma through this process. Major lymph vessels have enlarged regions called lymph nodes that filter pathogens from the lymph.

The heart is a muscular, four-chambered organ that pumps blood into the blood vessels, as shown in Figure 8.2. The two upper chambers of the heart are the **atria** (singular, *atrium*) and the two lower chambers of the heart are the **ventricles.**

Oxygen-poor blood from the body returns to the right atrium through two large veins. It flows from the right atrium into the right ventricle from which it is pumped through the pulmonary arteries to the lungs. In the lungs, carbon dioxide, water vapor, and other gaseous wastes move from the blood, and oxygen enters the blood. The oxygen-rich blood returns through the pulmonary veins to the left atrium. Then it flows into the left ventricle that pumps it into the **aorta,** the largest artery in the body. From the aorta, oxygen-rich blood flows to all parts of the body. When blood reaches cells, oxygen moves into cells and carbon dioxide and other cellular wastes move into blood.

✓ CHECK FOR UNDERSTANDING Describe the transport of oxygen-poor blood from body cells to the lungs.

Respiratory System

The human respiratory system is involved in breathing and gas exchange. It consists of two lungs and the network of passageways that connect the external environment and lungs. Air enters the respiratory system through the nose and/or mouth. In the nose, it moves into the nasal cavity that is lined with ciliated cells that secrete mucus. These cells clean, warm, and moisten the air.

From the nasal cavity, air enters the **pharynx,** or throat, and passes by the **epiglottis**—a protective flap of tissue that keeps food and liquids from entering the airway. Air moves down past the larynx, or vocal cords, into the trachea or windpipe. The **trachea** is a stiff tube lined with mucous-secreting ciliated cells. These cells also trap foreign material.

The lower end of the trachea splits to form two tubes called the bronchi (singular, *bronchus*) that extend into the lungs and branch into small tubes called bronchioles. Eventually, bronchioles branch into microscopic tubes that branch into hollow air sacs called **alveoli** (singular, *alveolus*), shown in Figure 8.3. The lungs consist of thousands of alveoli. Capillaries surround each alveolus where oxygen and carbon dioxide move by diffusion between the alveolus and capillaries.

✓ **CHECK FOR UNDERSTANDING** How does the exchange of oxygen and carbon dioxide take place in alveoli?

The rate of breathing is controlled by the brain in response to the level of carbon dioxide in blood. When the level increases, impulses that increase the contraction and relaxation of muscles are sent to rib muscles and to the **diaphragm**—the sheet of muscles below the lungs. When the diaphragm and the rib muscles contract, the chest's volume increases, which lowers air pressure in the chest. This process, known as inhalation, allows air to move into the lungs. The opposite condition, exhalation, forces air from the lungs. When the carbon dioxide level in the blood drops, the breathing rate decreases.

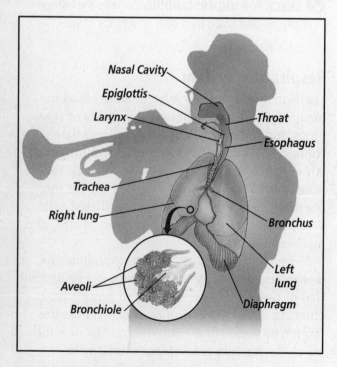

Figure 8.3 Air moves from the environment to the lungs through the respiratory system.

The Excretory System

Excretion is the removal of metabolic wastes, such as carbon dioxide, water, salts, and urea, from the body. These wastes move in the blood from body cells to organs, such as lungs, sweat glands, and kidneys, where they are excreted.

The skin contains sweat glands, which excrete water, salts, and small amounts of urea as perspiration. These substances move by diffusion from capillaries into sweat glands, and then into ducts that lead to pores on the skin's surface. When perspiration evaporates from the skin's surface, heat is absorbed from skin cells. This helps maintain the body's normal temperature.

The Urinary System

The human urinary system consists of the kidneys, ureters, urinary bladder, and urethra, as shown in Figure 8.4. The kidneys remove from blood urea that is produced by the liver from the breakdown of excess amino acids. They also regulate the concentrations of most of the substances in body fluids.

Each bean-shaped kidney consists of about one million small filtering units called **nephrons.** Blood flows into each nephron where water, salts, urea, glucose, vitamins, and some amino acids are forced out under pressure. Then, in another part of the nephron, water, glucose, amino acids, and some salts move back into the blood. The remaining fluid is known as urine. The kidneys produce about 2L of urine a day.

✓ **CHECK FOR UNDERSTANDING** What is the function of a nephron?

Urine flows from each kidney into a long tubule called the **ureter.** Each ureter carries the urine to the muscular sac called the urinary bladder where it is stored temporarily, and then, it passes through a tube called the **urethra** to outside the body.

The Nervous System

The human nervous system consists of the **central nervous system**—the brain and spinal cord—and the **peripheral nervous system**—all the nerves outside the central nervous system. With the endocrine system, the nervous system regulates the control and coordination of body activities.

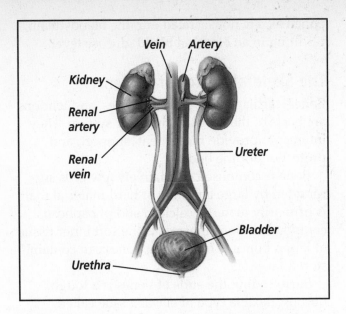

Figure 8.4 Some fluids are excreted from the body by the urinary system.

The **neuron,** or nerve cell, as shown in Figure 8.5, is the basic unit of structure and function in the nervous system. Impulses moving from neuron to neuron must cross a small gap called a **synapse.** When nerve impulses reach the terminal branches of a neuron, they stimulate the release of **neurotransmitters.** These chemicals diffuse across the synapse carrying the impulse to the next neuron and eventually to the targeted tissue. The brain is the control center of the nervous system. It is surrounded and protected by the skull and has three major regions—the cerebrum, the cerebellum and the medulla oblongata. Each part of the brain controls specific functions in the body.

The **cerebrum** is the upper region and largest part of the brain. It is the center for conscious activities, such as voluntary movements, memory, and learning. Below the cerebrum at the back of the head is the **cerebellum.** This region of the brain controls balance and muscle coordination. The **medulla oblongata** is located at the base of the brain. It connects the brain and the spinal cord and controls involuntary activities in the body, such as heartbeat and breathing.

☑ CHECK FOR UNDERSTANDING Explain why the brain is called the control center of the nervous system.

The spinal cord consists of bundled nerve cells and extends from the medulla oblongata through the center of the protective vertebral column. The spinal cord relays impulses to and from the brain and is the center of some **reflexes**—simple automatic actions that involve no conscious control.

The peripheral nervous system consists of the somatic and autonomic nervous systems and carries impulses to and from the central nervous system. The **somatic nervous system** controls the movements of voluntary muscles. The **autonomic nervous system** controls involuntary activities such as respiration, circulation, and peristalsis.

The Endocrine System

The organs of the endocrine system are glands. **Endocrine glands** produce chemicals called **hormones** and secrete them directly into the bloodstream. Hormones cause physiological changes in the body at specific sites called target cells that often are far from the endocrine gland.

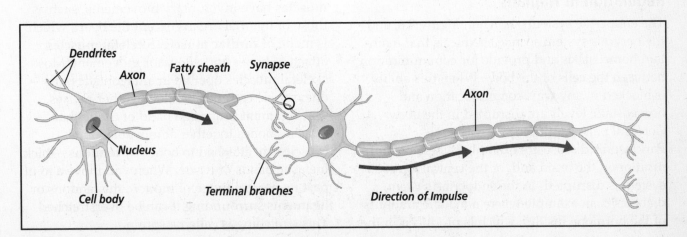

Figure 8.5 Impulses travel from nerve cell to nerve cell, but nerve cells do not touch.

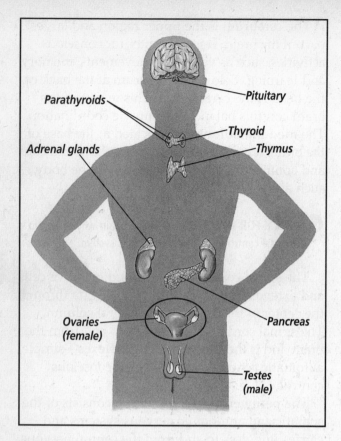

Figure 8.6 The endocrine system includes several glands.

Parathyroids

Pituitary

Adrenal glands

Thyroid

Thymus

Ovaries
(female)

Pancreas

Testes
(male)

Hormone secretion is regulated by an internal mechanism known as a **negative feedback system.** In this system, the level of one hormone inhibits the production of a second hormone, and the level of the second hormone inhibits the production of the first. This process helps to maintain homeostasis in your body, just like a thermostat regulates the temperature in a house.

Regulation in Humans

The endocrine system, shown in Figure 8.6, and the nervous system secrete chemicals that maintain homeostasis and provide for communication between the cells of the body. When this ability is blocked in any way, communication and homeostatic levels are disrupted in the body. Cerebral palsy, multiple sclerosis, and Parkinson's disease are examples where communication in the brain and/or the central nervous system is disrupted. In the endocrine system, diabetes is an example where adequate amounts of the hormone insulin, which is produced in the

pancreas, are not secreted into the bloodstream, resulting in an elevated blood glucose level.

The Skeletal-Muscular System

Bones, cartilage, ligaments, muscles, and tendons are parts of the skeletal-muscular system. They interact to provide movement, support, and protection for the body.

Bone is composed of relatively few cells surrounded by large amounts of hard material that is primarily made of calcium and phosphorus compounds. Bone marrow is the soft inner tissue of larger bones. Arm and leg bones can contain stored fat.

Surrounding the ends of bones is a tough, fibrous, flexible type of elastic tissue called **cartilage.** It provides cushioning at joints and flexibility and support in structures such as the nose and ears. In embryos, the skeleton is mostly cartilage, but after birth, it is replaced gradually by bone. This process of bone replacing cartilage continues until adulthood.

The human skeleton provides support and protection for the soft organs and tissues of the body, such as the brain and lungs. It also is where muscles are attached. A **joint** is where two bones meet. Joints are classified as immovable or movable. The joints of the skull are immovable joints. There are four types of movable joints in the human body, as shown in Figure 8.7.

Body movement involves the muscles. Muscle tissue consists of fibers bound together that have the capacity to contract, or shorten. There are three types of human muscle tissue—smooth muscle, cardiac muscle, and skeletal muscle. **Smooth muscles** have involuntary movements, such as those of internal organs except the heart, which is made of **cardiac muscle. Skeletal muscles** attach to bones and allow for movement. Most skeletal muscles operate in antagonistic pairs—one muscle contracts while the other relaxes.

A **ligament** is a tough band of tissue that attaches bones together at movable joints. Muscles are attached to bones by **tendons**—thick, inelastic bands of tissue. When you move a joint past its normal range of motion, the tendons or ligaments surrounding it can be overstretched. This stretching is called a sprain.

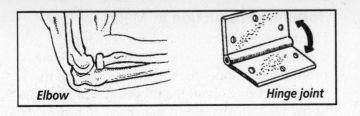 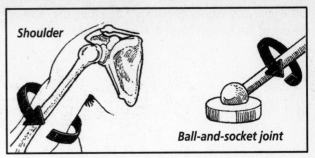

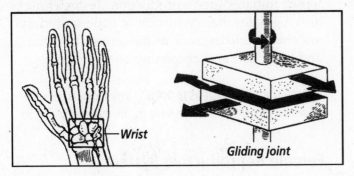 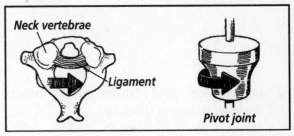

Figure 8.7 Four types of movable joints in humans are shown here.

Quick Review

1 Which structures secrete chemicals utilized for the completion of digestion within the small intestine?
(1) liver and pancreas
(2) glomerulus and villi
(3) esophagus and alveoli
(4) gallbladder and pharynx

2 Which structure shown in the diagram below, contracts, causing a pressure change in the chest cavity during breathing?

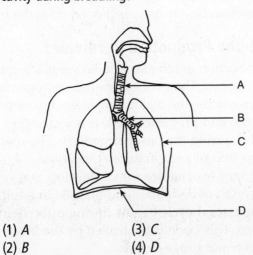

(1) A   (3) C
(2) B   (4) D

3 To determine heart rate, a student should count the pulsations per minute in
(1) a vein   (3) an artery
(2) a capillary   (4) a lymph vessel

4 Which system is responsible for transporting hormones from endocrine glands to various body tissues?
(1) circulatory
(2) digestive
(3) excretory
(4) nervous

5 Which two structures are directly involved in locomotion in humans?
(1) visceral muscle and fibrous tendons
(2) smooth muscle and ligaments
(3) skeletal muscle and bones
(4) cardiac muscle and immovable joints

6 In the diagram below, peristalsis occurs in structures

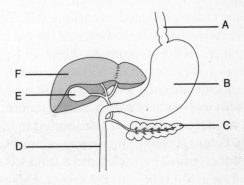

(1) A and D
(2) C and F
(3) C and E
(4) E and F

Base your answers to questions 7 and 8 on the diagram below of the human heart and on your knowledge of biology.

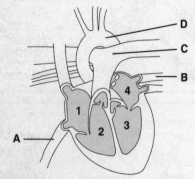

7 Deoxygenated blood from the body is returned to the heart by way of structure
(1) *A*   (3) *C*
(2) *B*   (4) *D*

8 Which heart chamber pumps blood toward the alveoli by way of the pulmonary arteries?
(1) 1   (3) 3
(2) 2   (4) 4

Human Reproduction

The survival of any species, including humans, depends on reproducing others of the species. Human reproductive systems make possible the continuation of the human species.

Male Reproductive System

The production of sperm—the male sex cells—and their delivery to the female reproductive system are key functions of the male reproductive system.

Sperm are produced by meiotic cell divisions of reproductive cells in the testes (singular, *testis*), which are in the scrotum, as shown in Figure 8.8. In males, meiotic cell divisions occur only in testes. Outside each testis is a coiled tube—the **epididymis**—where sperm mature. Sperm enter the **vas deferens** and are transported to the urethra. Before entering the urethra, a mucous fluid from the **seminal vesicles** and a fluid from the prostate gland mix with the sperm. This mixture of sperm and fluids is called **semen.**

The head portion of a sperm is covered by a cap and contains the nucleus. The cap contains enzymes that help a sperm penetrate an egg. Attached to the head is a tail that propels the sperm along.

Hormone Production in Males

Hormones coordinate the changes that occur at the onset of male puberty. The pituitary gland produces hormones that are transported to the testes and bring about the production of the male hormone, testosterone. The increase in testosterone initiates sperm production. Testosterone also regulates the production of male secondary sex characteristics, such as the growth of facial and body hair and deepening of the voice.

✓ CHECK FOR UNDERSTANDING What effects does the production of testosterone have on the male body?

Female Reproductive System

Functions of the female reproductive system include production of eggs (female sex cells), providing a pathway for sperm to reach the egg, and providing an environment where a fertilized egg can develop into an embryo. In a sexually mature female, egg production occurs in the **ovaries** that are located in the lower portion of the abdomen, as shown in Figure 8.8.

About once a month, a tiny sac called a **follicle** bursts and releases an egg from the ovary's surface. This is **ovulation.** The egg moves into the **oviduct** on its way to the **uterus**—a pear-shaped organ with thick muscular walls. Fertilization, if it occurs, takes place in the oviduct. If fertilization does not occur, the egg breaks down in about 24 hours and eventually is passed from the body.

Hormone Production in Females

Reproduction in females also is under the control of hormones. The ovaries produce estrogen and progesterone—the major female sex hormones. Estrogen and progesterone levels increase in females during the onset of puberty. The uterus, vagina, and ovaries mature at this time. Secondary sex characteristics develop, such as the growth of body hair and breasts. In addition, the **menstrual cycle** begins during puberty in females. This cycle is controlled by the levels of estrogen and progesterone.

The Menstrual Cycle

This cycle includes the production of an egg, the preparation of the uterus to receive the egg, and the shedding of the lining of the uterus if the egg is not fertilized. This shedding is called menstruation.

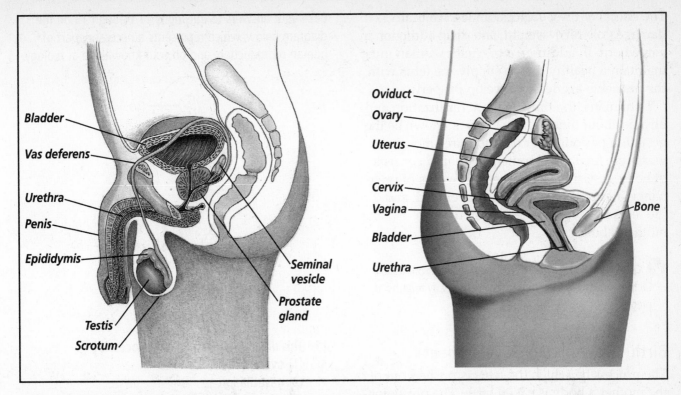

Figure 8.8 The different structures of the male reproductive system (left) and the female reproductive system (right) share a common function—continuation of the species.

The menstrual cycle occurs about every 28 days and continues for 30 to 40 years until egg production stops. It is controlled by hormones from the pituitary gland, which in turn stimulate the ovaries to produce estrogen and progesterone.

Fertilization

For fertilization to occur, sperm must be present in the oviduct. During sexual intercourse, 300–500 million sperm can enter a female's vagina. Most sperm are destroyed by the acidic environment of the vagina, but those that survive can swim through the cervix into the uterus and then, into the oviduct. Only one sperm can penetrate and fertilize the egg. When this occurs, an immediate change occurs in the egg's membrane that prevents other sperm from entering it. The fertilized egg is called a **zygote.**

After fertilization, the zygote moves to the uterus by the action of cilia that line the oviduct. As the zygote moves, it divides into a hollow ball of cells. This ball of cells attaches to the uterine wall and will eventually develop into an embryo.

From Embryo to Fetus

The changes that take place after fertilization, which continue throughout an organism's life are known as **development.** Dramatic changes occur to a human embryo during its early development, including the formation of the **placenta** and **umbilical cord.** Nutrients and oxygen are transported from the mother to the placenta and move from the placenta to the embryo through the umbilical cord. Then, the embryo's waste products travel through the umbilical cord to the placenta where they diffuse into the mother's blood. After about two months, major organ systems are formed, bones begin to harden, and muscles appear. The embryo now is called a **fetus.**

The embryo is most susceptible during the early months of pregnancy, when its body organs are developing. Problems usually are a result of inherited genes or associated with the mother's exposure to harmful environmental factors. Harmful factors that a woman should avoid during pregnancy include the uses of illegal drugs, alcohol, and tobacco, and exposure to damaging radiation (X rays).

The effects of these factors can lead to brain damage, low birth weight, and drug addiction in a newborn. In addition, a pregnant woman must maintain a healthy diet to supply the fetus with the nutrients needed to develop properly.

In humans, the time between fertilization and birth is about nine months. This is known as the gestation period. After the first three months of gestation, fetal development primarily consists of body growth. During the final weeks of pregnancy, all body systems have developed, and the fetus now can survive outside of the mother's body.

☑ CHECK FOR UNDERSTANDING What environmental factors may harm the embryo during the early months of pregnancy?

Birth, Growth, and Development

The process by which the fetus is pushed out of the mother's body is called birth. The physiological and physical changes that occur to the mother during the birthing process are called labor. Labor ends when the baby is expelled through the birth canal by strong uterine and abdominal contractions. After birth, the umbilical cord is cut near the baby's abdomen. Then the placenta is expelled from the uterus within 15 minutes after the birth.

A human's physical development continues until adulthood. During adulthood, the structures of the body go through a series of natural changes known as aging. The aging process eventually ends in death. The process of birth, growth, development, aging, and death is a pattern that exists in all organisms.

Quick Review

9   For a human zygote to become an embryo, it must undergo
    (1) meiosis   (3) regeneration
    (2) mitotic divisions (4) disjunction

10 The material that flows from the human female reproductive tract during menstruation is produced by the breakdown of the lining of the
    (1) ovary   (3) vagina
    (2) oviduct   (4) uterus

Base your answers to questions 11 through 13 on the diagram below, which represents a necessary part of human reproduction, and on your knowledge of biology.

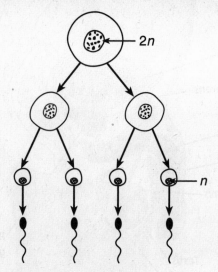

11 This diagram represents the process of
    (1) ovulation
    (2) gastrulation
    (3) mitotic cell division
    (4) sperm formation

12 In humans, this process is most influenced by the presence of
    (1) egg cells
    (2) testosterone
    (3) thyroxin
    (4) progesterone

13 This process occurs within the
    (1) corpus luteum
    (2) ovaries
    (3) testes
    (4) sperm duct

For *each* statement in questions 14 and 15, select the stage of the human menstrual cycle, *chosen from the list below*, that is most closely associated with that statement.

Stages of the Human Menstrual Cycle
    (1) Follicle
    (2) Ovulation
    (3) Corpus luteum
    (4) Menstruation

14 A mature egg is released. _____

15 It usually will *not* occur if a zygote is formed during the cycle.

_____

Content Questions for Regents Exam Practice

Part A

1 To communicate between cells, many multicellular animals use

(1) nerve signals and respiratory gases

(2) respiratory gases and hormones

(3) bones and muscles

(4) nerve signals and hormones

2 The diagram below can be used to illustrate a process directly involved in

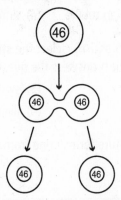

(1) tissue repair

(2) meiosis

(3) recombination

(4) sexual reproduction

3 Which statement accurately compares cells in the human circulatory system to cells in the human nervous system?

(1) Cells in the circulatory system carry out the same life function for the organism as cells in the nervous system.

(2) Cells in the circulatory system are identical in structure to cells in the nervous system.

(3) Cells in the nervous system are different in structure from cells in the circulatory system, and they carry out different specialized functions.

(4) Cells in the nervous system act independently, but cells in the circulatory system function together.

4 Communication between cells is affected if there is decreased ability to produce

(1) digestive enzymes and gametes

(2) antibodies and chloroplasts

(3) hormones and nerve impulses

(4) antibiotics and guard cells

5 A glucose-tolerance test was conducted to observe the effect of time on glucose concentration in the blood. An animal was fed 10 milliliters of glucose solution. At five different times after the ingestion of the solution, the blood glucose concentration was determined, and the results were recorded in the data table below.

Data Table	
Time After Glucose Ingestion (minutes)	Glucose Concentration in Blood (mg/100dL)
0	75
30	125
60	110
90	90
120	80
180	70

The change in glucose concentration in the blood between 0 and 30 minutes was probably due to

(1) the liver releasing glucose into the small intestine

(2) glucose being absorbed from the digestive system

(3) the synthesis of glucose from starch

(4) glucose being used for cellular respiration

6 The normal sodium level in human blood is 135 mEq/L. If a blood test taken immediately after a meal reveals a sodium level of 150 mEq/L, what will most likely result?

(1) Antibody production will increase.

(2) The person will move to an ecosystem with a lower sodium level.

(3) The nutritional relationships between humans and other organisms will change.

(4) An adjustment within the human body will be made to restore homeostasis.

7 If a human system fails to function properly, what is the most likely result?

(1) a stable rate of metabolism

(2) a disturbance in homeostasis

(3) a change in the method of cellular respiration

(4) a change in the function of DNA

8 When a pregnant woman ingests toxins such as alcohol and nicotine, the embryo is put at risk because these toxins can
  (1) diffuse from the mother's blood into the embryo's blood within the placenta
  (2) enter the embryo when it eats
  (3) transfer to the embryo since the mother's blood normally mixes with the embryo's blood
  (4) enter the uterus through the mother's navel

9 Which statement describes a feedback mechanism involving the human pancreas?
  (1) The production of estrogen stimulates the formation of gametes for sexual reproduction.
  (2) The level of oxygen in the blood is related to heart rate.
  (3) The level of sugar in the blood is affected by the amount of insulin in the blood.
  (4) The production of urine allows for excretion of cell wastes.

10 Which phrase does *not* describe a way the human body responds to fight disease?
  (1) destruction of infectious agents by white blood cells
  (2) production of antibodies by white blood cells
  (3) increase production of white blood cells
  (4) production of pathogens by white blood cells

11 Lymph is an intercellular fluid that originates from
  (1) bile   (3) urine
  (2) plasma   (4) water

12 In the human body, the blood with the greatest concentration of oxygen is found in the
  (1) left atrium of the heart
  (2) cerebrum
  (3) kidneys
  (4) right ventricle of the heart

13 Which type of vessel normally contains valves that prevent the backward flow of materials?
  (1) artery   (3) capillary
  (2) arteriole   (4) vein

14 The functional unit of the human kidney is known as a
  (1) nephridium   (3) nephron
  (2) Malpighian tubule   (4) urinary bladder

For questions 15 and 16, select the structure from the list below that best answers the question.
  (1) alveolus   (3) sweat gland
  (2) nephron   (4) liver

15 Which structure forms urine from water, urea, and salts?

_____

16 Which structure removes carbon dioxide and water from the blood?

_____

Part B

17 The graph below shows the relationship between kidney function and arterial pressure in humans.

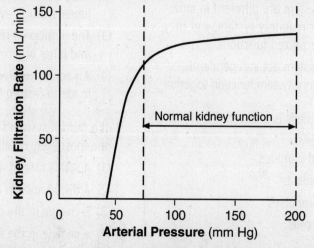

State how a steady decrease in arterial pressure will affect homeostasis in the human body. _____

_____

Base your answers to questions 18 through 20 on the diagram below illustrating one type of cellular communication and on your knowledge of biology.

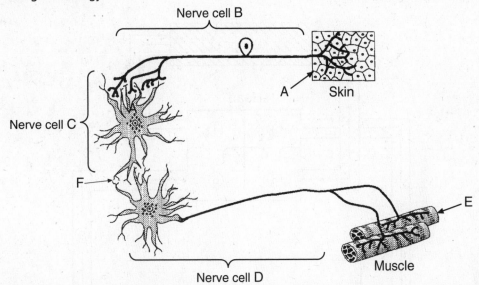

18 In region *F*, there is a space between nerve cells *C* and *D*. Cell *D* is usually stimulated to respond by

(1) a chemical produced by cell *C* moving to cell *D*

(2) the movement of a virus from cell *C* to cell *D*

(3) the flow of blood out of cell *C* to cell *D*

(4) the movement of material through a blood vessel that forms between cell *C* and cell *D*

19 If a stimulus is received by the cells at *A*, the cells at *E* will most likely use energy obtained from a reaction between

(1) fats and enzymes   (3) glucose and oxygen

(2) ATP and pathogens   (4) water and carbon dioxide

20 State one possible cause for the failure of muscle *E* to respond to a stimulus at *A*. _____

_____

Base your answers to questions 21 through 23 on the diagram to the right and on your knowledge of biology.

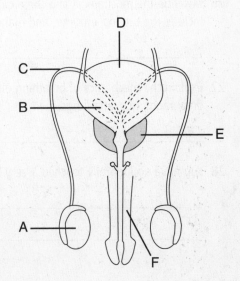

21 Which letter indicates a structure that secretes a hormone that promotes maturation of gametes?

_____

22 Which letter indicates a structure that is *not* involved in the production or delivery of gametes?

_____

23 Structures *B* and *E* provide nutrients and fluid for the gametes. Why are these substances necessary for fertilization?

_____

Base your answers to questions 24 and 25 on the diagram below, which represents the pathway of blood throughout the body, and on your knowledge of biology.

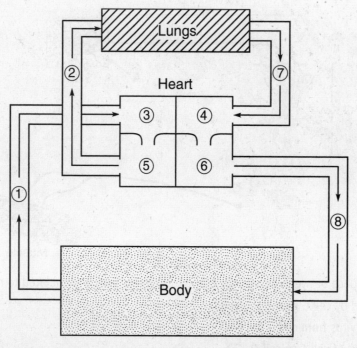

24 Which number indicates the structure that carries oxygenated blood to the body?

    (1) 1   (3) 7

    (2) 2   (4) 8

25 Which structure represents the chamber of the heart that receives oxygenated blood directly from the lungs?

    (1) 5   (3) 3

    (2) 6   (4) 4

Part C

26 Describe the mechanical and chemical digestion of a tuna fish sandwich from the mouth to the small intestine. Include the organs, enzymes and glands involved in the digestion of the sandwich.

_____

27 Explain the mechanics of breathing air into and out of your lungs. Include the following organs in your explanation: diaphragm, ribs, and lungs.

_____

28 You have accidentally touched a very hot pot. Explain how the reflex arc will work to pull your finger from the pot.

_____

Part D

Answer all questions in this part.

Directions (29–36): For those questions that are followed by four choices, circle the number of the choice that best answers the question. For all other questions in this part, follow the directions given in the question.

Base your answers to questions 29 and 31 on the information below and your knowledge of biology.

> The systems in your body work together to provide nutrients to the cells, to remove waste products, and to ensure that your cells have the nutrients needed to function properly.

29 Before performing the laboratory activity, you ate a sweet potato for lunch, which provided you with energy for metabolic processes. What is the original source of this energy?

(1) protein molecules stored in the potato

(2) starch molecules absorbed by the potato

(3) vitamins and minerals from the soil

(4) light energy transformed by photosynthesis

30 The system below breaks down the sweet potato into usable energy for the cells. Which system does this illustration represent?

(1) circulatory

(2) digestive

(3) endocrine

(4) excretory

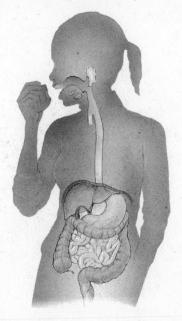

31 Which two systems are responsible for the increased breathing rate of a person who is exercising?

I   circulatory   III   endocrine

II   digestive   IV   respiratory

(1) I and IV

(2) II and III

(3) II and IV

(4) I and III

Directions (32): Base your answers on the information and diagram below and your knowledge of biology.

Diagrams of two major body systems are shown below.

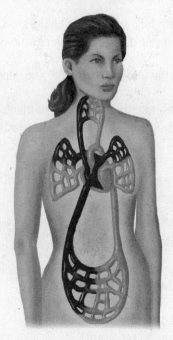

32 Which two systems are represented in the illustrations above?

(1) circulatory and endocrine

(2) nervous and reproductive

(3) respiratory and circulatory

(4) urinary and excretory

33 Red blood cells transport oxygen attached to which component?

(1) hemoglobin

(2) nitrogen

(3) nuclei

(4) plasma membrane

34 Which causes an increase in the breathing rate?

(1) high concentration of oxygen in the blood

(2) high concentration of blood in the lung capillaries

(3) high concentration of carbon dioxide in the blood

(4) low concentration of carbon dioxide in the blood

35 Explain why muscle capillaries dilate when you are exercising. _____

_____

_____

_____

VOCABULARY

autotroph
biodiversity
carrying capacity
commensalism

decomposer
ecology
ecosystem
heterotroph

mutualism
niche
parasitism
population

A squirrel gathers nuts to take to its nest in a tree. Two bighorn sheep butt heads, as shown in Figure 9.1. Insect larva and fungi consume a decaying apple. What do these observations have in common? They are all part of ecology. **Ecology** is the scientific study of the interactions among organisms and interactions of organisms with their environments. Ecologists study Earth's **ecosystems,** which are composed of the living organisms of a community and the nonliving components of an environment. The part of our planet that supports life often is called the biosphere. It is made of many different kinds of ecosystems.

Life in Ecosystems

Species that inhabit an environment are those that evolved, in part, because they successfully used the environment's resources. Some of these resources are living or from living things, such as nuts and apples. Other resources are not living, such as sunlight and water.

Survival and reproduction depend on organisms meeting their needs. Competition is fierce for limited resources and not all individuals or species can survive. One species may have success in one environment and another species may find success in a different environment. This is why we find many different life forms in the diverse ecosystems on Earth.

Producers

Photosynthetic organisms, such as plants, algae and other protists, and some bacteria contain a green pigment called chlorophyll. During photosynthesis, it is involved in chemical reactions that use light energy, water, and carbon dioxide and produce high-energy organic nutrients and oxygen. When a species can make its own nutrients, this is called autotrophic nutrition.

Figure 9.1 Head butting between male bighorn sheep is common during mating season.

Autotrophs not only make nutrients for themselves, but also are the source of nutrients for other organisms in an ecosystem. For this reason, they are called producers. If you go to the produce section of a supermarket, you can see items from a variety of producers including lettuce, tomatoes, potatoes, onions, cantaloupes, and apples.

The high-energy nutrients produced by photosynthesis are called simple sugars. The molecules in simple sugars are made of only carbon, hydrogen, and oxygen atoms. Producers use high-energy molecules in many ways. For example, they are the basis of larger complex carbohydrate and fat molecules.

Simple sugars are the energy source for the life processes of most organisms. Energy that holds the sugar molecules together is released during chemical reactions that occur as sugar molecules are broken down. One process, called cellular respiration, also releases carbon dioxide and water back into the environment. Released energy is used in the production of substances such as proteins. Protein molecules are formed from amino acids that contain atoms of hydrogen, oxygen, carbon, nitrogen, and, sometimes, sulfur.

Consumers

The ability to make nutrients benefits producers and other life forms, as illustrated in Figure 9.2. If an organism is not a producer, it is a consumer. Any organism that consumes other organisms is called a **heterotroph.** All animals are heterotrophs. Herbivores are animals that only eat producers, such as plants or algae. Carnivores are animals that eat other animals. Most people are omnivores since they eat both plant and animal products such as those found in pizza.

✓ CHECK FOR UNDERSTANDING How are autotrophic nutrition and heterotrophic nutrition different?

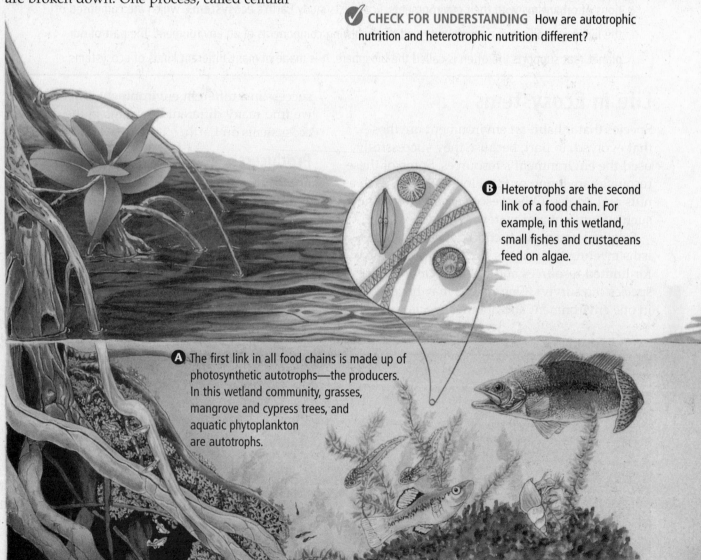

B Heterotrophs are the second link of a food chain. For example, in this wetland, small fishes and crustaceans feed on algae.

A The first link in all food chains is made up of photosynthetic autotrophs—the producers. In this wetland community, grasses, mangrove and cypress trees, and aquatic phytoplankton are autotrophs.

Figure 9.2 In this wetland environment, energy flows from the environment to producers then to consumers.

Decomposers

When leaves and fruits fall from trees, when animals excrete wastes, and when organisms die, their molecules eventually return to the environment. **Decomposers** are organisms such as bacteria and fungi that feed on the remains of dead organisms, or waste products of living organisms. Decomposers break down energy-rich nutrients contained in their food into molecules that are returned to the environment. For example, some carbon returns to the air as carbon dioxide, which plants can use to make more high-energy molecules. A form of nitrogen returns to the soil when amino acids are broken down. Plants take in this nitrogen and produce new proteins.

C Carnivores that make up the third link feed on second-link heterotrophs. The heron is a carnivorous bird that feeds on fishes, frogs, and other small animals of the wetland habitat.

D Other carnivores that feed on carnivorous heterotrophs, make up the fourth link level. Bacteria and fungi decompose all the links of the food chain when organisms die.

Cycles of Matter

According to the law of conservation of matter, matter is not created or destroyed; it only changes into different forms. This is true everywhere on Earth including in ecosystems. Consider an atom of carbon that is part of your brain. It was once carbon dioxide in the air. It might have become part of a high-energy molecule in a corn plant growing in Iowa. The corn might have been fed to cattle in upstate New York or made into cornflakes. The carbon atom might have become part of a protein molecule in milk. When you drank and digested that milk, the amino acids could have become part of a protein in your brain.

What if the carbon atom was part of a glucose molecule in your liver? When energy is needed, the glucose molecule can move into your blood and travel to a muscle cell. There it is broken down with a release of energy. The products of this breakdown are carbon dioxide and water that you eventually exhale. The carbon dioxide is again available for use by plants or algae. The flow of carbon from living things to the environment and back into living things is called the carbon cycle.

Other substances, such as water, nitrogen, and phosphorus, also cycle through the biosphere. These cycles are like permanent round-trip tickets for matter through an ecosystem. Therefore, atoms constantly cycle through the living and nonliving world.

Energy Flow

All of the life around you is solar-powered. Perhaps you have a friend that only eats pizza and who seems to be "pizza-powered." All the energy in a pizza, however, can be traced back to the Sun. The flour used to make the dough came

Figure 9.3 Compared to a food chain, a food web provides a more complete model of the feeding relationships in a community.

from wheat plants, the sauce came from tomatoes, and the cheese was made from milk.

Unlike the atoms that make up a pizza, energy cannot be recycled continually. Energy has only a one-way ticket through an ecosystem.

Producers transform light energy into chemical energy during the production of high-energy nutrients. If you exercise, your body breaks down food—high-energy nutrients—and energy is released. You exhale carbon dioxide and water, and you give off a great amount of heat—a form of the released energy. Molecules of matter can be used again, but not energy. The heat energy is lost to the environment. This is not a problem because the Sun provides a continuous supply of energy to the ecosystem.

✓ CHECK FOR UNDERSTANDING Compare and contrast the flow of matter and energy in an ecosystem.

Ecologists study the relationship between the flow of energy and matter in ecosystems. Plants grow and rabbits eat them. Wolves eat rabbits. The energy is transferred from the plants to the rabbits to the wolf. This is a food chain and is diagrammed as

plants $\longrightarrow$ rabbit $\longrightarrow$ wolf

You can probably think of other animals that eat plants such as squirrels, deer, or marmots. You also can probably think of other animals that eat rabbits such as hawks and coyotes. When you consider the many organisms in a community and try to draw lines to connect organisms that are eaten to the organisms that eat them, you get many lines and intersecting lines. Because the result looks like a spider's web, it is called a food web, such as the one shown in Figure 9.3.

Biomass

Ecologists study the number of producers, herbivores, and carnivores in ecosystems. Imagine that you are instructed to rope off one acre of land and to capture all the carnivores. Then, you are instructed to capture all the herbivores, so you capture animals that only eat plants. Finally, you are instructed to gather all the producers. You dig up plants, including their roots, and place them in a big pile.

Your next task is to find the mass of each type of living thing and the total mass of all of the organisms, often called the biomass. Which type of organism—carnivore, herbivore, or producer—would have the greatest biomass? If you think about all of the plants you gathered compared to the number of animals, you might realize that producers would have the greater mass. For the animals, herbivores would have a greater mass than the carnivores.

Pyramid of Energy

Imagine if you could burn all the producers and measure the amount of heat energy released. This would tell you how much energy was contained in the biomass of the producers.

Ecologists do not need to burn living things to determine the energy in their mass; they can calculate the amount of energy. If you were to calculate the total energy in an ecosystem, the producers would have the most energy, and the herbivores would have more energy than the carnivores.

An energy pyramid, such as the one shown in Figure 9.4, shows the relationships among the amounts of energy in the levels of the pyramid. It is important to note that as you go from producers to herbivores to carnivores, the amount of available energy at each level decreases. As the energy from sunlight flows through the ecosystem, an increasing amount is lost to the environment as heat.

Would an energy pyramid be different in an unbalanced ecosystem? For example, what if there were more herbivores than producers? The herbivores would not find enough food. In the same way, if there were more carnivores than herbivores, the carnivores would not have a sufficient food supply. In a balanced or self-sustaining ecosystem, the energy of the producers is greater than the energy of the herbivores, and the energy of the herbivores is greater than the energy of the carnivores.

Figure 9.4 This energy pyramid shows that each feeding level contains less energy than the level below it.

Quick Review

1 Which sequence shows a correct flow of energy in a food chain?
(1) bacteria → grass → fox → owl
(2) grass → grasshopper → frog → snake
(3) fungi → beetle → algae → mouse
(4) algae → snake → duck → deer

2 Decomposition, or the decay of organic matter, is carried out by the actions of
(1) green plants   (3) viruses and algae
(2) bacteria and fungi   (4) scavengers

3 For an ecosystem to be self-sustaining, many essential chemical elements must be
(1) converted to energy
(2) changed into fossil fuels such as oil and coal
(3) permanently removed from the environment
(4) cycled between organisms and the environment

4 Which sequence best represents the flow of energy in the cartoon below?

"Hey, wait a minute! This is grass! We've been eating grass!"

(1) prey → predator
(2) heterotroph → autotroph
(3) producer → herbivore
(4) autotroph → carnivore

5 Eating a sweet potato can provide energy for human metabolic processes. The original source of this energy is
(1) in protein molecules stored within the potato
(2) from starch molecules absorbed by the potato plant
(3) light energy that is transformed by photosynthesis
(4) in vitamins and minerals found in the soil

Use the diagram below to answer questions 6 through 8.

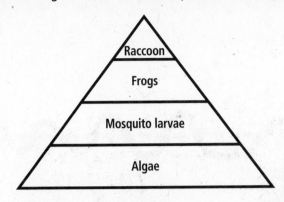

6 Which term best describes the mosquito larvae?
   (1) producer   (3) carnivore
   (2) parasite   (4) consumer

7 State *one* reason why algae form the base of this pyramid.

8 Explain why the size of each level of the pyramid *decreases* from bottom to top.

Populations

Imagine that you were given a few rats as a gift and you promised to supply them and their offspring with all they needed to survive. Your rats would survive and reproduce, and the number of rats you own would increase rapidly. Not only would your gift rats have offspring, but the offspring would reproduce, and so would the offspring's offspring. The number of rats would increase at a rate similar to the rate of increase in the number of houseflies as illustrated in Figure 9.5.

Ecologists call the number of organisms of one species in a given area a **population.** It could be the number of pet rats in your bedroom, the number of houseflies in a container, or the number of deer at Bear Mountain State Park.

Growing Populations

Under ideal conditions, all populations will grow in size. This is because organisms naturally create more offspring than can survive. For example, female rats can give birth to a new litter every month. Starting with one breeding pair of rats, after one year and under ideal conditions, there would be a colony of 2,000 rats.

In nature, however, conditions rarely are ideal. As a rat population grows, competition increases. Rat-to-rat competition is fierce because they have identical needs. They compete for water, food,

nesting spots, and mates. This competition tends to limit population growth, because there are not enough resources. Anything that slows or stops the growth of a population is called a limiting factor. Rat competition with other animal species also is a limiting factor. Even in an abandoned building, rats not only compete with other rats, but with mice, cockroaches, and ants. This also limits the rat population growth.

✔ CHECK FOR UNDERSTANDING What is a limiting factor of a population?

Predators also can limit population sizes. If there were a growing population of rats in an abandoned building, stray cats might discover this bountiful food supply and predation of rats would increase. As a result, the stray cat population in the abandoned building might increase and reduce the size of the rat population. Even though organisms can potentially reproduce many new individuals, limiting factors in the environment control population sizes.

Carrying Capacity

As the number of individuals in a population increases, the population's rate of growth slows down because of competition for limited resources. Eventually, the population reaches the carrying capacity of the environment. **Carrying capacity** is the average number of organisms of one species that an environment can support indefinitely.

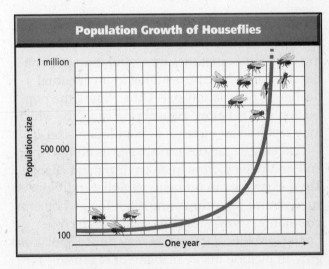

Figure 9.5 An ecologist graphed the rate of increase for the number of houseflies in his experiment. The rate of increase is exponential and its graph resembles the letter J.

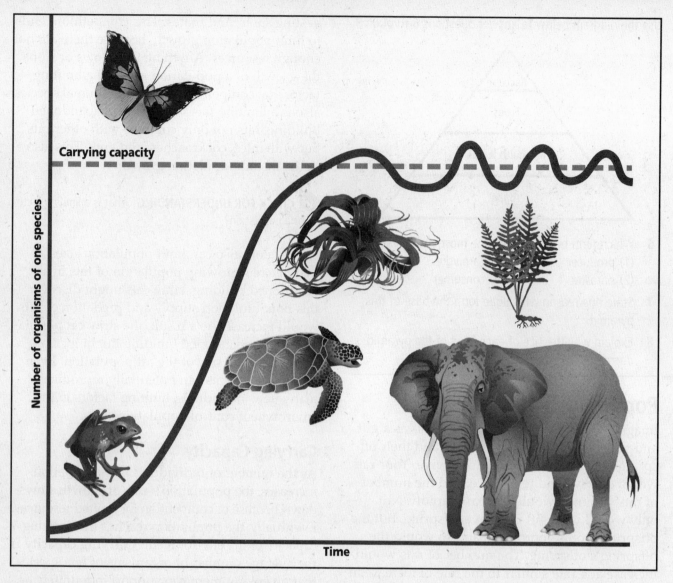

Carrying capacity

Number of organisms of one species

Time

Figure 9.6 Ecologists have learned that population increases follow a pattern.

As shown by the graph in Figure 9.6, the size of a population fluctuates after it reaches the carrying capacity. Sometimes the population exceeds the carrying capacity, resulting in an eventual decline in population size. Other times, the population size is below the carrying capacity, which may result in an increase in population size.

Carrying capacities can change as both living and nonliving factors in an environment change. These changes can influence whether individuals survive and reproduce, and, therefore, whether a population grows, remains stable, or declines. Living, or biotic, factors that may limit population growth include the availability of organisms for food and the presence of predators and disease causing organisms. Nonliving influences, often called abiotic factors, include temperature extremes; light intensity; soil conditions including the type of soil, its pH, and mineral content; and availability of water. For example, a drought can lower the carrying capacity of an ecosystem.

✔ CHECK FOR UNDERSTANDING What biotic and abiotic factors can affect carrying capacity?

Succession

Sometimes, the presence of populations in an ecosystem creates conditions for other populations to enter the same ecosystem. This happens in succession, which is the change in species as ecosystems change. Imagine a volcanic island in the ocean. Lichens and mosses are among the few producers that can grow in the crevices of lava.

Over time, these populations contribute to the breakdown of the lava. As old lichens and mosses die and decompose, soil forms that is a mixture of this decomposing organic matter and rock fragments. Eventually, conditions are created that allow for the growth of other plant species. The plants shade the soil, which reduces moisture loss. The roots of the plants help to limit soil erosion. In time, the soil becomes deeper and can support larger plant species, as shown in Figure 9.7. Eventually, a stable ecosystem forms called a climax community. The stages in succession resulting in the climax community occur because different populations change environmental conditions that allow new populations to survive. While repeated changes occur, such as changing seasons and small fires, the climax community might be considered in approximate equilibrium. Despite environmental changes, conditions can remain relatively unchanged for hundreds or thousands of years.

Succession also can occur after an environmental disturbance. Perhaps you live near a beech-maple forest. After a fire destroys the forest, grasses and small plants grow before conditions allow trees to grow in the burned areas.

As one population increases or decreases in size, it may cause other populations to increase or decrease. When fire or logging destroys trees, the populations that depend on these trees are affected. If environmental changes and disturbances in the size of populations are not too devastating, the ecosystem will usually recover.

Interacting Populations

Relationships between organisms may be positive, negative, or neutral. For example, when herbivores eat, the relationship is usually positive for herbivores and negative for plants. Sometimes it can be positive for both, such as when animals eat fruits. The animals get food and the plants' seeds are dispersed.

Mountain lions and deer are examples of predator-prey relationships, as shown in Figure 9.8 on page 120. As the predator, a mountain lion experiences a positive outcome by obtaining food, and a fallen deer experiences a negative outcome. However, the removal of organisms from a prey population may be beneficial because weak, old, or sick deer are usually the ones attacked. Removing unhealthy or old individuals can help ensure there is enough food to support a healthy population.

Symbiotic Relationships

Not all relationships are as obvious as the predator-prey relationship. Some species have evolved symbiotic relationships with other species. Symbiotic relationships include mutualism, commensalism, and parasitism.

In **mutualism,** both species benefit from their interaction. For example, a lichen consists of a fungus and a producer—an alga or a cyanobacterium. The producer gets a home where it can photosynthesize, and the fungus gets nutrients from the producer. Both species benefit. A broader example of mutualism is flowers and bees.

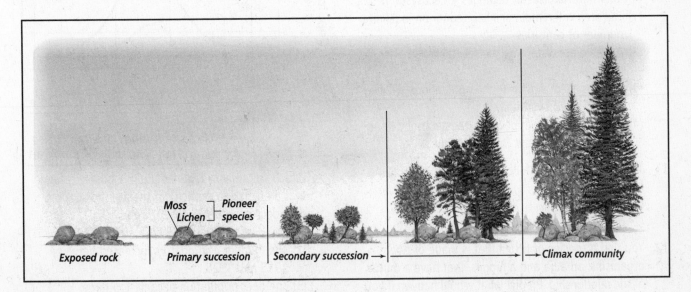

Figure 9.7 Changes in species occur over time during succession.

The flowers are pollinated while bees get pollen and nectar.

If one organism benefits and the other is neither helped nor harmed, the symbiotic relationship is called **commensalism.** This relationship can be observed between some epiphytic orchids and trees. Epiphytic orchids grow attached to the trees and other objects. The orchids benefit by getting a place to grow. Orchid plants are lightweight and do not absorb nutrients from the tree. They neither harm nor help the tree.

Parasitism is a relationship in which one organism benefits from it and the other

organism is harmed by it. The parasite usually gets nutrition at the host's expense. A tapeworm growing in the intestine of a pig, or a heartworm in a dog's heart are both examples of parasites.

Figure 9.8 Mountain lions often attack weak, lame, or old deer.

Quick Review

9 A new volcanic island is produced off the coast of Iceland. What most likely will be the first species to grow there?
(1) lichens   (3) pioneer trees
(2) grasses   (4) weeds

10 Which of the following will most likely occur if a fire or other natural disaster damages an ecosystem?
(1) The area will remain uninhabited for an indefinite number of centuries.
(2) A stable ecosystem will be reestablished after one year.
(3) An ecosystem similar to the original one will be reestablished eventually.
(4) A stable ecosystem becomes reestablished in an area that is different from the original.

11 The number of individuals of one species that lives in an area is
(1) population   (3) niche
(2) biodiversity   (4) symbiosis

12 You find a species of lichen that is made of two organisms, an alga and a fungus, that have a mutualistic relationship. Predict what would happen if you tried to grow the fungus separately from the alga.

13 The graph below provides information about the population of deer in a given area between 1900 and 1945.

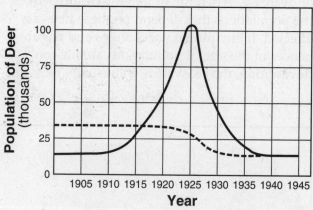

Which statement identifies the most likely reason that the carrying capacity of the area to support deer decreased between 1925 and 1930?
(1) The deer population decreased in 1926.
(2) The number of predators increased between 1915 and 1925.
(3) The deer population became too large.
(4) An unusually cold winter occurred in 1918.

14 Certain bacteria that live in a human's large intestine help to produce vitamin K. This relationship is an example of
(1) parasitism
(3) commensalism
(2) predator-prey
(4) mutualism

For questions 15, 16, and 17, select the number from the list below that most closely matches the described interaction. An interaction may be used more than once or not at all.

Interactions

(1) Organism A ⟶ Organism B
Organism B ⟶ Organism A

(2) Organism A --- ▸ Organism B
Organism B ⟶ Organism A

(3) Organism A ·········▸ Organism B
Organism B ⟶ Organism A

(4) Organism A --- ▸ Organism B
Organism B --- ▸ Organism A

Key	
⟶	= Positive effect
---	= Negative effect
·········	= No effect

15 The rhinoceros bird (organism *A*) feeds on parasites that live on the body of a rhinoceros (organism *B*). The rhinoceros allows the birds to feed on the parasites.

16 Ants (organism *A*) defend acacia trees (organism *B*) from attacks by insects that are herbivores. The ants live in the hollow thorns of the trees.

17 Wasp larvae (organism *A*) obtain nutrition from tomato hornworms (organism *B*). The tomato hornworms do *not* survive.

18 For many decades, certain areas of New York State have remained hardwood forests that are predominantly oak and hickory trees. These forested areas will most likely
(1) remain indefinitely and not be affected by environmental influences
(2) reach maturity and change in the near future
(3) be destroyed by environmental changes and never return to their present forms
(4) continue in their present forms unless affected by environmental changes

Biodiversity: Pieces in the Puzzle

From food webs to symbiosis to succession, it is clear that life depends on populations in a community that influence each other. Scientists are aware of some of the interactions between species, but suspect most relationships are undiscovered.

Interdependence of Species

The interactions of a species with other species are a large part of an organism's niche. The **niche** of a species includes its adaptations for survival and the role the species plays in the community.

The number of species in an area is a measure of biological diversity or **biodiversity.** In an ecosystem, biodiversity is important because the loss of one species could have tragic consequences for other species. Imagine if insecticidal sprays killed all the bees and other pollinating insects in an area. How would this impact plant life? Plants that depend on these insects for pollination would not produce fertile seeds and, thus, a generation would be lost. Herbivores that eat these plants would suffer, as would carnivores that eat the herbivores. The removal of pollinating insects would adversely affect many organisms in the ecosystem.

How would the removal of predators affect an ecosystem? Without predators, the number of herbivores could rise, leading to the destruction and disappearance of plants. Eventually, the herbivores would starve.

Factors Increasing Biodiversity

Some areas of the world naturally contain greater biodiversity than others. For example, a tropical rain forest has more biodiversity than a desert. Areas that receive a lot of sunlight and rain have ideal growing conditions for most producers. The producers can create large amounts of nutrients. An abundance of food supports a greater biodiversity.

The tall trees of rain forests provide organisms with a variety of places to live. These provide more niches for organisms, as shown in Figure 9.9 on page 122. Another reason for the great biodiversity in tropical rain forests is that they have been undisturbed environments for many years. This has allowed many species that have unique niches in this complex community to evolve.

Figure 9.9 The layers of a tropical rain forest are niches for thousands of species. **A** The canopy is home to monkeys and birds. **B** The understory is more humid and darker than the canopy. Vines, broad-leaved shrubs, and smaller trees that grow there are inhabited by many animal species. **C** The forest floor is dark and moist. Rodents, cats, many insects, and decomposers occupy niches there.

A Canopy

B Understory

C Ground

Biodiversity and Stable Ecosystems

Biodiversity can bring stability to an ecosystem. Therefore, protecting biodiversity is important. Ecosystems that are rich in biodiversity tend to be more resilient than ecosystems that lack biodiversity. When an environment changes, biodiversity makes it less likely that the ecosystem will be damaged and more likely that it will survive the changes.

Consider two plots of land—one with only walnut trees and one that is a natural forest with many tree species including the walnut species. What if a pest that only affects walnut trees came into both areas? The pest would spread rapidly through the walnut forest. Soon, all of the trees in the walnut forest would die. The habitats of animals that live in and around the walnut trees would disappear. In the natural forest, the pest would spread more slowly because other tree species separate the infested walnut trees. Even if the pest did infest and eventually kill all of the walnut trees, the other tree species would not be affected. The forest community would continue. The biodiversity of the natural forest would make the damage from one pest less severe.

CHECK FOR UNDERSTANDING Why is a rich biodiversity important to an ecosystem?

Humans Benefit from Biodiversity

Protecting biodiversity is important for protecting ecosystems. It also is important for human needs because we depend on living things for food, medicines, and other resources. Plants from the wild often are used to improve cultivated crops. For example, genes from some wild plants have been identified as providing resistance to insect attacks. By breeding these genes into cultivated crops, the crops become more resistant to insect attacks thus reducing the need for insecticides. Many varieties of corn and rice have been improved by breeding them with strains found in the wild.

Wild plants are sources of other potential plant uses and improvements. These plants not only provide chemicals to cure headaches, such as the willow in Figure 9.10, and malaria, but they might also provide chemicals for treating other diseases such as cancer or HIV. When species are lost, however, their potential use is gone forever. It is like losing pieces to a puzzle while you are still working on the puzzle.

Extinctions

When the last individual of a species dies, that species becomes extinct. Extinction occurs naturally when a species is unable to adapt to a changed environment. For example, many species became extinct because of the last ice age.

Figure 9.10 Biodiversity provides the basis for many important medicines. **A** Taxol, an anticancer drug, is derived from the bark and needles of the Pacific yew. **B** Rosy periwinkle is the source of a substance found in medicines used to treat Hodgkin's disease and leukemia. **C** Willow bark was the original source of an aspirinlike substance.

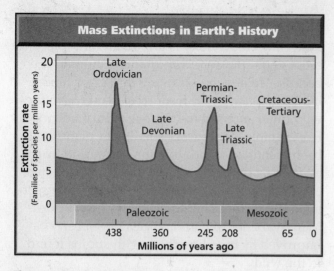

Figure 9.11 The peaks on this graph represent five mass extinctions in Earth's history.

Figure 9.11 shows the rates of natural extinctions in Earth's history.

Today, many organisms are endangered and some are on the brink of extinction. This means that their population sizes are so small that scientists are concerned about their long-term survival. Evidence shows humans can affect the rate of extinction and increase the number of endangered species.

Quick Review

19 The number of species in an area is a measure of
 (1) population   (3) niche
 (2) biodiversity   (4) autotrophs

20 Compared to a natural forest, a farmer's wheat field lacks
 (1) heterotrophs   (3) significant biodiversity
 (2) autotrophs   (4) stored energy

21 The adaptations of a species and its role in the community describes its
 (1) population   (3) ecosystem
 (2) niche   (4) biodiversity

22 Recently, scientists have been sent to rain forests by pharmaceutical and agricultural corporations to collect samples of seeds, fruits, and leaves before these densely vegetated areas are destroyed. State one reason these corporations are interested in obtaining these samples.

23 The widest variety of genetic material that can be used by humans for future agricultural or medical research would most likely be found in
 (1) a large field of a genetically engineered crop
 (2) an ecosystem having significant biodiversity
 (3) a forest that is planted and maintained by a forest service
 (4) areas that contain only one or two species

24 Which of the following is the best definition of biodiversity?
 (1) the number of organisms an area can support
 (2) the niche of an organism
 (3) the number of species that live in an area
 (4) the number of extinctions in an area

25 Base your answer to this question on the graph below and your knowledge of biology.

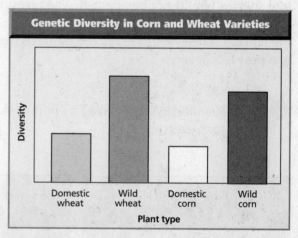

If the environment were to change dramatically or a new plant disease were to break out, which plant type would most likely survive?
 (1) wild wheat   (3) wild corn
 (2) domestic wheat   (4) domestic corn

Part A

1 In an ecosystem, what happens to the atoms of certain chemical elements such as carbon, oxygen, and nitrogen?

(1) They move into and out of living systems.

(2) They are never found in living systems.

(3) They move out of living systems and never return.

(4) They move into living systems and remain there.

2 The diagram below shows the relationships between the organisms in and around a pond.

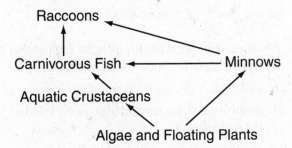

One additional biotic factor needed to make this a stable ecosystem is the presence of

(1) producers   (3) decomposers

(2) herbivores   (4) consumers

3 The diagram below shows a food chain.

grasses ⟶ rabbits ⟶ bobcats

If the population of bobcats decreases, what will most likely be the long-term effect on the rabbit population?

(1) It will increase, only.

(2) It will decrease, only.

(3) It will increase and then decrease.

(4) It will decrease and then increase.

4 The dense needles of Douglas fir trees can prevent most light from reaching the forest floor. This situation would have an immediate effect on

(1) producers   (3) herbivores

(2) carnivores   (4) decomposers

5 Which statement best describes a characteristic of an ecosystem?

(1) It must have producers and consumers but not decomposers.

(2) It is stable because it has consumers to recycle energy.

(3) It always has two or more different autotrophs filling the same niche.

(4) It must have organisms that carry out autotrophic nutrition.

6 Which statement illustrates a biotic resource interacting with an abiotic resource?

(1) A rock moves during an earthquake.

(2) A sea turtle transports a pilot fish to food.

(3) A plant absorbs sunlight, which is used for photosynthesis.

(4) A wind causes waves to form on a lake.

7 Which relationship best describes the interactions between lettuce and a rabbit?

(1) predator-prey   (3) parasite-host

(2) producer-consumer   (4) decomposer-scavenger

8 The diagram below represents an energy pyramid.

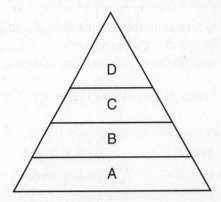

Which organisms would most likely be found at level A?

(1) birds   (3) mammals

(2) worms   (4) algae

9 The dotted line on the graph below represents the potential size of a population based on its reproductive capacity. The solid line on this graph represents the actual size of the population. Which statement best explains why the actual population growth is less than the potential population growth?

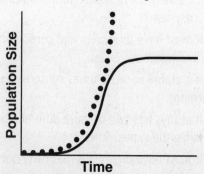

(1) Resources in the environment are limited.
(2) More organisms migrated into the population than out of the population.
(3) The birthrate gradually became greater than the death rate.
(4) The final population size is greater than the carrying capacity.

10 An ecosystem will most likely remain stable if
(1) it has more predators than prey
(2) it has a high level of biodiversity
(3) biotic factors decrease
(4) finite resources decrease

11 *Monocystis* is an organism that feeds on the sperm cells of earthworms. The activities of *Monocystis* eventually cause the infected earthworm to become sterile. The relationship between the earthworm and *Monocystis* is classified as
(1) host-parasite
(2) predator-prey
(3) producer-consumer
(4) scavenger-decomposer

12 Organisms that eat cows obtain less energy from the cows than the cows obtain from the plants they eat because the cows
(1) pass on most of the energy to their offspring
(2) convert solar energy to food
(3) store all their energy in milk
(4) use energy for their own metabolism

13 Which change would usually increase competition among the squirrel population in a certain area?
(1) an epidemic of rabies among squirrels
(2) an increase in the number of squirrels killed on the highways
(3) an increase in the number of hawks that prey on squirrels
(4) a temporary increase in the squirrel reproduction rate

Part B

14 Two species of microorganisms were placed in the same culture dish, which included basic materials necessary for life. The size of each population increased during the first three days. After one week, the population size of one species began to decline each day. State *one* possible reason for this decline.

Base your answers to questions 15 through 17 on the energy pyramid below and on your knowledge of biology.

15 The greatest amount of available energy is transferred from level
(1) A to level B   (3) B to level A
(2) A to level C   (4) D to level A

16 Which energy levels could contain carnivores?
(1) A and B   (3) C and D
(2) B and C   (4) D and A

17 In a community where grass, cats, insects, and mice are found, which of these organisms would fill level A?

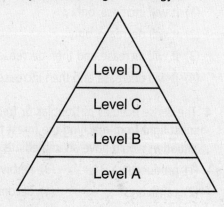

Base your answers to questions 18 through 20 on the information and graph below and on your knowledge of biology.

A Closer Look at Cycles in Predator and Prey Populations

Scientists have hypothesized that the populations of both lynx and snowshoe hares should show cyclic changes with increases in the predator population size lagging behind increases in prey population size, if the assumption is made that snowshoe hares are eaten only by lynx.

Does this out-of-phase population cycle of predators and prey actually occur in nature? A classic example of such a cycle was observed by counting all the fur pelts (skins) from northern Canada lynx and snowshoe hares purchased by the Hudson Bay Company between 1845 and 1935. Population cycles of snowshoe hares and their lynx predators, based on the number of pelts received by the Hudson Bay Company, are shown in the graph below.

As with any field investigation, many variables could influence the relationship between hare and lynx. One problem is that hare populations have been shown to fluctuate even without lynx present, possibly because the carrying capacity of their environment had been exceeded.

To test this hypothesis about population cycles more scientifically, investigators turned to controlled laboratory studies on populations of small predators and their prey.

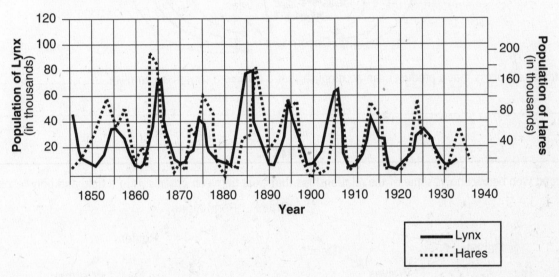

18 Identify *two* variables other than the size of the lynx population that can affect the size of the hare population.

_____

19 The phrase "carrying capacity" refers to

(1) storing extra food for the winter

(2) the number of organisms a habitat can support

(3) transporting food to organisms in an area

(4) the maximum possible weight of an individual organism

20 Why would scientists want to have a laboratory study on populations of different predators and their prey?

_____

_____

_____

_____

21 The diagram below represents a food web. Select and record the name of *one* species in the food web, and explain how its removal could affect *one* of the other species in the food web.

_____

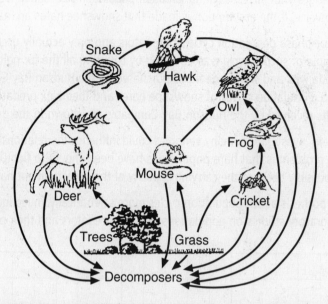

Snake, Hawk, Owl, Frog, Deer, Mouse, Cricket, Trees, Grass, Decomposers

22 Identify *one* process that a producer can accomplish that a carnivore cannot accomplish. _____

_____

Part C

23 The food web below shows some of the relationships that exist between organisms in a field and pond ecosystem.

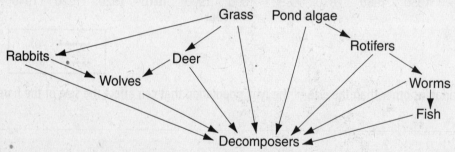

Grass, Pond algae, Rotifers, Rabbits, Deer, Wolves, Worms, Fish, Decomposers

a Write one or more paragraphs describing some of the relationships in this food web. In your answer, be sure to:

- identify a carnivore from the food web
- describe the complete path of energy from the Sun to that carnivore
- explain why decomposers are necessary in this web

_____

b A significant decrease in the wolf population occurs. After a period of one year, what change in the grass population would most likely be observed?

_____

c A farmer sprayed pesticides on a field next to the pond. Using one or more complete sentences, explain why several years later the fish population would contain higher pesticide levels than any other pond organisms would contain.

_____

24 An aquatic food web is presented in the diagram below.

Algae $<$ Zooplankton $\longrightarrow$ Yellow Perch $\longrightarrow$ Walleyed Pike
Zebra Mussels

Using one or more complete sentences, predict how one of the populations in the food web will most likely change if the yellow perch population increases over a period of three years.

_____

Part D

Answer all questions in this part.

Directions (25–32): For those questions that are followed by four choices, circle the number of the choice that best answers the question. For all other questions in this part, follow the directions given in the question.

Base your answers to questions 25 through 28 on your knowledge of biology.

25 Are the plants classified as producers or consumers that you used in the laboratory activity? Explain. _____

_____

26 State one reason why safety goggles should be used while in the laboratory even if you are not conducting an experiment yourself.

_____

27 Give one reason why an indicator would be used during a laboratory activity. _____

_____

28 Identify the autotroph(s) and heterotroph(s) in the illustration below.

Directions (29–32): Base your answers on your knowledge of biology.

29 Which is the best explanation for explaining the term *carrying capacity*?

(1) storing extra food for winter

(2) the number of organisms a habitat can support

(3) transporting food to organisms in an area

(4) the maximum possible weight of an individual organism

30 A laboratory activity is conducted in which plants from the same species are introduced into an environment. By accident, too many of the plants are introduced, exceeding the carrying capacity of the environment. Which is most likely?

(1) The plant population will decrease.

(2) The plant population will increase.

(3) The plant population will experience exponential growth.

(4) The plant population will experience linear growth.

31 What does the line graph below show? _____

_____

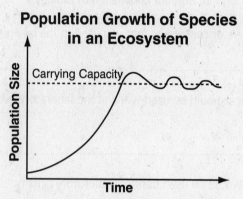

Population Growth of Species in an Ecosystem

32 Populations in an ecosystem will most likely remain stable if which is true?

(1) They have more predators than prey.

(2) They have a high level of biodiversity.

(3) Biotic factors decrease.

(4) Finite resources decrease.

Humans and the Environment

acid precipitation
conservation biology
endangered species

exotic species
habitat corridors
habitat fragmentation

ozone layer
reintroduction programs
threatened species

Take a deep breath of air or think about your favorite foods and clothes. What do you like to do or where do you like to go? The lifestyles we enjoy are possible because we use resources from our environments.

Environmental Threats

While all living things affect the environment in which they live, humans can have a greater impact than other organisms. Humans can alter the environment in the pursuit of natural resources, such as food, coal, and wood. As humans use resources, they also generate wastes and pollution that affect the environment.

Human activities can upset the basic processes of ecosystems, such as the generation of soils, cycling of water, flow of energy, and recycling of nutrients. The ever-increasing human population threatens the environment. When humans change the environment, it can result in harm to other organisms and lower the quality of our lives.

Depleting Resources

The unwise use of resources can result in their depletion. When the Vikings first settled Iceland in A.D. 874, the island was about 30 percent forest-covered. After a few hundred years, all the trees on the island had been cut down. The settlers' livestock grazed on growing seedlings and prevented the regeneration of forests. Growing conditions deteriorated as soil erosion increased because of vegetation loss. In addition, the harsh Icelandic climate resulted in slow growth of any trees that survived, and still today trees are rare in Iceland.

As late as 1850, U.S. skies east of the Rocky Mountains often were filled with flocks of passenger pigeons, such as the one in Figure 10.1. Unfortunately, excessive hunting of these birds

for meat and sport resulted in the species' extinction in 1910.

Many resources are finite—that means there is a fixed amount of them on Earth and they cannot be replaced. These are called nonrenewable resources. For example, there is a finite amount of aluminum on Earth, and mining and using aluminum depletes the supply. This is one reason why many people recycle aluminum.

It takes at least 50 million years for the remains of once-living organisms to be transformed into fossil fuels such as coal, natural gas, and oil.

Figure 10.1 The now extinct passenger pigeon was once a common bird species east of the Rocky Mountains.

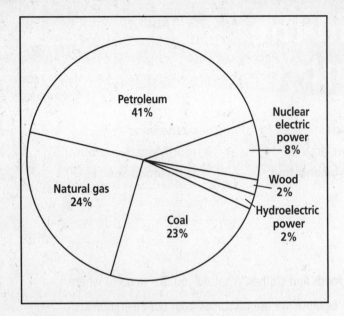

Figure 10.2 Eighty-eight percent of the energy used in the United States comes from fossil fuels.

Because of the vast length of time required for the formation of fossil fuels, they also are considered nonrenewable resources.

Earth's ever-increasing human population, increasing use of fossil-fuel-powered vehicles, and continual industrialization has accelerated the depletion of fossil fuels. Figure 10.2 shows the relationship between fossil fuels and energy consumption in the United States.

Some resources are replaceable in a relatively short period of time. For example, new corn can be grown each summer to replace corn that was harvested the preceding year. These resources are called renewable resources.

✓ CHECK FOR UNDERSTANDING How are renewable and nonrenewable resources different?

The use of a resource does not always result in the exhaustion of the resource, but great demand or a limited supply can increase its cost. For example, during exceptionally cold winters, the demand for home-heating fuels may exceed the supply and prices increase dramatically. Unwise use of resources today may decrease their availability tomorrow and increase their costs.

Pollution

As we use resources, we generate wastes. These wastes can pollute our environment by changing the chemical composition of air, soil, and water.

Air pollution affects our lives in many ways. You might have inhaled fumes from a passing car or truck. Smoke from wood and other fires might have irritated your eyes. Not all air pollution is as obvious as these are. For example, acid precipitation and the thinning ozone layer also are a result of air pollution.

Rain, snow, sleet, or hail that has a pH value less than 5.6 is considered **acid precipitation.** Acid precipitation begins with burning fossil fuels that release sulfur oxides and/or nitrogen oxides into the air. These pollutants combine with water in the atmosphere to produce sulfuric acid and nitric acid that fall to Earth as acid precipitation, which can harm organisms and structures. Many sugar maple trees in New York and plants in other regions of the United States, such as those in Figure 10.3, have been affected by acid precipitation. It can wash nutrients from the soil and essential compounds from plant tissues. Acid precipitation can lower the pH of lakes and ponds, and as a result, adversely affect aquatic organisms. Buildings and statues can be damaged by acid rain because it can dissolve some substances, such as marble and limestone.

✓ CHECK FOR UNDERSTANDING What is acid precipitation?

Figure 10.3 Acid precipitation can cause the decline and eventual death of trees.

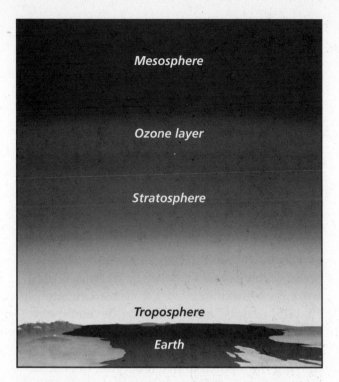

Figure 10.4 The atmosphere's ozone layer absorbs large amounts of ultraviolet radiation, preventing it from reaching Earth's surface.

The release of pollutants called chlorofluoro-carbons or CFCs has been linked to the thinning of Earth's ozone layer, shown in Figure 10.4. The **ozone layer,** at 15 km to 35 km altitude, reduces the amount of ultraviolet rays that enters Earth's lower atmosphere. Ultraviolet rays can damage DNA in cells and cause harmful mutations.

One of the products of burning is carbon dioxide gas. Evidence suggests that the burning of fossil fuels increases the amount of carbon dioxide in Earth's atmosphere. Carbon dioxide is one of the heat-trapping atmospheric gases known as greenhouse gases. Sunlight passes through greenhouse gases in the atmosphere and warms Earth's surface. When this heat is reemitted into the atmosphere, some of it is trapped by greenhouse gases near Earth, as shown in Figure 10.5.

Some scientists hypothesize that this increase in carbon dioxide is resulting in an increase of average temperatures on Earth—a phenomenon called global warming. If these scientists are correct, global warming could result in climatic changes. For example, warming temperatures could increase the rate at which polar ice melts and increase the levels of Earth's oceans. These increases could have catastrophic impacts on coastal areas.

Water pollution has negative effects on humans and other living things. Pollution of lakes and rivers with sewage can raise bacteria levels so that the water is unfit for consumption or even swimming. Fertilizer-rich runoff can result in rapid algal growth that causes a severe imbalance in aquatic ecosystems. Industrial pollutants, such as mercury and PCBs (polychlorinated biphenyls), can kill or damage aquatic life. The harmful chemicals can build up in the bodies of organisms in these food webs. These pollutants can harm humans who eat the aquatic life.

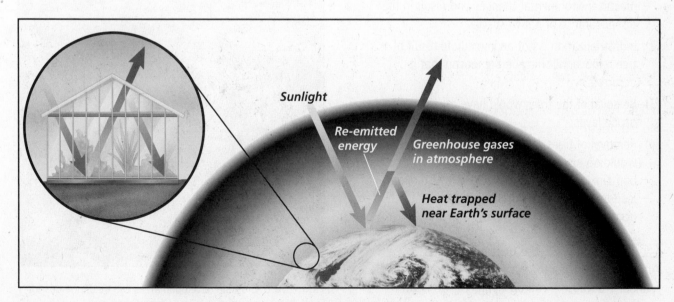

Figure 10.5 Greenhouse gases near Earth's surface trap reemitted heat similar to the way that the glass roof of a greenhouse traps heat.

Land pollution can be unsightly and dangerous. Besides causing immediate harm to organisms, some pollutants remain in the soil for years. Pollutants from landfills can enter water supplies. This can cause problems for humans and other organisms that depend on the water. When landfills located near cities become full, trash must be moved greater distances to other landfills. This increases the cost of trash removal.

Threats to Ecosystems and Species

Human activities are disturbing the balance of ecosystems worldwide. Increased human population growth can result in the death of organisms. The loss of species reduces biodiversity.

REGENTS EXAM

Strategies for Success

STEP 1 READ the Regents Question . . .
Deforestation would most immediately result in

(1) the disappearance of native species

(2) industrialization of an area

(3) the depletion of the ozone layer

(4) global warming

STEP 2 ANALYZE each choice . . .

(1) Many organisms depend on the trees for their needs. Also, trees affect environmental conditions in a forest. Removal of the trees would cause drastic environmental changes and result in the disappearance of native species.

(2) Industrialization is not an immediate result of tree removal but may be the reason that it occurred.

(3) Removal of the trees would have no effect on the ozone layer.

(4) Removal of trees would mean these producers would no longer absorb carbon dioxide. Thus, carbon dioxide levels might increase, which might lead to global warming. However, this would not occur immediately.

STEP 3 CHOOSE the best answer . . .
After considering all the options, the correct answer is number 1 because it can be an immediate result of deforestation.

The biggest threat to ecosystems and biodiversity is habitat loss. It occurs as land is cleared for residential, commercial, industrial, or recreational uses. Habitat loss also occurs in the world's forests, as trees are cut for lumber and/or to clear land for farms or cattle ranches. When all trees are cut or the land is bulldozed, the ecosystem is severely damaged. Organisms in such ecosystems lose their habitats and the resources that allowed them to survive and reproduce. Recovery from such damage is slow, if at all.

Another threat to ecosystems and biodiversity is **habitat fragmentation.** As homes, businesses, and roads are built in previously undeveloped areas, many isolated patches or fragments of natural environments are left. These become "habitat islands" surrounded by development. Observe the isolated islands of forest in Figure 10.6. Many organisms have difficulty moving from patch to patch because of obstructions such as buildings, fences, and roads. This is especially a problem for carnivores, such as foxes or wild felines. These animals' hunting territories often cover large areas of land.

Figure 10.6 Crossing developed areas can be dangerous for animals that must move between the few remaining areas of natural environments.

Figure 10.7 Exotic species can cause problems when they are intentionally or accidentally brought into an ecosystem. **A** Kudzu was brought to the United States from Japan in 1876. It was promoted as a garden plant, cattle forage, and control of soil erosion. **B** Zebra mussels entered the Great Lakes ecosystem from ship-ballast waters.

Habitat degradation also is a threat to wildlife. Prime causes of this are land, water, and air pollution. For example, water pollution is causing the death of sensitive corals in coral reefs. As a result, the ecosystem that these reefs support also is threatened. Global warming could affect the climate of different regions with drastic results on the local ecosystems.

The introduction of nonnative species can damage ecosystems and threaten biodiversity. These introduced species often are called **exotic species.** In the early 1800s, settlers introduced goats to Santa Catalina Island off the coast of California. The goats overgrazed the area, exposing bare patches of soil. Hardy weeds took root in the bare soil and completely eliminated 48 native species from the island. In the nineteenth century, the completion of the Erie Canal, from the Hudson River to Lake Ontario, made it possible for the sea lamprey to migrate from the ocean to the Great Lakes. This predator eliminated some fish species from the Great Lakes ecosystem. Figure 10.7 shows other introduced species that have adversely affected ecosystems and biodiversity.

✓ CHECK FOR UNDERSTANDING What is an example of a problem-causing exotic species?

Another threat to biodiversity and ecosystems occurs when humans overharvest or overcollect organisms. This may cause species to become threatened. **Threatened species** are species that are likely to become endangered in the near future. Elephants became a threatened species because they were hunted for their ivory tusks. When aquatic areas are overfished, it takes years for the fish to recover. This is not only difficult for the ecosystem, but also on the fishermen who depend on the fish for their livelihood.

Quick Review

1 Which factor is *not* considered by ecologists when they evaluate the impact of human activities on an ecosystem?
   (1) amount of energy released from the Sun
   (2) quality of the atmosphere
   (3) degree of biodiversity
   (4) location of power plants

2 Human impact on the environment often is more dramatic than the impact of most other living things because humans have a greater
   (1) need for water
   (2) need for food
   (3) ability to adapt to change
   (4) ability to alter the environment

3 Toxic chemicals called PCBs, produced as a result of manufacturing processes, were dumped into the Hudson River. What was most likely a result of this action on fish in the Hudson River?
(1) Some fish became unfit to eat.
(2) The fish populations increased.
(3) Thermal pollution of the river increased, decreasing the fish population.
(4) The carrying capacity for fish increased in the river.

4 Fertilizers used to improve lawns and gardens may interfere with the equilibrium of an ecosystem because they
(1) cause mutations in all plants
(2) cannot be absorbed by roots
(3) can be carried into local water supplies
(4) cause atmospheric pollution

5 In the early 1980s, scientists discovered holes in the ozone shield surrounding Earth. State one negative effect this environmental change could have on humans.

6 The tall wetland plant, purple loosestrife, was brought from Europe to the United States in the early 1800s as a garden plant. The plant's growth is now so widespread across the United States that it is crowding out a number of native plants. This situation is an example of
(1) the results of the use of pesticides
(2) the recycling of nutrients
(3) the flow of energy present in all ecosystems
(4) an unintended effect of adding a species to an ecosystem

7 Choose one ecological problem from the following list:
    Ecological Problems
    A Global warming
    B Destruction of the ozone shield
    C Loss of biodiversity
Discuss the ecological problem you chose. In your answer be sure to state:
• the problem you selected and one human action that may have caused the problem
• one way in which the problem may negatively affect humans
• one positive action that could be taken to reduce the problem

8 All living organisms are dependent on a stable environment. Describe how humans have made the environment less stable by:
• changing the chemical composition of air, soil, and water
• reducing the biodiversity of an area
• introducing technologies

Conservation—Preserving Earth's Resources

As the human population grows, it will use greater amounts of resources and generate more wastes. This could adversely affect life on Earth by causing a decline in biodiversity. If we practice wise conservation strategies, we can use resources wisely; keep the air, land, and water cleaner; and protect the world's ecosystems and biodiversity.

Using Resources Wisely

The three Rs of conservation are reduce, reuse, and recycle. We can reduce our use of resources by not wasting them. Actions such as switching off lights when no one is in a room and turning off water while you brush your teeth help conserve resources. Instead of driving alone, people who carpool or use public transportation reduce the use of fuels.

Reuse means using an item over and over again or using it for purposes other than its original use. For example, bringing your own paper bags to the grocery store and reusing them saves trees and the energy used to cut down the trees, transport the lumber, manufacture the paper, and make the bags. If the bag becomes torn, the paper can be used for other things.

☑ CHECK FOR UNDERSTANDING What is an example of (a) reduction and (b) reuse?

Today, many communities have recycling programs, as illustrated in Figure 10.8. Residents might sort their recyclable trash items, such as aluminum cans, certain plastics, and glass bottles, from things that are not recyclable. In recycling, raw materials are extracted from recyclable items. These raw materials can be reused in many different ways. For example, when aluminum cans are recycled, pure aluminum is gathered. This can be reused to produce aluminum foil, parts for airplanes, or cans.

Renewable Resources

The use of renewable resources, such as solar power, can help preserve the nonrenewable resources. For example, passive solar houses are designed so that sunlight can enter the south-facing windows in the winter when the Sun is lower in the sky. The sunlight helps to heat the house so less fuel or electricity is needed.

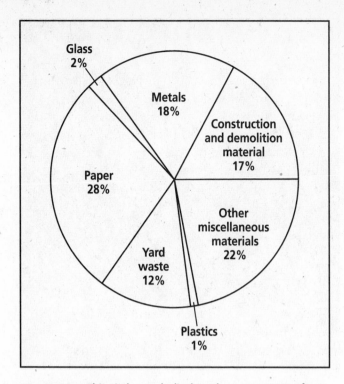

Glass
2%

Metals
18%

Construction
and demolition
material
17%

Paper
28%

Other
miscellaneous
materials
22%

Yard
waste
12%

Plastics
1%

Figure 10.8 This circle graph displays the percentages of specific materials recycled based on the total amount of materials recovered from the waste stream in 1998 as reported by New York State planning units.

In the summer when the Sun is more directly overhead, an overhang prevents sunlight from directly entering through these windows. Other uses of solar energy include heating hot water and generating electricity, as shown in Figure 10.9.

Another renewable resource used in some developing countries is methane gas. It is collected from large vats of animal manure. This odorless gas can be burned to provide light, heat, and cooking fuel in remote areas. Because people can use methane gas, they do not need to cut down trees for firewood.

Reducing Pollution

Another benefit of following the three Rs of conservation is a reduction in pollution. For example, recycling aluminum requires less mining and less fuel use. Using solar energy technologies also can reduce pollution.

Other technologies also can help reduce pollution. Perhaps there is a water treatment plant near you. In these facilities, human wastes are processed and made safe before they enter rivers or streams. Smoke stacks that are equipped with scrubbers can help to remove sulfur from coal-burning emissions, and thus reduce amounts of

acid precipitation that are produced. Introduced in 1975, catalytic converters in car, truck, and some other gasoline-powered engines have decreased the amount of nitrogen oxide and carbon monoxide emissions that enter the atmosphere.

Pesticides can reduce the numbers of pests but they can harm other living things and damage ecosystems. For example, insecticides usually kill many types of insects. If you spray a plant that has aphids, you also are killing beneficial insects such as ladybugs and praying mantises. The pesticides also can enter the food web and damage other organisms.

Biological control methods can be used to reduce or eliminate the need for pesticides. For example, in early summer, it is common to find some plants covered with aphids. Many gardeners release ladybugs to consume the aphids instead of spraying pesticides. Other methods of biological control include releasing parasitic nematodes and spores of *Bacillus thuringiensis* (Bt)—a bacterium. When ingested, Bt paralyzes the guts of insect pests.

Biological controls also can be used effectively to contain plants, such as when nonnative plant species grow out of control. By introducing the natural enemies of the exotic species, that population is controlled. For example, settlers to Australia introduced prickly pear cactus, and by the 1800s, it was growing out of control.

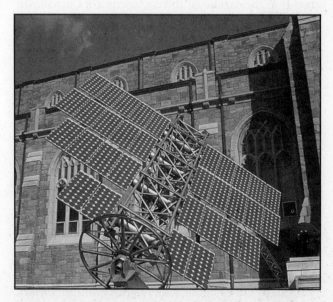

Figure 10.9 Rensselaer Polytechnic Institute in Troy, NY installed a 1.910 kWac photovoltaic system to provide AC power to the Voorhees Computing Center on campus.

Figure 10.10 In only two years, cactus moth larvae reduced the population of prickly pear cactus from about 12,000 per hectare (left photo) to about 27 per hectare (right photo).

By 1925, 12 million hectares of land became useless for farming or grazing animals because of this cactus, as shown in Figure 10.10. Australian entomologists came to the Americas in search of insects that feed on the prickly pear. They identified about 50 insect species and took them back to Australia for testing to make sure they would not eat the native Australian plants. It was discovered that the larvae of the cactus moth, *Cactoblastis cactorum*, only eats prickly pear. The cactus moth was released, and Australia's rangelands were almost cleared of prickly pear cactus by 1935. The moth continues to control the size of the prickly pear populations today.

☑ CHECK FOR UNDERSTANDING What is biological control?

Organic farming methods do not use pesticides or chemical fertilizers. Rather, they usually rely on biological control methods for pest control and composted organic material such as leaves, grass, and manure to improve and fertilize soils. This reduces the pollution problems of chemical pesticides and excess chemical fertilization.

In many cases, technology is not enough. Often, laws must be passed that require people to use newer technologies. For example, the Clean Air Act that was amended in 1990 provided rules that led to reduced acid-rain-producing emissions and the reduced release of materials that damage the ozone layer.

Protecting Biodiversity

Conserving resources and reducing pollution not only help humans survive, but also help other species survive. However, it is not enough to help species that are almost extinct. Ecologists identify species that are in danger of becoming extinct and classify them as **endangered species.** Once a species is identified as endangered, steps are taken to protect it and its habitat. **Conservation biology** is a branch of science that studies and implements ways to protect endangered and threatened species.

Since the largest threat to biodiversity is the loss of habitat, reserving land for species survival is important. Natural areas, such as those in Gateway National Recreation Area and the Adirondack Forest Preserve, provide needed habitats for many organisms. However, restricting land use can create resentment and problems. In the United States, there are debates about whether or not oil drilling should occur in the Arctic National Wildlife Refuge and about whether or not to cut down old growth forests that are rich in biodiversity.

Strategies that help developing countries establish protected areas help maintain biodiversity. Creating parks and protected areas is a first step. Unfortunately, in many cases, designating an area as protected does not automatically protect it. Rules need to be enforced. For example, in East Africa, national parks are protected areas for many species, but poachers still sneak in and kill elephants for their tusks and rhinos for their horns. Armed guards help reduce these violations.

One goal of wildlife management, such as practiced by the New York State Department of Environmental Conservation, is to allow people to use natural areas for recreation, such as hiking, hunting, and fishing. At the same time, park management limits the negative effects of human use, such as restricting the number of hunting permits issued to ensure that a species is not overhunted. Allowing recreation, limited hunting, or resource gathering can motivate people to protect these areas. For example, in the United States, people who hunt or fish often are strong advocates for protecting natural areas.

Habitat fragmentation, as discussed earlier, is a threat to biodiversity. Planning can avoid the formation of small habitat islands surrounded by buildings or roads by developing communities with one large natural area, rather than several small areas. Planning also can allow for **habitat corridors** that provide animals with a way to pass freely from one area to another. Knowing about the daily or seasonal movements of animals can allow scientists to plan safe habitat corridors. For example, tunnels can be built under highways, as shown in Figure 10.11, that allow animals to complete their normal migrations.

✓ CHECK FOR UNDERSTANDING How do habitat corridors help with the problem of habitat fragmentation?

Another strategy to help species is to reintroduce the native organisms into areas where they once lived. Programs that use this strategy are called **reintroduction programs.** For example, to save the population of California condors—an endangered bird species—surviving condors were captured and kept in captivity. After successful breeding programs, condor offspring were reintroduced into areas of Arizona and California where the species once lived.

Other reintroduction programs move members of a species from where they now live to where they used to live. For example, brown pelicans once were plentiful along the Gulf of Mexico.

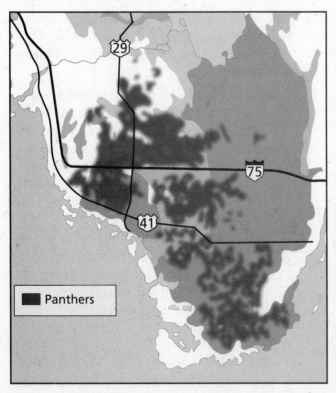

Figure 10.11 Over time, the Florida panther's habitat became fragmented, however wildlife corridors allow it to move safely from one area to another.

The presence of the pesticide DDT in the brown pelican's food chain resulted in weak-shelled pelican eggs and the loss of chicks. Over time, the brown pelican population disappeared from coastal areas of Louisiana. After DDT was banned in the United States in 1972, brown pelicans were brought to the Louisiana coast from Florida. Today, brown pelicans have been successfully reestablished along Louisiana's Gulf shores.

Many of the successes in preserving ecosystems and biodiversity were the result of government intervention. For example, governments create national and state parks that preserve wilderness areas. Governments also create laws to protect species. In 1973, the U.S. Endangered Species Act became law. This made it illegal to harm any species on an endangered- or threatened-species list. It also made it illegal for any federal agencies to fund any project that would harm organisms on these lists.

Striking a Balance

The world provides resources to enjoy life. It is obvious that humans use resources and create pollution. Unfortunately, some human activities damage environments and living organisms. There are many competing interest groups that strive to use resources or protect resources. Some groups want development and others want preservation of natural areas. As a future voter or as a leader, you will make decisions about how we can find acceptable balances. There are no simple answers. For each problem, the advantages and disadvantages of possible solutions need to be thoroughly considered. Decisions that you make will affect your life and the lives of future generations. Through a blend of conservation, knowledge of ecology, and technology, it is hoped that we can enjoy our lifestyles and protect Earth's resources.

Quick Review

9   Mountain lions in a protected forest have difficulty getting enough food because a highway has prevented them from accessing large portions of wilderness. Which is most likely the best solution to ensure access?
(1) habitat corridors
(2) biological control
(3) using renewable resources
(4) recycling

10   To minimize negative environmental impact, a community should
(1) approve the weekly spraying of pesticides on the plants in a local park
(2) grant a permit to a chemical manufacturing company to build a factory by one of its lakes, which has no restrictions on waste disposal
(3) make a decision about building a new road in a hiking area based only on the economic advantages
(4) set policy after considering both the risks and benefits involved in building a toxic waste site within its boundaries

11   A new type of fuel gives off excessive amounts of smoke. Before this type of fuel is widely used, an ecologist would most likely want to know
(1) what effect the smoke will have on the environment
(2) how much it will cost to produce the fuel
(3) how long it will take to produce the fuel
(4) if the fuel will be widely accepted by consumers

12   To ensure environmental quality for the future, each individual should
(1) acquire and apply knowledge of ecological principles
(2) continue to take part in deforestation
(3) use Earth's finite resources
(4) add and take away organisms from ecosystems

13   State one environmental impact of reduced funding for public transportation (e.g., trains, city buses, school buses, etc.) on future generations. Explain your answer.

14   There are several possible methods to control an invasion of gypsy moths in a city park. Write the letter of the method listed below that you would use and give an ecologically sound reason for your choice.
A   A band of material can be placed around each tree trunk that prevents larvae from crawling up the trunk. The larvae can be picked off each day and destroyed.
B   An effective chemical insecticide can be sprayed from an airplane. The chemical disappears rapidly, but some may run off into ponds and lakes.
C   Trees can be sprayed with naturally occurring bacteria that feed on gypsy moths. The bacteria are believed to be harmless, but the spray is expensive.
D   Allow nature to take its course, which results in major changes in the area concerned. The damage can then be repaired.

Part A

1 Which human activity would have the most direct impact on the oxygen-carbon dioxide cycle?

(1) reducing the rate of ecological succession

(2) decreasing the use of water

(3) destroying large forest areas

(4) enforcing laws that prevent the use of leaded gasoline

2 In some areas, foresters plant one tree for every tree they cut. This activity is an example of

(1) lack of management of nonrenewable natural resources

(2) a good conservation practice for renewable natural resources

(3) a good conservation practice for nonrenewable natural resources

(4) lack of concern for renewable natural resources

3 Before it was banned, the insecticide DDT was used to combat an organism called the red mite. An unexpected result of the use of DDT was that the population of the red mite increased rather than decreased, while the population of insect predators of the red mite decreased. What can be inferred from this situation?

(1) Environmental changes that affect one population can affect other populations.

(2) The red mite and its insect predators were all competing for the same resources.

(3) The red mites were immune to the effects of insecticides.

(4) Using insecticides is a reliable way to eliminate all insect predators.

4 When humans use more ground water for industry than is being replaced, the soil above the ground water may collapse and disrupt natural habitats. This human activity is an example of

(1) species exploitation

(2) renewal of natural resources

(3) a disposal problem

(4) poor use of finite resources

5 Chittenango Falls State Park in central New York State is the only known habitat for an endangered species of aquatic snail. Contamination of its water supply and reduction of its habitat have threatened the future of this snail. Which step could be taken to protect this species of snail?

(1) banning human activities that damaged the habitat

(2) introducing a new snail predator into the habitat

(3) transferring the snail to a terrestrial environment

(4) crossbreeding the snail with another species

6 Which human activity has probably contributed most to the acidification of lakes in the Adirondack region?

(1) passing environmental protection laws

(2) establishing reforestation projects in lumbered areas

(3) burning fossil fuels that produce air pollutants containing sulfur and nitrogen

(4) using pesticides for the control of insects that feed on trees

7 Car exhaust has been blamed for increasing the amount of carbon dioxide in the air. Some scientists believe this additional carbon dioxide in the air may cause

(1) global warming

(2) increased biodiversity

(3) habitat preservation

(4) ozone destruction

8 Which statement illustrates how human activities can most directly change the dynamic equilibrium of an ecosystem?

(1) A hurricane causes a stream to overflow its banks.

(2) Increased wind increases water evaporation from a plant.

(3) Water pollution causes a decrease in fish populations in a river.

(4) The ozone shield helps prevent harmful radiation from reaching the surface of Earth.

Part B

Base your answers to questions 9 through 13 on the passage below and on your knowledge of biology.

Help Wanted—Bacteria for Environmental Cleanup

The location of a former fuel storage depot and packaging operation in the industrial port of Toronto, Canada, is the proposed site of a sports arena and entertainment complex. The problem is that the soil in this area was contaminated with gasoline, diesel fuel, home heating oil, and grease from the operation of the previous facility. Unless these substances are removed, the project cannot proceed.

The traditional method of cleaning up such sites is the "dig and dump" method, in which the contaminated soil is removed, deposited in landfills, and replaced with clean soil. This "dig and dump" method is messy and costly and adds to landfills that are already over-loaded. A technique known as bio-remediation, which was used to help in the cleanup of the *Exxon Valdez* oil spill in Alaska, offered a relatively inexpensive way of dealing with this pollution problem. This cleanup process cost $1.4 million, one-third of the cost of the "dig and dump" method, and involved encasing 85,000 tons of soil in a plastic "biocell" the size of a football field. This plastic-encased soil contained naturally occurring bacteria that would eventually have cleaned up the area after 50 years or more with the amounts of oxygen and nutrients naturally found in the soil. Air, water, and fertilizer were piped into the biocell, stimulating the bacteria to reproduce rapidly and speed up the process. The cleanup by this technique was begun in August and completed in November of the same year. The bacteria attack parts of the contaminating molecules by breaking the carbon-to-carbon bonds that hold them together. This helps to change these molecules in the soil into carbon dioxide and water.

Although this method is effective for cleaning up some forms of pollution, bio-remediation is not effective for inorganic materials such as lead or other heavy metals since these wastes are already in a base state that cannot be degraded any further.

9 The use of bio-remediation by humans is an example of

   (1) interfering with nature so that natural processes cannot take place

   (2) using a completely unnatural method to solve a problem

   (3) solving a problem by speeding up natural processes

   (4) being unaware of and not using natural processes

10 The bacteria convert the contaminants into

   (1) carbon dioxide and water

   (2) toxic substances

   (3) proteins and fats

   (4) diesel fuel and grease

11 State an ecological drawback to the use of the "dig and dump" method. _____

_____

12 Explain why the cleanup took only 3 months. _____

_____

13 Bio-remediation is not an effective method for breaking down

(1) grease

(2) gasoline

(3) fuel for diesel engines and furnaces

(4) heavy metals such as lead

Part C

Base your answers to questions 14 and 15 on the passage below and on your knowledge of biology.

In a rural area, there is a swamp with a large population of mosquitoes. Nearby residents are concerned because the mosquitoes are always annoying and occasionally carry diseases. The community decides to have an insecticide sprayed from an airplane on the area during the prime mosquito season. Whenever they stop spraying, the mosquito population quickly rebounds to a higher level than existed before the spraying program began. After 10 years, the spraying became much less effective at reducing the mosquito population. Higher doses of insecticide were required to accomplish the same population decreases.

14 State *one* possible *disadvantage* of spraying the insecticide from an airplane. _____

_____

15 State *one* alternative method of mosquito control that may have a more lasting impact on the mosquito population.

_____

_____

Base your answers to questions 16 and 18 on the passage below and on your knowledge of biology.

Predators Contribute to a Stable Ecosystem

In nature, energy flows in only one direction. Transfer of energy must occur in an ecosystem because all life needs energy to live, and only certain organisms can change solar energy into chemical energy.

Producers are eaten by consumers that are, in turn, eaten by other consumers. Stable ecosystems must contain predators to help control the populations of consumers.

Since ecosystems contain many predators, exterminating predators would require a massive effort that would wipe out predatory species from barnacles to blue whales. Without the population control provided by predators, some organisms would soon overpopulate.

16 Draw an energy pyramid that illustrates the information underlined in the second paragraph. Include *three* different, specific organisms in the energy pyramid.

_____

17 Explain the phrase "only certain organisms can change solar energy into chemical energy," in the underlined portion of the first paragraph. In your answer be sure to identify:

• the type of nutrition carried out by these organisms

• the process being carried out in this type of nutrition

• the organelles present in the cells of these organisms that are directly involved in changing solar energy into chemical energy

_____

18 Explain why an ecosystem with a variety of predator species might be more stable over a long period of time than an ecosystem with only one predator species.

_____

Base your answers to questions 19 and 20 on the information below and on your knowledge of biology. Use one or more complete sentences to answer each question.

> In July 1997, about 25,000 *Galerucella pusilla* beetles were released at Montezuma Wildlife Refuge in western New York State. These beetles eat purple loosestrife, a beautiful but rapidly spreading weed that chokes wetlands. Purple loosestrife is native to Europe, but here it crowds out native wetland plants, such as cattails, and does not support wildlife the way the native plants do. Purple loosestrife grows too thick to allow birds to nest. Most native insects do not eat it, leaving little for insect-eating birds to eat. Bernd Blossey, a professor at Cornell University, spent 6 years in Europe trying to find out what limited the loosestrife population there.

19 Explain why the introduction of the beetle is an advantage over the use of herbicides to control the purple loosestrife population.

_____

20 Describe one possible environmental problem that may result from the introduction of this beetle. _____

_____

_____

Answer all questions in this part.

Directions (21–25): For those questions that are followed by four choices, circle the number of the choice that best answers the question. For all other questions in this part, follow the directions given in the question.

21 Use the diagram below to explain what the greenhouse effect is and why it might impact the biodiversity in coastal areas.

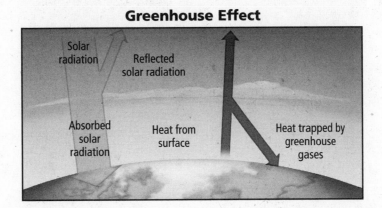

_____

_____

_____

_____

22 What does the drawing below illustrate and how is it used to preserve biodiversity?

_____

_____

_____

_____

23 Identify one way that the object above can preserve biodiversity in plants.

_____

_____

24 How are species described when the number of organisms of that species drops to a level so low that extinction is possible?

(1) degraded

(2) endangered

(3) exploited

(4) fragmented

25 Which has been a cause of extinctions of populations on islands?

(1) Native species often move back and forth between islands.

(2) Island populations easily develop resistance to introduced species.

(3) Introduced species are usually kept in check by predators on the islands.

(4) Introduced species have no natural predators.

Laboratory Skills

compound light microscope
safety symbol

A requirement of the Regents Living Environment course is that all students are expected to develop proficiency in specific science skills. These skills include the application of scientific methods, which was discussed in Section 1 of this book, and the application of laboratory techniques and procedures, which will be discussed in this section.

Safety in the Laboratory

Safety rules, such as those in the following list, help to make the laboratory experience safer for everyone. Laboratory safety is the responsibility of every student who participates in biology laboratory and field investigations.

- Read and follow all laboratory procedures before you begin an investigation. Ask your teacher to clarify anything about the lab that you do not understand before you begin.
- Begin the laboratory procedure only after you are directed by your teacher to do so.

- Wear safety goggles and other safety apparel that are indicated by the safety symbols at the beginning of each lab for the entire lab. **Safety symbols,** as shown in Figure 1, also warn of dangers that may exist for a lab.
- Handle chemicals and equipment only as instructed by your teacher.
- Never taste or directly inhale laboratory chemicals. Never eat or drink in the lab.
- Report and do not use any broken or atypical laboratory equipment.
- Inform your teacher of allergies and health conditions that can affect your participation in a lab.

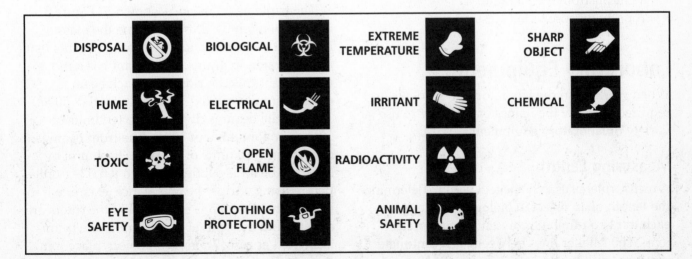

Figure 1 Safety symbols are a quick way of warning students of potential dangers in a laboratory.

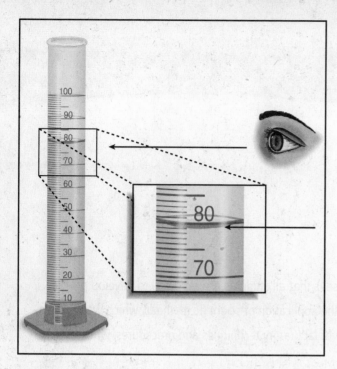

Figure 2 Liquid volume is measured at the lowest point of the meniscus. This liquid measures 79 mL.

- Immediately report to your teacher any spills and injuries during a lab.
- When heating or rinsing a liquid in a test tube or flask, always point it away from yourself and others.
- Do not pour excess, unused chemicals back into stock bottles or switch bottle stoppers.
- Make sure you know the location of and how to use the eyewash station, safety shower, and fire prevention equipment.
- Do not remove any equipment, materials, or chemicals from the laboratory.
- Properly dispose of lab wastes.

Laboratory Equipment

When working in the laboratory, all students are required to know the names of and how to use a variety of laboratory equipment.

Measuring Length

A metric ruler is usually the tool used to determine the length of an object in biology. On the ruler, each marked number represents a centimeter (cm). The smaller lines between each centimeter represent millimeters (mm). There are 10 mm in each centimeter and 100 cm in one meter (m).

Measuring Volume

A graduated cylinder is used to measure the volume of a liquid in the laboratory. The metric unit for measuring liquid volume is the liter (L).

In a graduated cylinder, the surface of a liquid curves upward along the sides of the cylinder. This curved surface—the meniscus—is formed because the liquid's molecules are attracted to the sides of the cylinder, as shown in Figure 2. When making an accurate measurement with a cylinder, it should be placed on a flat surface and the measurement read at eye level at the lowest point of the meniscus.

✔ CHECK FOR UNDERSTANDING What is a meniscus? How is it used to determine the volume of a liquid?

Measuring Temperature

In the metric system, temperature is measured in degrees Celsius, (°C). The freezing point of water is 0°C, the boiling point of water is 100°C, and human body temperature is 37°C. Alcohol thermometers are usually the tools used to measure temperature. Sometimes, electronic thermometers, called temperature probes, are used to record temperature over time or to give more precise temperature readings.

Measuring Mass

In the biology laboratory, mass—the quantity of matter in an object—is measured with a balance. The metric unit of mass is the kilogram (kg), but most biological items are massed in grams, (g). There are 1000 g in 1 kg.

The triple-beam balance, shown in Figure 3, is the tool often used to determine the mass of objects. It has a pan and three bars or beams that are calibrated in grams. Each beam has a moveable weight called a rider. The back beam is divided into five 100-g units for a total of 500 g. The middle beam is divided into ten units of 10 g each, for a total of 100 g. The front beam is divided into 10 units of 1 g each. Each unit of the front beam is subdivided into ten 0.1-g units. Before using a triple-beam balance, examine it to be sure that the pan is empty, all of the riders are at zero, and the pointer at the end of the beams is aligned at zero. To mass an object, place it in the pan. Begin by moving the 100-g rider to the right, one notch at a time, until the pointer stays

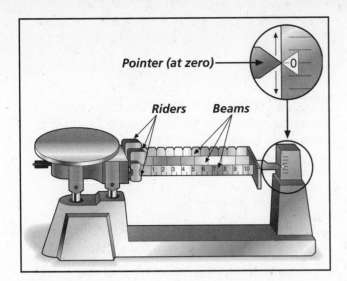

Figure 3 The triple beam balance is used to measure an object's mass.

down, and then move the rider back one notch. Next, move the 10-g rider following the same procedure. Last, move the 1-g rider along its beam until the pointer at the end of the beam aligns at zero. The mass of the object is the sum of all rider positions on the three beams.

Using a Compound Light Microscope

This instrument uses light and a series of lenses to magnify an object up to 1500 times its original size.

The **compound light microscope** can contain one or two eyepieces, or ocular lenses, and several objective lenses, as shown in Table 1. Light passes through the object being magnified—the specimen—then through an objective lens. Light travels up the tube to the eyepiece and then passes into the viewer's eye. Both the ocular and objective lens magnify the observed image. The total magnification for a specimen is calculated by multiplying the magnification of the eyepiece by the magnification of the objective lens. For example, if you were using a 10× eyepiece and a 10× objective lens, the total magnification of the specimen would be 100×.

The image of the object viewed under a compound light microscope is enlarged, reversed (backward), and inverted (upside down). For example, the letter "**e**" appears as "**ə**" under this microscope. When viewing living organisms, the slide should be moved in the opposite direction that the organism is moving. If the organism appears to be moving up, you should move the slide toward you; if down, move the slide away from you. If the organism appears to be moving to the right, then you should move the slide to the left, and vice versa.

To use a compound light microscope, place a specimen slide on the stage over the opening and then anchor it with stage clips.

Table 1 • Parts of the Compound Light Microscope	
Part	**Function**
Base	Supports the microscope
Arm	Used to carry the microscope
Stage	Platform where the slide with specimen is placed
Stage clip	Holds the slide in place on the stage
Eyepiece	Magnifies image for the viewer
Objective Lenses	Low-power and high-power lenses that magnify the specimen
Coarse Adjustment	Large knob used for focusing the image under low-power ONLY.
Fine Adjustment	Smaller knob used for focusing the image with the high-power objective.
Diaphragm	Controls the amount of light that passes through the specimen
Light Source	Provides light for viewing the specimen

Arm

Eyepieces

Low-power objective

Stage clip

Coarse adjustment

High-power objectives

Stage

Diaphragm

Fine adjustment

Light source

Base

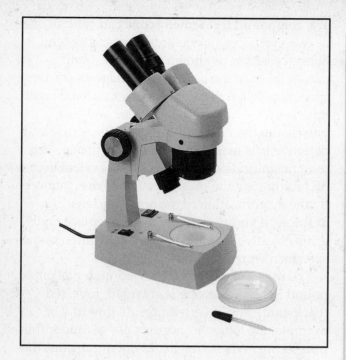

Figure 4 The dissecting microscope is used to view whole specimen or parts of specimen that are too large or too thick to view under a compound light microscope.

The observer first views the specimen using the low-power objective. Bring the object into focus using the coarse adjustment only. Once the object is in focus with low-power, a higher power of objective can be used. The fine adjustment is used only with higher power objectives. When switching from a low- to high-power objective, adjust the diaphragm to allow more light to reach the specimen.

Using Stereomicroscopes

Microscopes with two eyepieces, such as those in Table 1 and Figure 4, are referred to as stereomicroscopes. The image is three-dimensional because of the two eyepieces. The dissecting microscope—also called the stereoscope—is used to observe parts of objects such as flowers, insects, or the organs of dissected specimens. The total magnification of this type of microscope is much less than for a compound light microscope. The image seen is not reversed or inverted.

Determining the Size of Your Specimen

To estimate the size of a specimen under a microscope, you need to determine the diameter of the microscope's field of view in micrometers (μm). One millimeter contains 1000 micrometers.

Strategies for Success

STEP 1 **READ the Regents Question . . .**
What information from the list below must be used to estimate the length of a cell under the low-power objective of a compound light microscope?

Information

A Type of cell in the field

B Magnification of the low-power objective

C Magnification of the high-power objective

D Diameter of the low-power field of view

E Number of cells that fit end-to-end across the diameter of the low-power field of view

(1) *A* and *C* only

(2) *A, B, C,* and *E* only

(3) *D* and *E* only

(4) *A, B, C, D,* and *E*

STEP 2 **ANALYZE each choice . . .**

(1) The sizes of cells can vary because of the environment in which an organism lives. This can only give the viewer some idea about what size to expect. The magnification of the objective is only one of the factors for total magnification of the microscope.

(2) The magnifications of both objectives are not both used when figuring the magnification of an image.

(3) Diameter of the field of view and the number of cells that fit across the diameter would be used to estimate a cell's length.

(4) All of this information is not needed for reasons stated in (1) and (2).

STEP 3 **CHOOSE the best answer . . .**
After considering all of the options, the best answer is number 3 because the other choices give incorrect or incomplete information.

The field of view can be estimated using a clear plastic metric ruler. Place the millimeter section of the ruler over the opening of the stage under low power and focus. Locate the lines of the ruler so that a millimeter line is visible at the left edge of your field of view and another is seen to the right, as shown in Figure 5, then determine the diameter.

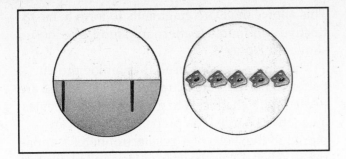

Figure 5 This field of view is approximately 1.5 mm in diameter.

If the estimated diameter is 1.5 mm, then the field of view at low power is 1500 μm. Once you know the field's diameter, you can estimate the size of a specimen. For example, if you viewed a specimen that took up half of this field of view under low power, the specimen would be approximately 750 μm in length.

Preparing a Wet-Mount Slide

A wet mount is a temporary slide prepared for viewing specimens under the compound light microscope. The specimen must be thin enough to allow light to pass through it. To prepare a wet mount:

1. Use a pipette or dropper to place a drop of water in the center of the slide.
2. Place the specimen in the drop of water.
3. Place a coverslip on the slide at the edge of the water, and slowly lower a coverslip over the specimen.

Applying Stains

Staining the specimen with iodine or methylene blue allows many cell parts to be seen and identified more easily. After preparing a wet mount, add a drop of stain to one edge of the coverslip. Next, touch a small piece of paper towel to the opposite edge of the coverslip to draw the stain across the slide and over the specimen.

Using stains, the nucleus becomes clearly visible as a round, stained structure within the cytoplasm. The cell membrane becomes visible as the outer boundary of the cell. In plant cells, the cell wall also can be viewed as the rectangular outer boundary on the outside of the cell membrane. Vacuoles are often viewed as colorless areas in the cytoplasm of plant cells and some animal cells. Chromosomes can be observed in cells undergoing cell division. However, even with stains, organelles such as the endoplasmic reticulum, ribosomes, and the mitochondria are too small to be seen under the compound light microscope.

✓ CHECK FOR UNDERSTANDING Why is staining important to observing a specimen under the microscope?

Using Indicators

Indicators are used to test for the presence of specific substances or chemicals. An indicator will change color when it contacts or reacts with a specific type of substance. Table 2 lists commonly used indicators, what they test for, and how they react.

Table 2 • Indicators		
Indicator	In a solution, indicates	Reaction
Litmus paper	acid or base	red litmus turns blue if a base; blue litmus turns red if an acid
pH paper	pH	color change compared to a color chart to estimate the pH
Bromthymol blue	presence of carbon dioxide	turns yellow if carbon dioxide is present; changes back to blue from yellow when carbon dioxide is removed
Phenolphthalein solution	presence of carbon dioxide or a basic solution	turns from clear to a bright pink in the presence of either substance
Benedict's solution	presence of simple sugars when heated	high sugar concentration, changes from blue to red; low sugar concentration, changes from blue to yellow.
Biuret solution	presence of protein	turns from light blue to purple
Lugol's solution	presence of starch	turns from deep brown to blue-black

Lab Techniques

Two important lab techniques used to identify molecules are gel electrophoresis and chromatography. Both techniques are important diagnostic tools in the biology laboratory.

Gel Electrophoresis

A technique used by scientists to separate mixtures of large molecules according to their size is gel electrophoresis. This technique is most often used in separating DNA and protein molecules.

DNA gel electrophoresis uses special enzymes to cut a DNA sample at specific nucleotide sequences. Next, small amounts of cut DNA are placed in wells located on one side of a semisolid gelatinlike substance. The gel is placed in a solution between two electrodes that are connected to a power supply. When an electric current is applied, one end of the gel has a positive charge and the other end has a negative charge. The negatively charged DNA fragments move toward the positive end of the gel plate. The smaller the fragment, the farther it moves through the gel.

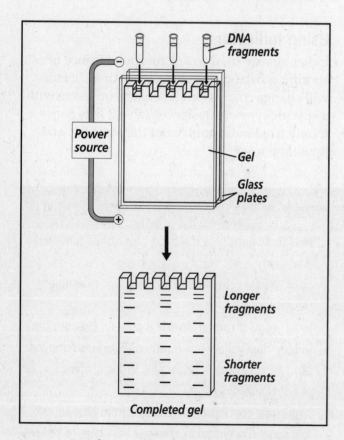

Figure 6 DNA fragments separate according to size during gel electrophoresis.

This allows the DNA fragments to form a distinctive and unique pattern for study, like those shown in Figure 6.

This process also is used to examine protein patterns. Proteins are extracted from cells and are treated with chemicals to give protein molecules a negative charge. The prepared proteins are placed in the wells of a gel electrophoresis apparatus. When an electric current is applied, protein molecules move through the gel. The separation of protein molecules is based on their size, shape, and charge.

✔ **CHECK FOR UNDERSTANDING** What is gel electrophoresis? How is it most often used in the laboratory?

Chromatography

A commonly used technique in the biology laboratory for separating mixtures of molecules is chromatography. In chromatography, the substance to be separated is placed on filter paper or special chromatography paper. Chlorophyll extract from leaves can be separated by chromatography. A dot of the extract is placed near one end of the strip of paper. The end of the paper nearest the dot is placed in a solvent, such as alcohol when using chlorophyll. The solvent should not touch the extract to be separated, but should be just below it. The solvent then moves up the paper and picks up substances in the solvent. Substances in the extract that are tightly held to the paper will move slowly up the paper, while extract substances that are not as tightly held move quickly up the paper. This results in bands of different substances on the chromatography paper.

Dichotomous Keys

Organisms and biological objects can be classified by their observable characteristics using a dichotomous key. A dichotomous key begins with two statements that separate organisms or objects into two groups. Each succeeding statement again will divide the objects or organisms into two more groups until each item is classified and/or identified. An example of a dichotomous key that could be used to identify a goldfish, a robin, an elephant, and a whale is shown in Table 3.

Table 3 • Animal Key		
Step 1 Length of organism		
a less than 1 m in length		go to Step 2
b 1 m or more in length		go to Step 3
Step 2 Type of appendages		
a fins		goldfish
b wings		robin
Step 3 Habitat		
a land		elephant
b water		whale

Quick Review

1   The diagram below represents two cells next to a metric ruler under low-power objective of a compound light microscope.

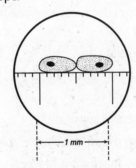

What is the approximate length of a nucleus in one of these cells?

(1) 100 µm   (3) 1000 µm
(2) 500 µm   (4) 1500 µm

2   The diagram below shows a microscopic field containing a portion of the cross section of a root tip.

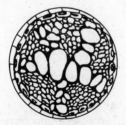

How should a student adjust the microscope in order to view a greater portion of the root tip?

(1) stay at the same power and adjust the focus
(2) stay at the same power but increase the size of the opening of the diaphragm
(3) switch to a lower power and decrease the size of the opening of the diaphragm
(4) switch to a higher power and adjust the focus

3   Which substance is a suitable indicator for detecting the presence of starch in a plant cell?

(1) Fehling's solution   (3) bromthymol blue
(2) pH paper   (4) iodine solution

Base your answer to question 4 on the diagram below and your knowledge of biology. The diagram represents the measurements of two leaves.

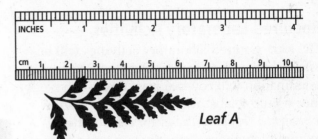

Leaf A

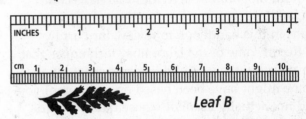

Leaf B

4   The difference in length between leaves *A* and *B* is closest to

(1) 20 mm   (3) 0.65 m
(2) 20 cm   (4) 1.6 µm

5   The diagram below represents a hydra as viewed with a compound light microscope.

If the hydra moves toward the right of the slide preparation, which diagram best presents what will be observed through the microscope?

(1)   (3)

(2) 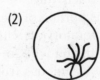   (4)

Preparing for Part D

Since June 2004, the Regents Examination in Living Environment includes Part D. The questions in this part relate to required laboratory activities you have performed in class. Part D of the exam includes both multiple-choice and open-ended questions.

Required Laboratory Activities

The four required laboratory activities will be established each year. Part D on the Regents examination will cover at least three of the four required labs. Your teacher will provide a *Student Laboratory Packet* for each of the required laboratory activities you have completed. Use these packets and the practice questions in this handbook to review for Part D.

Recall some of the laboratory techniques that you used in the required laboratory activities. Some might have been based on equipment you did not actually use, but whose data you can interpret. This might include gel electrophoresis or DNA sequencing. Others involved equipment you did use, such as compound light microscopes, paper chromatography, and chemical indicators. The laboratory techniques above are reviewed earlier in the Laboratory Skills section of this handbook.

What to Expect on Part D

The questions in Part D are intended to assess both your understanding of lab techniques and your ability to interpret lab results. Technique questions might cover how a particular technique works, what safety precautions one should take with a particular technique, and what can happen if the technique is not followed properly. Questions about lab results might ask you to interpret sample experimental results or even to design your own experiment. As always, you also will be expected to understand the basic biology behind these laboratory activities.

The key to doing well on this portion of the exam is not memorizing the laboratory activities you do in the classroom. Instead, you will do best by understanding the way techniques work, the problems to avoid when using a technique, and the biology behind the laboratory acitivities.

6 What change would occur in the cells of a fresh-water fish when it is placed in water that has a higher salt concentration?

(1) no change

(2) cells swell

(3) cells shrink

(4) cells shrink and then swell

7 Imagine you are testing the effect of exercise on pulse rate. You take the resting pulse rate of 100 people. Next you have half of the people exercise for 30 minutes and take everyone's pulse again. What do you call the group of people who did not exercise?

(1) control group   (3) experimental group

(2) data group   (4) indicator group

8 Gel electrophoresis separates molecules based on their

(1) charge and size.

(2) pH and light absorption.

(3) length and color.

(4) enzyme and substrate.

9 When using a light microscope, specimens should be

(1) thick so that light is blocked.

(2) thick so there are many layers of cells.

(3) thin so that light can pass through.

(4) thin so that only partial cells are present.

10 Mixing an unknown solution with Benedict's solution causes the solution to change from blue to red. What can you conclude about the unknown solution?

(1) No glucose is present.

(2) Glucose is present.

(3) No starch is present.

(4) Starch is present.

11 What would you see, using chromatography, that would allow you to conclude that two plants had the same kind of chlorophyll?

(1) identical band movement only

(2) identical band size

(3) identical colors and identical band movement

(4) identical solvent height

Part A

1 A cell in the field of view of a compound light microscope is shown in the diagram below

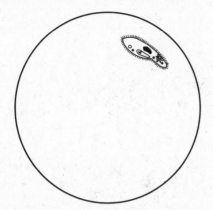

In which direction should the slide be moved to center this cell in the microscopic field?
(1) to the right and up
(2) to the right and down
(3) to the left and up
(4) to the left and down

2 The diagram below shows three cells in the field of view of a microscope. The diameter of the field of view is 1.5 millimeters.

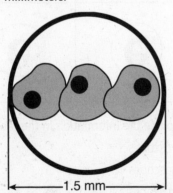

What is the approximate diameter of each cell?
(1) 50 μm   (3) 500 μm
(2) 250 μm   (4) 4,500 μm

3 Which statement best describes the procedure for removing excess methylene blue from a wet mount slide preparation?
(1) Remove the coverslip and drop water onto the specimen.
(2) Place a piece of paper towel at one edge of the coverslip to absorb the methylene blue, and then add water at the opposite edge of the coverslip.
(3) Insert a pipette under the coverslip and withdraw some methylene blue.
(4) Remove the coverslip, allow the methylene blue to dry, and then replace the coverslip.

4 A student views a wet mount of a specimen with the low-power objective of a compound light microscope. After the student switches to high power, which procedure would most likely produce a better view of the specimen?
(1) increasing the amount of light by adjusting the diaphragm
(2) increasing the distance between the slide and the low-power objective, using the coarse adjustment
(3) removing the water from the slide
(4) removing the coverslip from the slide

5 A wet mount of unstained elodea (a green aquatic plant) is observed using high power (400×) of a compound light microscope. Which structures would most likely be observed?
(1) cytoplasm, endoplasmic reticulum, and nucleolus
(2) ribosome, Golgi complex, and vacuole
(3) nucleus, chloroplast, and cell wall
(4) centrosome, lysosome, and plasma membrane

6 A compound light microscope has a 10× eyepiece, 10× objective, 40× objective, and low-power field diameter of 1,600 micrometers. What is the diameter of the field of view when the high-power objective lens is used?
(1) 10 μm   (3) 400 μm
(2) 40 μm   (4) 1,600 μm

7 What is the volume of water in the graduated cylinder shown below?

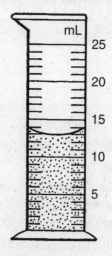

(1) 10.3 mL (3) 13.5 mL

(2) 13.0 mL (4) 14.0 mL

Part B

8 The table below shows the position of slides of the letter "e" on the stages of four microscopes. The image of the "e" as seen using each microscope is also shown.

	Microscope A	Microscope B	Microscope C	Microscope D
Position of slide on the stage	ǝ	e	ǝ	e
Image of specimen as seen using the microscope	e	e	ǝ	ǝ

Which letters correctly identify the microscopes most likely used to provide the information in the table?

(1) *A* and *D*—compound light microscopes; *B* and *C*—dissecting microscopes

(2) *B* and *C*—compound light microscopes; *A* and *D*—dissecting microscopes

(3) *C* and *D*—compound light microscopes; *A* and *B*—dissecting microscopes

(4) *B* and *D*—compound light microscopes; *A* and *C*—dissecting microscopes

9 Two views of the same onion epidermal cells, as seen with a compound light microscope, are shown in the diagram below.

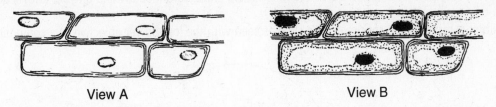

View A   View B

What was most likely done to change the view from *A* to *B?*

(1) Lugol's iodine solution was added to the cells.

(2) The 40× objective was switched to the 10× objective.

(3) The 10× objective was switched to the 40× objective.

(4) Salt water was added to the cells.

10 In preparing to dissect a preserved grasshopper, a student put on a laboratory apron. Then the student obtained the specimen, dissecting pins, instruments, and trays and returned to the laboratory work area. Using one or more complete sentences, state a safety procedure not mentioned that the student should follow before beginning the dissection. You may use pen or pencil for your answer.

_____

_____

Base your answer to question 11 on the diagram below and on your knowledge of biology

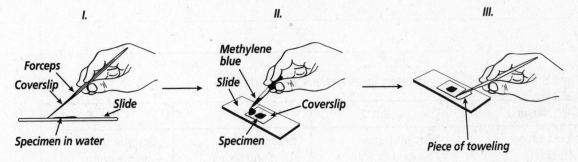

11 Which laboratory technique is illustrated in the diagram?

(1) testing a specimen for amino acids

(2) determining the pH of a specimen

(3) measuring the photosynthetic rate in a specimen

(4) preparing a wet mount of a specimen

Part C

Base your answers to questions 12 and 13 on the information and diagram below and on your knowledge of biology.

The diagram below represents a specimen on a slide as seen with the low-power objective of a compound light microscope.

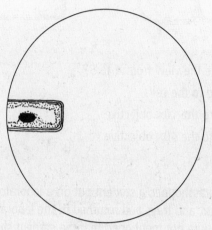

12 Using one or more complete sentences, explain how the slide should be moved to observe the entire specimen.

_____

_____

13 Which type of cell is most likely represented in this diagram?

_____

_____

14 The materials from four different laboratory investigations are listed below.

Set 1	Set 2	Set 3	Set 4

Test tubes
Beaker
Water
Hot plate
Pipette
Test-tube clamp
Benedict's solution
	Brown paper
	Source of light
		Beaker
		Drinking straw
		Bromthymol blue
			Compound
			  microscope
			Slide
			Coverslip
			Lugol's iodine
			  solution

Select one of the four sets of materials. Record the number of the set chosen, and using one or more complete sentences, state a laboratory investigation that could be carried out using this set. You may use pen or pencil for your answer.

_____

_____

_____

_____

174 • Content Questions for Regents Exam Practice

Base your answers to questions 15 through 17 on the figure below and on your knowledge of biology.

The diagram below shows the results of a test that was done using DNA samples from three bears. Each DNA sample was cut into fragments using special enzymes. The samples then were separated using gel electrophoresis.

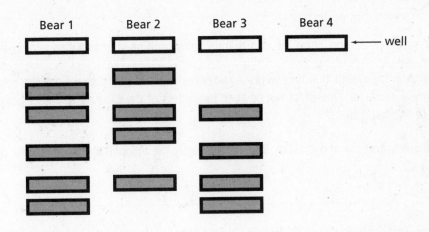

15 Sketch the band pattern for a fourth bear that could be the offspring of bears 1 and 2, but not bear 3.

16 Which bear had the DNA fragment with the greatest size, and how do you know? _____

_____

17 One of the bands is determined to have the following sequence:

GATTGAACCATGCGGCTTAGT

What is the corresponding mRNA sequence for this band? _____

_____

Base your answers to questions 18 through 20 on the figure below and on your knowledge of biology.

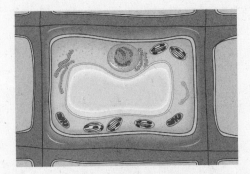

18 You are interested in determining where starch is stored in plant cells. Which indicator would you use, and what color would you look for in structures containing starch?

_____

19 Based on where you see the stain, which organelle of the plant cell is used for storing starch? _____

_____

20 If you prepare the above as a slide with distilled water, what happens to the cell structure you identified in question 19?

_____

Base your answers to questions 21 and 22 on the information below and on your knowledge of biology.

> A research article claims that resting pulse increases as the time interval since the most recent meal increases. This effect can be seen regardless of the exercise habits or general health of the test subject.

21 Design an experiment to test the above claim. Be sure to specify the independent variable, the dependent variable, and the sample size.

_____

22 Imagine one of your test subjects just came from gym class. Why might this affect your results? _____

_____

Base your answers to questions 23 and 24 on the information below and on your knowledge of biology.

> In an experiment testing ability to gather different kinds of seeds using different tools, you find that pliers are good for the large seed. For small seeds, however, pliers tend to crush the seed. Tweezers cannot fit around the large seed, but are quite efficient at acquiring small seeds.

23 Under what conditions would you expect a "pliers" species and a "tweezers" species to coexist? _____

_____

24 It turns out that a needle works for both sizes of seeds, but not as well as tweezers or pliers for each seed size. Suggest a scenario that would allow a "needle" species to coexist with at least one of the other species.

_____

Part A

Answer all questions in this part. [30]

Directions (1–30): For *each* statement or question, write on your separate answer sheet the *number* of the word or expression that, of those given, best completes the statement or answers the question.

1 The diagram below represents levels of organization in living things.

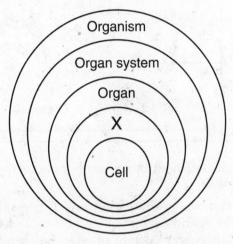

Which term would best represent *X*?

(1) human   (3) stomach
(2) tissue   (4) organelle

2 The evolutionary pathways of ten different species are represented in the diagram below.

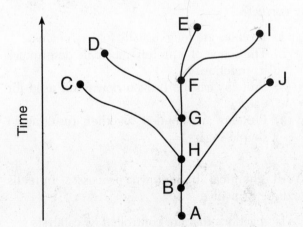

Which two species are the most closely related?

(1) *C* and *D*   (3) *G* and *J*
(2) *E* and *I*   (4) *A* and *F*

3 Which row in the chart below best describes the active transport of molecule *X* through a cell membrane?

Row	Movement of Molecule X	ATP
(1)	high concentration → low concentration	used
(2)	high concentration → low concentration	not used
(3)	low concentration → high concentration	used
(4)	low concentration → high concentration	not used

4 Hereditary information is stored inside the

(1) ribosomes, which have chromosomes that contain many genes
(2) ribosomes, which have genes that contain many chromosomes
(3) nucleus, which has chromosomes that contain many genes
(4) nucleus, which has genes that contain many chromosomes

5 A human liver cell is very different in structure and function from a nerve cell in the same person. This is best explained by the fact that

(1) different genes function in each type of cell
(2) liver cells can reproduce while the nerve cells cannot
(3) liver cells contain fewer chromosomes than nerve cells
(4) different DNA is present in each type of cell

6 Most of the starch stored in the cells of a potato is composed of molecules that originally entered these cells as

(1) enzymes   (3) amino acids
(2) simple sugars   (4) minerals

7 Hereditary traits are transmitted from generation to generation by means of

(1) specific sequences of bases in DNA in reproductive cells
(2) proteins in body cells
(3) carbohydrates in body cells
(4) specific starches making up DNA in reproductive cells

8 Which process can produce new inheritable characteristics within a multicellular species?

(1) cloning of the zygote
(2) mitosis in muscle cells
(3) gene alterations in gametes
(4) differentiation in nerve cells

9 Which two processes result in variations that commonly influence the evolution of sexually reproducing species?

(1) mutation and genetic recombination
(2) mitosis and natural selection
(3) extinction and gene replacement
(4) environmental selection and selective breeding

10 The illustration below shows an insect resting on some green leaves.

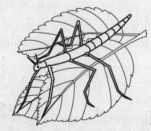

The size, shape, and green color of this insect are adaptations that would most likely help the insect to

(1) compete successfully with all birds
(2) make its own food
(3) hide from predators
(4) avoid toxic waste materials

11 A food web is represented below.

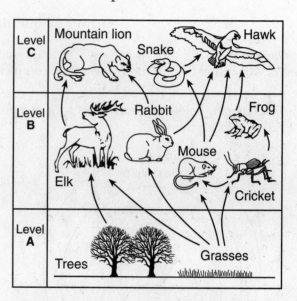

Which statement best describes energy in this food web?

(1) The energy content of level *B* depends on the energy content of level *C*.
(2) The energy content of level *A* depends on energy provided from an abiotic source.
(3) The energy content of level *C* is greater than the energy content of level *A*.
(4) The energy content of level *B* is transferred to level *A*.

12 Which statement concerning proteins is *not* correct?

(1) Proteins are long, usually folded, chains.
(2) The shape of a protein molecule determines its function.
(3) Proteins can be broken down and used for energy.
(4) Proteins are bonded together, resulting in simple sugars.

13 All chemical breakdown processes in cells directly involve

(1) reactions that are controlled by catalysts
(2) enzymes that are stored in mitochondria
(3) the production of catalysts in vacuoles
(4) enzymes that have the same genetic base sequence

14 Steps in a reproductive process used to produce a sheep with certain traits are listed below.

Step 1 — The nucleus was removed from an unfertilized egg taken from sheep A.

Step 2 — The nucleus of a body cell taken from sheep B was then inserted into this unfertilized egg from sheep A.

Step 3 — The resulting cell was then implanted into the uterus of sheep C.

Step 4 — Sheep C gave birth to sheep D.

Which sheep would be most genetically similar to sheep D?

(1) sheep A, only
(2) sheep B, only
(3) both sheep A and B
(4) both sheep A and C

15 Which diagram best illustrates an event in sexual reproduction that would most directly lead to the formation of a human embryo?

(1)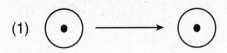

(2)

(3)

(4)

16 Offspring that result from meiosis and fertilization each have

(1) twice as many chromosomes as their parents
(2) one-half as many chromosomes as their parents
(3) gene combinations different from those of either parent
(4) gene combinations identical to those of each parent

17 Which developmental process is represented by the diagram below?

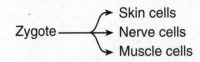

(1) fertilization
(2) differentiation
(3) evolution
(4) mutation

18 The diagram below represents human reproductive systems.

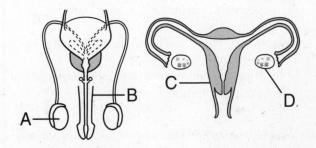

Which statement best describes part of the human reproductive process?

(1) Testosterone produced in A is transferred to D, where it influences embryonic development.
(2) Testosterone produced in D influences formation of sperm within B.
(3) Estrogen and progesterone influence the activity of C.
(4) Progesterone stimulates the division of the egg within C.

19 Which order of metabolic processes converts nutrients consumed by an organism into cell parts?

(1) digestion → absorption → circulation → diffusion → synthesis
(2) absorption → circulation → digestion → diffusion → synthesis
(3) digestion → synthesis → diffusion → circulation → absorption
(4) synthesis → absorption → digestion → diffusion → circulation

20 The diagram below represents a cell organelle involved in the transfer of energy from organic compounds.

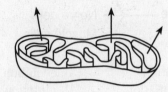

The arrows in the diagram could represent the release of

(1) ATP from a chloroplast carrying out photosynthesis
(2) oxygen from a mitochondrion carrying out photosynthesis
(3) glucose from a chloroplast carrying out respiration
(4) carbon dioxide from a mitochondrion carrying out respiration

21 Which process illustrates a feedback mechanism in plants?

(1) Chloroplasts take in more nitrogen, which increases the rate of photosynthesis.
(2) Chloroplasts release more oxygen in response to a decreased rate of photosynthesis.
(3) Guard cells change the size of leaf openings, regulating the exchange of gases.
(4) Guard cells release oxygen from the leaf at night.

22 Which human activity would have the most positive effect on the environment of an area?

(1) using fire to eliminate most plants in the area
(2) clearing the area to eliminate weed species
(3) protecting native flowers and grasses in the area
(4) introducing a foreign plant species to the area

23 What impact do the amounts of available energy, water, and oxygen have on an ecosystem?

(1) They act as limiting factors.
(2) They are used as nutrients.
(3) They recycle the residue of dead organisms.
(4) They control environmental temperature.

24 Many years ago, a volcanic eruption killed many plants and animals on an island. Today the island looks much as it did before the eruption. Which statement is the best possible explanation for this?

(1) Altered ecosystems regain stability through the evolution of new plant species.
(2) Destroyed environments can recover as a result of the process of ecological succession.
(3) Geographic barriers prevent the migration of animals to island habitats.
(4) Destroyed ecosystems always return to their original state.

25 The growth of a population is shown in the graph below.

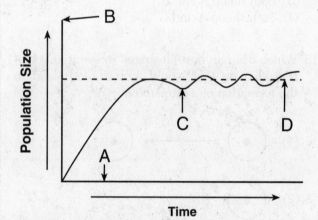

Which letter indicates the carrying capacity of the environment for this population?

(1) A   (3) C
(2) B   (4) D

26 When habitats are destroyed, there are usually fewer niches for animals and plants. This action would most likely *not* lead to a change in the amount of

(1) biodiversity
(2) competition
(3) interaction between species
(4) solar radiation reaching the area

27 Which set of terms best identifies the letters in the diagram below?

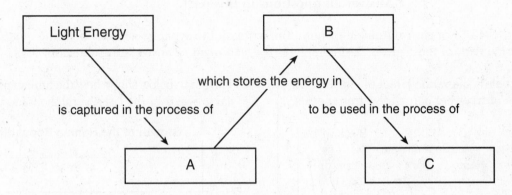

	A	B	C
(1)	photosynthesis	inorganic molecules	decomposition
(2)	respiration	organic molecules	digestion
(3)	photosynthesis	organic molecules	respiration
(4)	respiration	inorganic molecules	photosynthesis

28 The diagram below represents some energy transfers in an ecosystem.

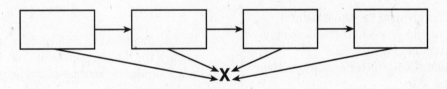

Which type of organism is most likely represented by letter *X*?

(1) decomposer
(2) autotroph
(3) producer
(4) herbivore

29 Some farmers currently grow genetically engineered crops. An argument *against* the use of this technology is that

(1) it increases crop production
(2) it produces insect-resistant plants
(3) its long-term effects on humans are still being investigated
(4) it always results in crops that do not taste good

30 The removal of nearly all the predators from an ecosystem would most likely result in

(1) an increase in the number of carnivore species
(2) a decrease in new predators migrating into the ecosystem
(3) a decrease in the size of decomposers
(4) an increase in the number of herbivores

Part B–1

Answer all questions in this part. [13]

Directions (31–43): For *each* statement or question, write on the separate answer sheet the *number* of the word or expression that, of those given, best completes the statement or answers the question.

31 The graph below shows the effect of moisture on the number of trees per acre of five tree species.

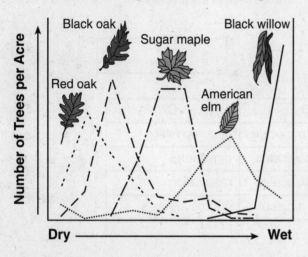

Which observation best represents information shown in the graph?

(1) All five species grow in the same habitat.
(2) The American elm grows in the widest range of moisture conditions.
(3) Red oaks can grow in wetter conditions than black willows.
(4) Sugar maples can grow anywhere black oaks can grow.

32 A science researcher is reviewing another scientist's experiment and conclusion. The reviewer would most likely consider the experiment *invalid* if

(1) the sample size produced a great deal of data
(2) other individuals are able to duplicate the results
(3) it contains conclusions not explained by the evidence given
(4) the hypothesis was not supported by the data obtained

33 The graph below shows how the human population has grown over the last several thousand years.

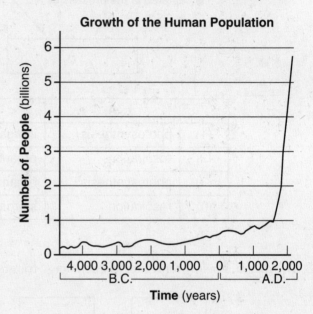

Which statement is a valid inference that can be made if the human population continues to grow at a rate similar to the rate shown between 1000 A.D. and 2000 A.D.?

(1) Future ecosystems will be stressed and many animal habitats may be destroyed.
(2) Global warming will decrease as a result of a lower demand for fossil fuels.
(3) One hundred years after all resources are used up, the human population will level off.
(4) All environmental problems can be solved without a reduction in the growth rate of the human population.

34 Cellular communication is illustrated in the diagram below.

Cell A   **Cell B**

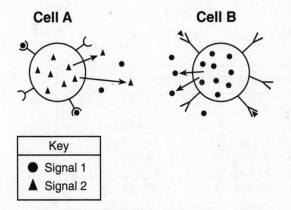

Key
● Signal 1
▲ Signal 2

Information can be sent from

(1) cell *A* to cell *B* because cell *B* is able to recognize signal 1
(2) cell *A* to cell *B* because cell *A* is able to recognize signal 2
(3) cell *B* to cell *A* because cell *A* is able to recognize signal 1
(4) cell *B* to cell *A* because cell *B* is able to recognize signal 2

35 The diagram below represents single-celled organism *A* dividing by mitosis to form cells *B* and *C*.

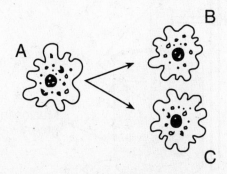

Cells *A*, *B*, and *C* all produced protein *X*. What can best be inferred from this observation?

(1) Protein *X* is found in all organisms.
(2) The gene for protein *X* is found in single-celled organisms, only.
(3) Cells *A*, *B*, and *C* ingested food containing the gene to produce protein *X*.
(4) The gene to produce protein *X* was passed from cell *A* to cells *B* and *C*.

Base your answers to questions 36 and 37 on the information in the diagram below and on your knowledge of biology.

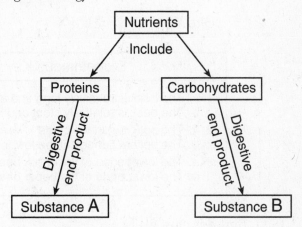

36 In an autotrophic organism, substance *B* functions as a

(1) source of energy   (3) vitamin
(2) hormone   (4) biotic resource

37 In a heterotrophic organism, substance *A* could be used directly for

(1) photosynthesis
(2) synthesis of enzymes
(3) a building block of starch
(4) a genetic code

38 The dichotomous key shown below can be used to identify birds *W, X, Y,* and *Z.*

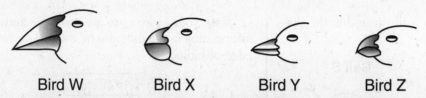

Bird W   Bird X   Bird Y   Bird Z

Dichotomous Key to Representative Birds
1. a. The beak is relatively long and slender...............................*Certhidea*
b. The beak is relatively stout and heavy....................................go to 2
2. a. The bottom surface of the lower beak is flat and straight ......*Geospiza*
b. The bottom surface of the lower beak is curved ....go to 3
3. a. The lower edge of the upper beak has a distinct bend ....*Camarhynchus*
b. The lower edge of the upper beak is mostly flat ....*Platyspiza*

Bird *X* is most likely

(1) *Certhidea*
(2) *Geospiza*
(3) *Camarhynchus*
(4) *Platyspiza*

39 An experimental setup is shown in the diagram below.

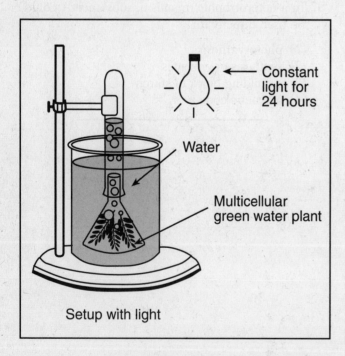
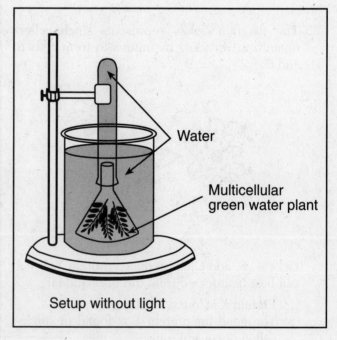

Which hypothesis would most likely be tested using this setup?

(1) Green water plants release a gas in the presence of light.
(2) Roots of water plants absorb minerals in the absence of light.
(3) Green plants need light for cell division.
(4) Plants grow best in the absence of light.

Base your answers to questions 40 through 42 on the passage below which describes an ecosystem in New York State and on your knowledge of biology.

The Pine Bush ecosystem near Albany, New York, is one of the last known habitats of the nearly extinct Karner Blue butterfly. The butterfly's larvae feed on the wild green plant, lupine. The larvae are in turn consumed by predatory wasps. The four groups below represent other organisms living in this ecosystem.

Group A	Group B	Group C	Group D
algae mosses ferns pine trees oak trees	rabbits tent caterpillars moths	hawks moles hognosed snakes toads	soil bacteria molds mushrooms

40 The Karner Blue larvae belong in which group?

(1) A
(2) B
(3) C
(4) D

41 Which food chain best represents information in the passage?

(1) lupine → Karner Blue larvae → wasps
(2) wasps → Karner Blue larvae → lupine
(3) Karner Blue larvae → lupine → wasps
(4) lupine → wasps → Karner Blue larvae

42 Which group contains decomposers?

(1) A
(2) B
(3) C
(4) D

43 A graph of the population growth of two different species is shown below.

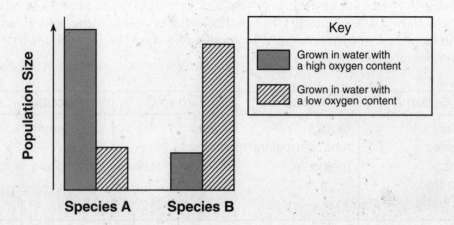

Which conclusion can be drawn from information in the graph?

(1) Oxygen concentration affects population sizes of different species in the same manner.
(2) Species A requires a high oxygen concentration for maximum population growth.
(3) Species B requires a high oxygen concentration to stimulate population growth.
(4) Low oxygen concentration does not limit the population size of either species observed.

Part B–2

Answer all questions in this part. [12]

Directions (44–55): For those questions that are followed by four choices, circle the *number* of the choice that best completes the statement or answers the question. For all other questions in this part, follow the directions given in the question.

Base your answers to questions 44 through 48 on the passage and data table below and on your knowledge of biology.

The amount of oxygen gas dissolved in water is important to the organisms that live in a river. The amount of dissolved oxygen varies with changes in both physical factors and biological processes. The temperature of the water is one physical factor affecting dissolved oxygen levels as shown in the data table below. The amount of dissolved oxygen is expressed in parts per million (ppm).

Dissolved Oxygen Levels at Various Temperatures

Water Temperature (°C)	Level of Dissolved Oxygen (ppm)
1	14
10	11
15	10
20	9
25	8
30	7

Directions (44–45): Using the information given, construct a line graph on the grid on page 13, following the directions below.

44 Mark an appropriate scale on each labeled axis. [1]

45 Plot the data for dissolved oxygen on the grid. Surround each point with a small circle and connect the points. [1]

Example:

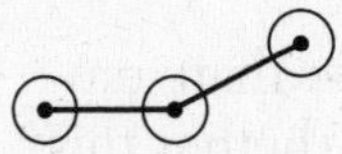

Dissolved Oxygen Levels at Various Temperatures

Level of Dissolved Oxygen (ppm)

Water Temperature (°C)

44 ☐

45 ☐

46 If the trend continues as shown in the data, what would the dissolved oxygen level most likely be if the temperature of the water was 35°C? [1]

_____ **ppm**

46 ☐

47 State the relationship between the level of dissolved oxygen and water temperature. [1]

_____

_____

_____

_____

47 ☐

48 Identify *one* physical or biological process taking place within the river, other than temperature change, that would affect the level of dissolved oxygen and state whether this process would increase or decrease the level of dissolved oxygen. [1]

_____

_____

_____

48 ☐

In Search of a Low-Allergy Peanut

Many people are allergic to substances in the environment. Of the many foods that contain allergens (allergy-inducing substances), peanuts cause some of the most severe reactions. Mildly allergic people may only get hives. Highly allergic people can go into a form of shock. Some people die each year from reactions to peanuts.

A group of scientists is attempting to produce peanuts that lack the allergy-inducing proteins by using traditional selective breeding methods. They are searching for varieties of peanuts that are free of the allergens. By crossing those varieties with popular commercial types, they hope to produce peanuts that will be less likely to cause allergic reactions and still taste good. So far, they have found one variety that has 80 percent less of one of three complex proteins linked to allergic reactions. Removing all three of these allergens may be impossible, but even removing one could help.

Other researchers are attempting to alter the genes that code for the three major allergens in peanuts. All of this research is seen as a possible long-term solution to peanut allergies.

49 Allergic reactions usually occur when the immune system produces

   (1) antibiotics against usually harmless antigens

   (2) antigens against usually harmless antibodies

   (3) antibodies against usually harmless antigens

   (4) enzymes against usually harmless antibodies

49 ☐

50 How does altering the DNA of a peanut affect the proteins in peanuts that cause allergic reactions?

   (1) The altered DNA is used to synthesize changed forms of these proteins.

   (2) The altered DNA leaves the nucleus and becomes part of the allergy-producing protein.

   (3) The altered DNA is the code for the antibodies against the allergens.

   (4) The altered DNA is used as an enzyme to break down the allergens in peanuts.

50 ☐

51 Explain how selective breeding is being used to try to produce commercial peanuts that will *not* cause allergic reactions in people.   [1]

_____

_____

_____

_____

51 ☐

Base your answers to questions 52 through 55 on the diagram below and on your knowledge of biology. The arrows in the diagram represent biological processes.

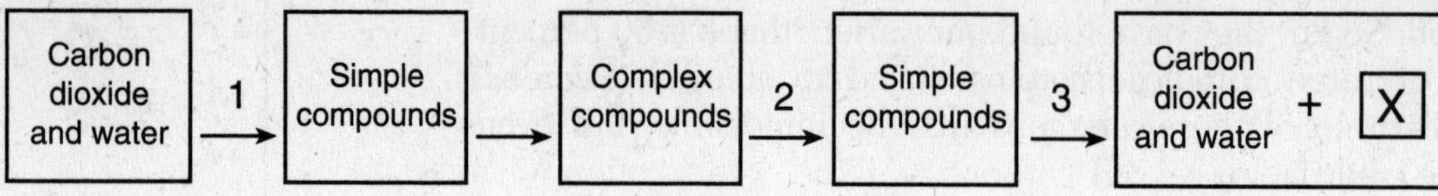

| Carbon dioxide and water | 1 → | Simple compounds | → | Complex compounds | 2 → | Simple compounds | 3 → | Carbon dioxide and water + | X |

52 Identify *one* type of organism that carries out process 1.   [1]

_____

52 ☐

53 Explain why process 2 is essential in humans.   [1]

_____

_____

53 ☐

54 Identify process 3.   [1]

_____

54 ☐

55 Identify what letter *X* represents.   [1]

_____

_____

55 ☐

Part C

Answer all questions in this part. [17]

Directions (56–62): Record your answers in the spaces provided in this examination booklet.

56 Growers of fruit trees have always had problems with insects. Insects can cause visible damage to fruits, making them less appealing to consumers. As a result of this damage, much of the fruit cannot be sold. Insecticides have been useful for controlling these insects, but, in recent years, some insecticides have been much less effective. In some cases, insecticides do nothing to stop the insect attacks.

Provide a biological explanation for this loss of effectiveness of the insecticides. In your answer, be sure to:

- identify the original event that resulted in the evolution of insecticide resistance in some insects [1]
- explain why the percentage of resistant insects in the population has increased [1]
- describe *one* alternative form of insect control, other than using a different insecticide, that fruit growers could use to protect their crops from insect attack [1]

For Teacher Use Only

_____

_____

_____

_____

_____

_____

_____

_____

_____

56 ☐

Regents Examination • 191

57 The concentration of salt in water affects the hatching of brine shrimp eggs. Brine shrimp eggs will develop and hatch at room temperature in glass containers of salt solution. Describe a controlled experiment using three experimental groups that could be used to determine the best concentration of salt solution in which to hatch brine shrimp eggs. Your answer must include at least:

- a description of how the control group and each of the three experimental groups will be different [1]
- *two* conditions that must be kept constant in the control group and the experimental groups [2]
- data that should be collected [1]
- *one* example of experimental results that would indicate the best concentration of salt solution in which to hatch brine shrimp eggs [1]

_____

_____

_____

_____

_____

_____

_____

_____

_____

_____

57 ☐

Base your answers to questions 58 and 59 on the statement and diagram below and on your knowledge of biology.

Women are advised to avoid consuming alcoholic beverages during pregnancy.

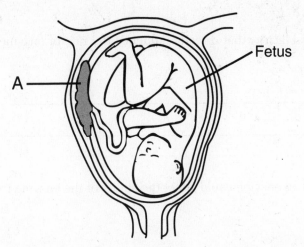

58 Identify the structure labeled A and explain how the functioning of structure A is essential for the normal development of the fetus. [2]

Structure A: _____

_____

_____

_____

59 Explain why consumption of alcoholic beverages by a pregnant woman is likely to be more harmful to her fetus than to herself. [1]

_____

_____

_____

Base your answers to questions 60 and 61 on the statement below and on your knowledge of biology.

Some internal environmental factors may interfere with the ability of an enzyme to function efficiently.

60 Identify *two* internal environmental factors that directly influence the rate of enzyme action. [2]

_____

_____

60 ☐

61 Explain why changing the shape of an enzyme could affect the ability of the enzyme to function. [1]

_____

_____

_____

61 ☐

62 Deforestation is viewed as a problem in the world today. Describe a cause and an effect of deforestation and a way to lessen this effect. In your answer, be sure to:

- state *one* reason deforestation is occurring [1]
- state *one* environmental problem that results from widespread deforestation [1]
- state *one* way to lessen the effects of deforestation, other than planting trees [1]

_____

_____

_____

_____

_____

_____

_____

_____

62 ☐

Part D

Answer all questions in this part. [13]

Directions (63–74): For those questions that are followed by four choices, circle the *number* of the choice that best completes the statement or answers the question. For all other questions in this part, follow the directions given in the question.

Base your answers to questions 63 through 65 on the Universal Genetic Code Chart on page 21 and on your knowledge of biology. Some DNA, RNA, and amino acid information from four similar sequences of four plant species is shown in the chart below.

63 Using the information given, fill in the missing mRNA base sequence for species *B* in the chart below. [1]

64 Using the Universal Genetic Code Chart on page 21, fill in the missing amino acid sequence for species *C* in the chart below. [1]

Species A	DNA base sequence	CCG	TGC	ATA	CAG	GTA
	mRNA base sequence	GGC	ACG	UAU	GUC	CAU
	Amino acid sequence	**GLY**	**THR**	**TYR**	**VAL**	**HIS**
Species B	DNA base sequence	TGC	TGC	ATA	CAG	GTA
	mRNA base sequence	___	___	___	___	___
	Amino acid sequence	**THR**	**THR**	**TYR**	**VAL**	**HIS**
Species C	DNA base sequence	CCG	TGC	ATA	CAG	GTT
	mRNA base sequence	GGC	ACG	UAU	GUC	CAA
	Amino acid sequence	___	___	___	___	___
Species D	DNA base sequence	CCT	TGT	ATG	CAC	GTC
	mRNA base sequence	GGA	ACA	UAC	GUG	CAG
	Amino acid sequence	**GLY**	**THR**	**TYR**	**VAL**	**GLN**

63 ☐

64 ☐

65 According to these amino acid sequences, which *two* plant species are the most closely related? Support your answer. [1]

Species _____ and _____

_____

_____

_____

65 ☐

_____

Universal Genetic Code Chart
Messenger RNA Codons and the Amino Acids They Code For

		SECOND BASE				
		U	C	A	G	
FIRST BASE	**U**	UUU } PHE UUC UUA } LEU UUG	UCU } SER UCC UCA UCG	UAU } TYR UAC UAA } STOP UAG	UGU } CYS UGC UGA } STOP UGG } TRP	U C A G
	C	CUU } LEU CUC CUA CUG	CCU } PRO CCC CCA CCG	CAU } HIS CAC CAA } GLN CAG	CGU } ARG CGC CGA CGG	U C A G
	A	AUU } ILE AUC AUA AUG } MET or START	ACU } THR ACC ACA ACG	AAU } ASN AAC AAA } LYS AAG	AGU } SER AGC AGA } ARG AGG	U C A G
	G	GUU } VAL GUC GUA GUG	GCU } ALA GCC GCA GCG	GAU } ASP GAC GAA } GLU GAG	GGU } GLY GGC GGA GGG	U C A G

(THIRD BASE on right side)

66 A student was comparing preserved specimens of three plant species, *X*, *Y*, and *Z*, in a classroom. Which statement is an example of an observation the student could have made and *not* an inference?

(1) The leaves produced by plant *X* are 4 cm across and 8 cm in length.

(2) Plant *Y* has large purple flowers that open at night.

(3) Plant *X* produces many seeds that are highly attractive to finches.

(4) The flowers of plant *Z* are poisonous to household pets.

66 ☐

Base your answers to questions 67 and 68 on the information below and on your knowledge of biology.

A student squeezes and releases a clothespin as often as possible for 2 minutes and then takes his pulse for 20 seconds. After a 2-minute rest, he repeats the procedure. This pattern is repeated one more time. The student's 20-second pulse counts were 23, 26, and 21.

67 Complete the "Pulse/Min" column in the data table below for all three trials as well as the average pulse rate per minute. [1]

Pulse Rate After Activity

Trial	20-Second Pulse Counts	Pulse/Min
1	23	
2	26	
3	21	
Average		

67 ☐

68 What additional data should the student have collected in order to determine the effect of squeezing a clothespin on his pulse rate? [1]

_____

_____

_____

68 ☐

Base your answers to questions 69 through 71 on the passage below and on your knowledge of biology.

When Charles Darwin traveled to the Galapagos Islands, he observed 14 distinct varieties of finches on the islands. Darwin also observed that each finch variety ate a different type of food and lived in a slightly different habitat from the other finches. Darwin concluded that the finches all shared a common ancestor but had developed different beak structures.

69 The 14 varieties of finches are most likely the result of

(1) absence of biodiversity

(2) biological evolution

(3) asexual reproduction

(4) lack of competition

69 ☐

70 The second sentence best describes

(1) an ecosystem

(2) a food web

(3) a niche

(4) a predator/prey relationship

70 ☐

71 The different beak structures mentioned in the last sentence were most likely influenced by

(1) selection for favorable variations

(2) environmental conditions identical to those of the common ancestor

(3) abnormal mitotic cell division

(4) characteristics that are acquired during the bird's lifetime

71 ☐

72 The diagram below represents a laboratory setup used by a student during an investigation of diffusion.

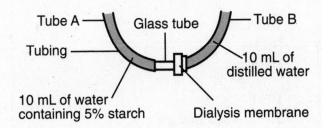

Tube A — Glass tube — Tube B

Tubing —

10 mL of distilled water

10 mL of water containing 5% starch

Dialysis membrane

Which statement best explains why the liquid in tube *A* will rise over a period of time?

(1) The starch concentrations are equal on both sides of the membrane.

(2) The water will pass from a region of lower starch concentration to one of higher starch concentration.

(3) Water and starch volumes are the same in both tubes *A* and *B*.

(4) The fluids in both tubes *A* and *B* will change from a higher temperature to a lower temperature.

72

73 A red onion cell has undergone a change, as represented in the diagram below.

This change is most likely due to the cell being placed in

(1) distilled water

(2) light

(3) salt water

(4) darkness

73

74 A laboratory setup for a demonstration is represented in the diagram below.

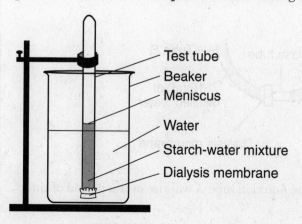

Test tube
Beaker
Meniscus
Water
Starch-water mixture
Dialysis membrane

Describe how an indicator can be used to determine if starch diffuses through the membrane into the beaker. In your answer, be sure to include:

• the procedure used   [1]
• how to interpret the results   [1]

_____

_____

_____

_____

_____

_____

74 ☐

Part A

Answer all questions in this part. [30]

Directions (1–30): For *each* statement or question, write on your separate answer sheet the *number* of the word or expression that best completes the statement or answers the question.

1 The levels of organization for structure and function in the human body from least complex to most complex are

(1) systems → organs → tissues → cells
(2) cells → organs → tissues → systems
(3) tissues → systems → cells → organs
(4) cells → tissues → organs → systems

2 Genes are inherited, but their expressions can be modified by the environment. This statement explains why

(1) some animals have dark fur only when the temperature is within a certain range
(2) offspring produced by means of sexual reproduction look exactly like their parents
(3) identical twins who grow up in different homes have the same characteristics
(4) animals can be cloned, but plants cannot

3 Meat tenderizer contains an enzyme that interacts with meat. If meat is coated with tenderizer and then placed in a refrigerator for a short time, how would the enzyme be affected?

(1) It would be broken down.
(2) Its activity would slow down.
(3) Its shape would change.
(4) It would no longer act as an enzyme.

4 Which row in the chart below contains correct information concerning synthesis?

Row	Building Blocks	Substance Synthesized Using the Building Blocks
(1)	glucose molecules	DNA
(2)	simple sugars	protein
(3)	amino acids	enzyme
(4)	molecular bases	starch

5 Molecule X moves across a cell membrane by diffusion. Which row in the chart below best indicates the relationship between the relative concentrations of molecule X and the use of ATP for diffusion?

Row	Movement of Molecule X	Use of ATP
(1)	high concentration → low concentration	used
(2)	high concentration → low concentration	not used
(3)	low concentration → high concentration	used
(4)	low concentration → high concentration	not used

6 Which statement best compares a multicellular organism to a single-celled organism?

(1) A multicellular organism has organ systems that interact to carry out life functions, while a single-celled organism carries out life functions without using organ systems.
(2) A single-celled organism carries out fewer life functions than each cell of a multicellular organism.
(3) A multicellular organism always obtains energy through a process that is different from that used by a single-celled organism.
(4) The cell of a single-celled organism is always much larger than an individual cell of a multicellular organism.

7 Which statement indicates that different parts of the genetic information are used in different kinds of cells, even in the same organism?

(1) The cells produced by a zygote usually have different genes.
(2) As an embryo develops, various tissues and organs are produced.
(3) Replicated chromosomes separate during gamete formation.
(4) Offspring have a combination of genes from both parents.

8 Three structures are represented in the diagram below.

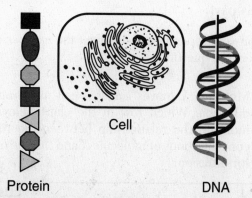

Protein   DNA

What is the relationship between these three structures?

(1) DNA is made up of proteins that are synthesized in the cell.
(2) Protein is composed of DNA that is stored in the cell.
(3) DNA controls the production of protein in the cell.
(4) The cell is composed only of DNA and protein.

9 In a group of mushrooms exposed to a poisonous chemical, only a few of the mushrooms survived. The best explanation for the resistance of the surviving mushrooms is that the resistance

(1) was transmitted to the mushrooms from the poisonous chemical
(2) resulted from the presence of mutations in the mushrooms
(3) was transferred through the food web to the mushrooms
(4) developed in response to the poisonous chemical

10 Which statement correctly describes the genetic makeup of the sperm cells produced by a human male?

(1) Each cell has pairs of chromosomes and the cells are usually genetically identical.
(2) Each cell has pairs of chromosomes and the cells are usually genetically different.
(3) Each cell has half the normal number of chromosomes and the cells are usually genetically identical.
(4) Each cell has half the normal number of chromosomes and the cells are usually genetically different.

11 In an environment that undergoes frequent change, species that reproduce sexually may have an advantage over species that reproduce asexually because the sexually reproducing species produce

(1) more offspring in each generation
(2) identical offspring
(3) offspring with more variety
(4) new species of offspring in each generation

12 Mutations that occur in skin or lung cells have little effect on the evolution of a species because mutations in these cells

(1) usually lead to the death of the organism
(2) cannot be passed on to offspring
(3) are usually beneficial to the organism
(4) lead to more serious mutations in offspring

13 The teeth of carnivores are pointed and are good for puncturing and ripping flesh. The teeth of herbivores are flat and are good for grinding and chewing. Which statement best explains these observations?

(1) Herbivores have evolved from carnivores.
(2) Carnivores have evolved from herbivores.
(3) The two types of teeth most likely evolved as a result of natural selection.
(4) The two types of teeth most likely evolved as a result of the needs of an organism.

14 What would most likely happen if most of the bacteria and fungi were removed from an ecosystem?

(1) Nutrients resulting from decomposition would be reduced.
(2) Energy provided for autotrophic nutrition would be reduced.
(3) The rate of mutations in plants would increase.
(4) Soil fertility would increase.

15 A certain bacterial colony originated from the division of a single bacterial cell. Each cell in this colony will most likely

(1) express adaptations unlike those of the other cells
(2) replicate different numbers of genes
(3) have a resistance to different antibiotics
(4) synthesize the same proteins and enzymes

16 Removal of one ovary from a human female would most likely

(1) affect the production of eggs
(2) make fertilization impossible
(3) make carrying a fetus impossible
(4) decrease her ability to provide essential nutrients to an embryo

17 Which substance usually passes in the greatest amount through the placenta from the blood of the fetus to the blood of the mother?

(1) oxygen
(2) carbon dioxide
(3) amino acids
(4) glucose

18 An enzyme known as rubisco enables plants to use large amounts of carbon dioxide. This enzyme is most likely active in the

(1) nucleus
(2) vacuoles
(3) mitochondria
(4) chloroplasts

19 Starch molecules present in a maple tree are made from materials that originally entered the tree from the external environment as

(1) enzymes
(2) simple sugars
(3) amino acids
(4) inorganic compounds

20 Which change in a sample of pond water could indicate that heterotrophic microbes were active?

(1) increase in ozone level
(2) increase in glucose level
(3) decrease in oxygen level
(4) decrease in carbon dioxide level

21 Some human white blood cells help destroy pathogenic bacteria by

(1) causing mutations in the bacteria
(2) engulfing and digesting the bacteria
(3) producing toxins that compete with bacterial toxins
(4) inserting part of their DNA into the bacterial cells

22 Four students each drew an illustration to show the flow of energy in a field ecosystem. Which illustration is *most* accurate?

(1)
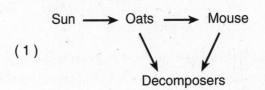

(2)
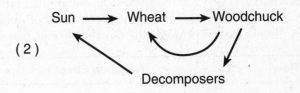

(3)
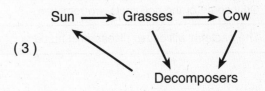

(4)
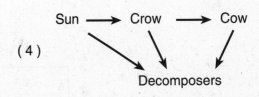

23 As succession proceeds from a shrub community to a forest community, the shrub community modifies its environment, eventually making it

(1) more favorable for itself and less favorable for the forest community
(2) more favorable for itself and more favorable for the forest community
(3) less favorable for itself and more favorable for the forest community
(4) less favorable for itself and less favorable for the forest community

24 The diagram below represents a series of events in the development of a bird.

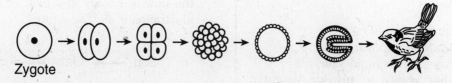

Zygote

Which series of terms best represents the sequence of processes shown?

(1) meiosis → growth → differentiation
(2) meiosis → differentiation → growth
(3) mitosis → meiosis → differentiation
(4) mitosis → differentiation → growth

25 Bacteria that are removed from the human intestine are genetically engineered to feed on organic pollutants in the environment and convert them into harmless inorganic compounds. Which row in the table below best represents the most likely negative and positive effects of this technology on the ecosystem?

Row	Negative Effect	Positive Effect
(1)	Inorganic compounds interfere with cycles in the environment.	Human bacteria are added to the environment.
(2)	Engineered bacteria may out-compete native bacteria.	The organic pollutants are removed.
(3)	Only some of the pollutants are removed.	Bacteria will make more organic pollutants.
(4)	The bacteria will cause diseases in humans.	The inorganic compounds are buried in the soil.

26 An energy pyramid is represented below.

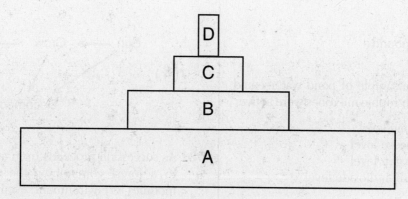

How much energy would be available to the organisms in level *C*?

(1) all of the energy in level *A*, plus the energy in level *B*
(2) all of the energy in level *A*, minus the energy in level *B*
(3) a percentage of the energy contained in level *B*
(4) a percentage of the energy synthesized in level *B* and level *D*

27 Which graph illustrates changes that indicate a state of dynamic equilibrium in a mosquito population?

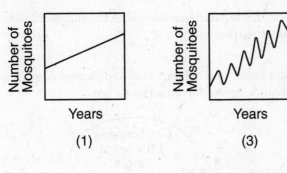

(1)

(3)

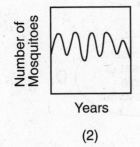

(2)

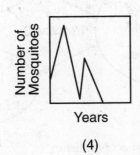

(4)

28 Which condition is necessary for enzymes and hormones to function properly in the human body?

(1) These chemicals must have a specific shape.
(2) These chemicals must be able to replicate.
(3) Body temperature must be above 40°C.
(4) Body pH must be above 10.

29 Four environmental factors are listed below.

A. energy
B. water
C. oxygen
D. minerals

Which factors limit environmental carrying capacity in a land ecosystem?

(1) A, only
(2) B, C, and D, only
(3) A, C, and D, only
(4) A, B, C, and D

30 Which human activity would have the *least* negative impact on the quality of the environment?

(1) adding animal wastes to rivers
(2) cutting down tropical rain forests for plywood
(3) using species-specific sex attractants to trap and kill insect pests
(4) releasing chemicals into the groundwater

Part B–1

Answer all questions in this part. [10]

Directions (31–40): For *each* statement or question, write on the separate answer sheet the *number* of the word or expression that best completes the statement or answers the question.

Base your answers to questions 31 through 34 on the diagram below and on your knowledge of biology. The diagram represents a single-celled organism, such as an ameba, undergoing the changes shown.

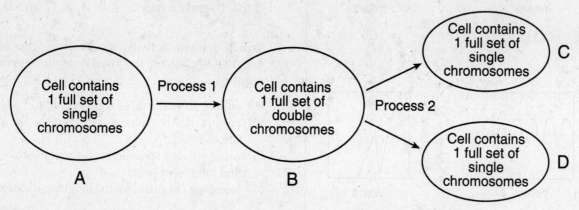

31 As a result of these processes, the single-celled organism accomplishes

(1) gamete production
(2) energy production
(3) sexual reproduction
(4) asexual reproduction

32 Process 1 is known as

(1) replication
(2) meiosis
(3) differentiation
(4) digestion

33 Process 1 and process 2 are directly involved in

(1) meiotic cell division
(2) mitotic cell division
(3) fertilization
(4) recombination

34 The genetic content of *C* is usually identical to the genetic content of

(1) *B* but not *D*
(2) both *B* and *D*
(3) *D* but not *A*
(4) both *A* and *D*

Base your answers to questions 35 through 37 on the diagram below that shows some evolutionary pathways. Each letter represents a different species.

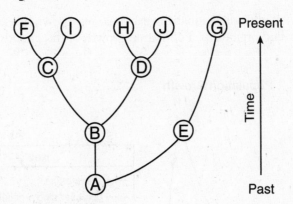

35 Which two organisms are most closely related?

(1) *F* and *I*   (3) *A* and *G*
(2) *F* and *H*   (4) *G* and *J*

36 The most recent ancestor of organisms *D* and *F* is

(1) *A*   (3) *C*
(2) *B*   (4) *I*

37 If *A* represents a simple multicellular heterotrophic organism, *B* would most likely represent

(1) a single-celled photosynthetic organism
(2) an autotrophic mammal
(3) a complex multicellular virus
(4) another type of simple multicellular heterotroph

38 A scientist studied iguanas inhabiting a chain of small ocean islands. He discovered two species that live in different habitats and display different behaviors. His observations are listed in the table below.

Observations of Two Species of Iguanas

Species A	Species B
spends most of its time in the ocean	spends most of its time on land
is rarely found more than 10 meters from shore	is found many meters inland from shore
eats algae	eats cactus and other land plants

Which statement best describes these two species of iguanas?

(1) Both species evolved through the process of ecological succession.
(2) Each species occupies a different niche.
(3) The two species can interbreed.
(4) Species *A* is a scavenger and species *B* is a carnivore.

Base your answers to questions 39 and 40 on the information and graph below and on your knowledge of biology.

A population of paramecia (single-celled aquatic organisms) was grown in a 200-mL beaker of water containing some smaller single-celled organisms. Population growth of the organisms for 28 hours is shown in the graph below.

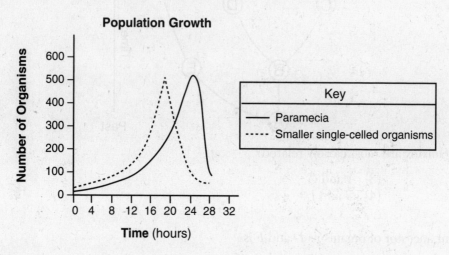

39 Which factor most likely accounts for the change in the paramecium population from 8 to 20 hours?

(1) an increase in the nitrogen content of water
(2) an increase in wastes produced
(3) an increase in available food
(4) an increase in water pH

40 One likely explanation for the change in the paramecium population from 26 hours to 28 hours is that the

(1) carrying capacity of the beaker was exceeded
(2) rate of reproduction increased
(3) time allowed for growth was not sufficient
(4) oxygen level was too high

Part B–2

Answer all questions in this part. [15]

Directions (41–55): For those questions that are followed by four choices, circle the *number* of the choice that best completes the statement or answers the question. For all other questions in this part, follow the directions given in the questions and record your answers in the spaces provided.

Base your answers to questions 41 through 45 on the passage below and on your knowledge of biology.

Better Rice

The production of new types of food crops will help raise the quantity of food grown by farmers. Research papers released by the National Academy of Sciences announced the development of two new superior varieties of rice—one produced by selective breeding and the other by biotechnology.

One variety of rice, called Nerica (New Rice for Africa), is already helping farmers in Africa. Nerica combines the hardiness and weed resistance of rare African rice varieties with the productivity and faster maturity of common Asian varieties.

Another variety, called Stress-Tolerant Rice, was produced by inserting a pair of bacterial genes into rice plants for the production of trehalose (a sugar). Trehalose helps plants maintain healthy cell membranes, proteins, and enzymes during environmental stress. The resulting plants survive drought, low temperatures, salty soils, and other stresses better than standard rice varieties.

41 Why is the production of new varieties of food crops necessary?

(1) Essential food crops are rapidly becoming extinct.

(2) Technology for producing fresh water for agriculture has improved.

(3) Burning fossil fuels has decreased agricultural areas.

(4) World population continues to increase.

42 Which substance from bacteria was most likely inserted into rice plants in the development of the trehalose-producing rice?

(1) sugar

(2) enzymes

(3) DNA

(4) trehalose

43 Nerica was most likely produced by

(1) crossing a variety of African rice with a variety of Asian rice

(2) cloning genes for hardiness and weed resistance from Asian rice

(3) using Asian rice to compete with rare African varieties

(4) inserting genes for productivity and faster maturity into Asian rice

For Teacher Use Only

43 ☐

44 Which strain of rice was produced as a result of genetic engineering? Support your answer. [1]

44 ☐

45 State *one* reason that further testing must be done before rice plants that produce trehalose are approved for human consumption. [1]

45 ☐

Base your answers to questions 46 through 49 on the information and data table below and on your knowledge of biology.

A number of bean seeds planted at the same time produced plants that were later divided into two groups, A and B. Each plant in group A was treated with the same concentration of gibberellic acid (a plant hormone). The plants in group B were not treated with gibberellic acid. All other growth conditions were kept constant. The height of each plant was measured on 5 consecutive days, and the average height of each group was recorded in the data table below.

Data Table

	Average Plant Height (cm)				
	Day 1	**Day 2**	**Day 3**	**Day 4**	**Day 5**
Group A	5	7	10	13	15
Group B	5	6	6.5	7	7.5

Directions (46–48): Using the information in the data table, construct a line graph on the grid on the next page, following the directions below.

46 Mark an appropriate scale on the axis labeled "Average Plant Height (cm)." [1]

47 Plot the data for the average height of the plants in group A. Surround each point with a small circle and connect the points. [1]

Example:

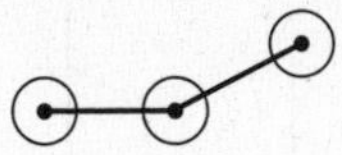

48 Plot the data for the average height of the plants in group B. Surround each point with a small triangle and connect the points. [1]

Example:

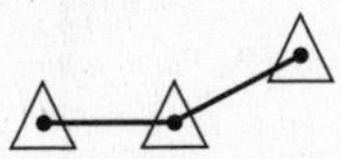

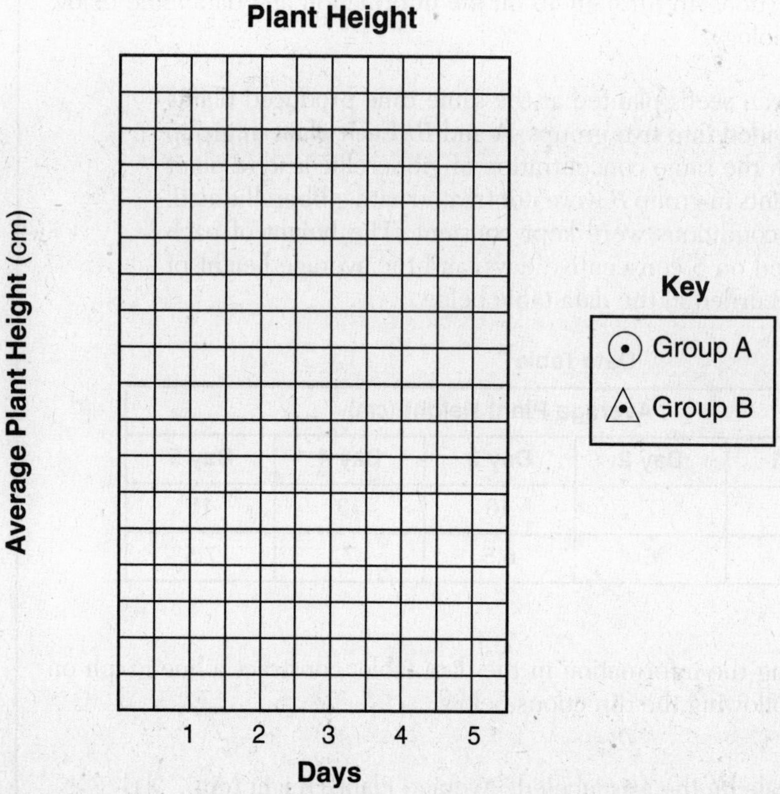

Plant Height

Average Plant Height (cm)

Days

Key

⊙ Group A

△ Group B

46

47

48

49 State a valid conclusion that can be drawn concerning the effect of gibberellic acid on bean plant growth. [1]

_____

_____

_____

_____

49

Base your answers to questions 50 through 55 on the data table below and on your knowledge of biology. The table contains information about glucose production in a species of plant that lives in the water of a salt marsh.

Temperature (°C)	Glucose Production (mg/hr)
10	5
20	10
30	15
40	5

50 Which terms describe temperature in this investigation?

(1) abiotic factor and independent variable

(2) abiotic factor and dependent variable

(3) biotic factor and independent variable

(4) biotic factor and dependent variable

50 [ ]

51 What evidence from the data table shows that a salt-marsh plant is sensitive to its environment? [1]

_____

_____

51 [ ]

52 At which temperature would the plants most likely use the greatest amount of carbon dioxide?

(1) 10°C

(2) 20°C

(3) 30°C

(4) 40°C

52 [ ]

53 How much oxygen will plants that live in water at 10°C most likely produce?

    (1)   twice the amount of oxygen produced at 20°C

    (2)   the same amount of oxygen produced at 40°C

    (3)   the most oxygen produced at any temperature

    (4)   more oxygen than is produced at 30°C

54 State *one* possible reason for the change in glucose production when the temperature was increased from 30°C to 40°C. [1]

_____

_____

55 Which level of the energy pyramid below would contain the plant species of this salt marsh?

    (1)   *A*

    (2)   *B*

    (3)   *C*

    (4)   *D*

Part C

Answer all questions in this part. [17]

Directions (56–59): Record your answers in the spaces provided in this examination booklet.

56 A scientist wants to determine the best conditions for hatching brine shrimp eggs. In a laboratory, brine shrimp hatch at room temperature in glass containers of salt water. The concentration of salt in the water is known to affect how many brine shrimp eggs will hatch.

Design an experiment to determine which of three saltwater concentrations (2%, 4%, or 6%) is best for hatching brine shrimp eggs. In your experimental design, be sure to:

- state how many containers to use in the experiment, and describe what would be added to each container in addition to the eggs [1]
- state *two* factors that must be kept constant in all the containers [1]
- state what data must be collected during this experiment [1]
- state *one* way to organize the data so that they will be easy to analyze [1]
- describe a result that would indicate the best salt solution for hatching brine shrimp eggs [1]

_____

_____

_____

_____

_____

_____

_____

_____

_____

_____

_____

_____

_____

_____

_____

_____

_____

56 ☐

57 Not all diseases are caused by pathogenic organisms. Other factors, such as inheritance, poor nutrition, and toxic substances, may also cause disease.

Describe a disease or disorder that can occur as a result of one of these other factors. Your answer must include at least:

- the name of the disease [1]
- *one* specific factor that causes this disease [1]
- *one* major effect of this disease on the body, other than death [1]
- *one* way this disease can be prevented, treated, or cured [1]

_____

_____

_____

_____

_____

_____

_____

_____

_____

_____

_____

_____

_____

_____

_____

_____

_____

_____

57

58 Describe how *two* of the cell structures listed below interact to help maintain a balanced internal environment in a cell.

mitochondrion
ribosome
cell membrane
nucleus
vacuole

In your answer be sure to:

- select *two* of these structures, write their names, and state *one* function of each [2]
- describe how each structure you selected contributes to the functioning of the other [2]

_____

_____

_____

_____

_____

_____

_____

_____

_____

_____

_____

58

59 Currently, Americans rely heavily on the burning of fossil fuels as sources of energy. As a result of increased demand for energy sources, there is a continuing effort to find alternatives to burning fossil fuels.

Discuss fossil fuels and alternative energy sources. In your answer be sure to:

- state *one disadvantage* of burning fossil fuels for energy   [1]
- identify *one* energy source that is an alternative to using fossil fuels   [1]
- state *one* advantage of using this alternative energy source   [1]
- state *one disadvantage* of using this alternative energy source   [1]

_____

_____

_____

_____

_____

_____

_____

_____

_____

_____

_____   59 [ ]

_____

Part D

Answer all questions in this part.   [13]

Directions (60–69): For those questions that are followed by four choices, circle the *number* of the choice that best completes the statement or answers the question. For all other questions in this part, follow the directions given in the questions and record your answers in the spaces provided.

Base your answers to questions 60 and 61 on the information and diagram below and on your knowledge of biology. The diagram illustrates an investigation carried out in a laboratory activity on diffusion. The beaker and the artificial cell also contain water.

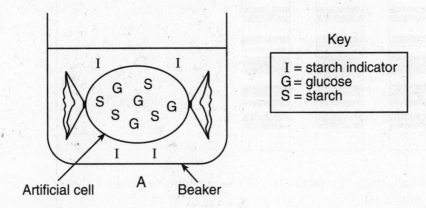

60 Predict what would happen over time by showing the location of molecules *I*, *G*, and *S* in diagram *B* below. [3]

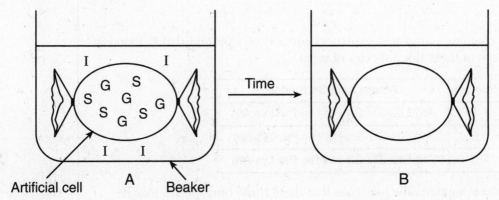

61 State what is observed when there is a positive test for starch using the starch indicator. [1]

60 ☐

_____

_____

_____

61 ☐

Base your answers to questions 62 through 64 on the information and diagram below and on your knowledge of biology.

The DNA of three different species of birds was analyzed to help determine if there is an evolutionary relationship between these species. The diagram shows the results of this analysis.

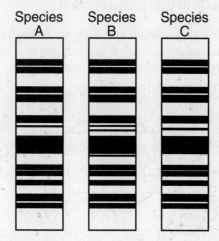

62 Identify the technique normally used to separate the DNA fragments to produce the patterns shown in the diagram.   [1]

_____   62 ☐

63 The chart below contains amino acid sequences for part of a protein that is found in the feathers on each of these three species of birds.

Species	Amino Acid Sequence
A	Arg-Leu-Glu-Gly-His-His-Pro-Lys-Arg
B	Arg-Gly-Glu-Gly-His-His-Pro-Lys-Arg
C	Arg-Leu-Glu-Gly-His-His-Pro-Lys-Arg

State *one* way this data supports the inference that these three bird species may be closely related.   [1]

_____

_____   63 ☐

64 State *one* type of additional information that could be used to determine if these three species are closely related.   [1]

_____

_____   64 ☐

Base your answers to questions 65 through 67 on the information and graph below and on your knowledge of biology.

Pulse-rate data were collected from some students during their lunch time for the lab activity, *Making Connections*. The data are represented in the histogram below.

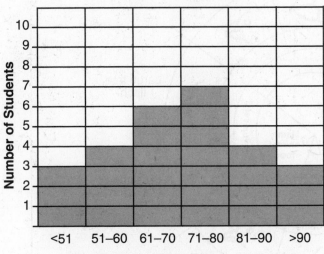

Student Pulse-Rate Data

65 The histogram includes data from a total of how many students?

(1) 6

(2) 7

(3) 10

(4) 27

65 ☐

66 Describe *one* way in which a pulse rate below 45 would disrupt homeostasis in an individual whose average resting pulse rate falls in the range of 71–80. [1]

_____

_____

66 ☐

67 State *one* way the data would most likely be different if the pulse rates were collected immediately after exercising instead of during lunch. [1]

_____

_____

67 ☐

Base your answers to questions 68 and 69 on the finch diversity chart below, which contains information concerning the finches found on the Galapagos Islands.

Finch Diversity

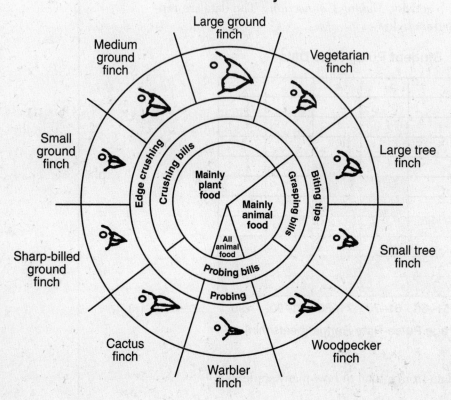

68 Identify *one* bird that would most likely compete for food with the large tree finch. Support your answer. [1]

_____

_____ 68 ☐

69 Identify *one* trait, other than beak characteristics, that would contribute to the survival of a finch species and state *one* way this trait contributes to the success of this species. [2]

_____

_____ 69 ☐

Part A

Answer all questions in this part. [30]

Directions (1–30): For *each* statement or question, write on your separate answer sheet the *number* of the word or expression that, of those given, best completes the statement or answers the question.

1 When brown tree snakes were accidentally introduced onto the island of Guam, they had no natural predators. These snakes sought out and ate many of the eggs of insect-eating birds. What probably occurred following the introduction of the brown tree snakes?

(1) The bird population increased.
(2) The insect population increased.
(3) The bird population began to seek a new food source.
(4) The insect population began to seek a new food source.

2 What will most likely happen to wastes containing nitrogen produced as a result of the breakdown of amino acids within liver cells of a mammal?

(1) They will be digested by enzymes in the stomach.
(2) They will be removed by the excretory system.
(3) They will be destroyed by specialized blood cells.
(4) They will be absorbed by mitochondria in nearby cells.

3 Which sequence represents the correct order of organization in complex organisms?

(1) tissues → organs → systems → cells
(2) organs → tissues → systems → cells
(3) systems → organs → cells → tissues
(4) cells → tissues → organs → systems

4 Which organelle is correctly paired with its specific function?

(1) cell membrane—storage of hereditary information
(2) chloroplast—transport of materials
(3) ribosome—synthesis of proteins
(4) vacuole—production of ATP

5 Homeostasis in unicellular organisms depends on the proper functioning of

(1) organelles   (3) guard cells
(2) insulin   (4) antibodies

6 Which statement best explains the change shown in the diagram below?

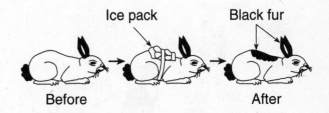

(1) Gene expression in an organism can be modified by interactions with the environment.
(2) Certain rabbits produce mutations that affect genes in specific areas of the body.
(3) Sorting and recombination of genes can be influenced by very cold temperatures.
(4) Molecular arrangement in existing proteins can be altered by environmental factors.

7 After a rabbit population reaches the carrying capacity of its habitat, the population of rabbits will most likely

(1) decrease, only
(2) increase, only
(3) alternately increase and decrease
(4) remain unchanged

8 Variation in the offspring of sexually reproducing organisms is the direct result of

(1) sorting and recombining of genes
(2) replication and cloning
(3) the need to adapt and maintain homeostasis
(4) overproduction of offspring and competition

9 An error in genetic information present in a body cell of a mammal would most likely produce

(1) rapid evolution of the organism in which the cell is found
(2) a mutation that will affect the synthesis of a certain protein in the cell
(3) an adaptation that will be passed on to other types of cells
(4) increased variation in the type of organelles present in the cell

10 Which process is illustrated in the diagram below?

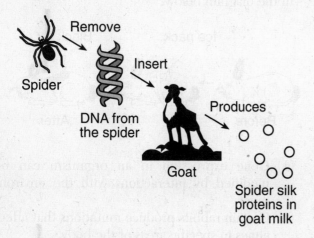

Remove
Insert
Spider
DNA from the spider
Goat
Produces
Spider silk proteins in goat milk

(1) chromatography
(2) direct harvesting
(3) meiosis
(4) genetic engineering

11 Which statement is most closely related to the modern theory of evolution?

(1) Characteristics that are acquired during life are passed to offspring by sexual reproduction.
(2) Evolution is the result of mutations and recombination, only.
(3) Organisms best adapted to a changed environment are more likely to reproduce and pass their genes to offspring.
(4) Asexual reproduction increases the survival of species.

12 In 1993, there were only 30 panthers in Florida. They were all closely related and many had reproductive problems. To avoid extinction and restore health to the population, biologists introduced 8 female panthers from Texas. Today, there are more than 80 panthers in Florida and most individuals have healthy reproductive systems. The success of this program was most likely due to the fact that the introduced females

(1) produced more reproductive cells than the male panthers in Texas
(2) solved the reproductive problems of the species by asexual methods
(3) increased the genetic variability of the panther population in Florida
(4) mated only with panthers from Texas

13 The *least* genetic variation will probably be found in the offspring of organisms that reproduce using

(1) mitosis to produce a larger population
(2) meiosis to produce gametes
(3) fusion of eggs and sperm to produce zygotes
(4) internal fertilization to produce an embryo

14 Woolly mammoths became extinct thousands of years ago, while other species of mammals that existed at that time still exist today. These other species of mammals most likely exist today because, unlike the mammoths, they

(1) produced offspring that all had identical inheritable characteristics
(2) did not face a struggle for survival
(3) learned to migrate to new environments
(4) had certain inheritable traits that enabled them to survive

15 Marine sponges contain a biological catalyst that blocks a certain step in the separation of chromosomes. Which cellular process would be directly affected by this catalyst?

(1) mitosis   (3) respiration
(2) diffusion   (4) photosynthesis

16 A tree produces only seedless oranges. A small branch cut from this tree produces roots after it is planted in soil. When mature, this new tree will most likely produce

(1) oranges with seeds, only
(2) oranges without seeds, only
(3) a majority of oranges with seeds and only a few oranges without seeds
(4) oranges and other kinds of fruit

17 The diagram below represents a human reproductive system.

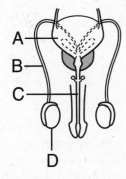

Meiosis occurs within structure

(1) *A*   (3) *C*
(2) *B*   (4) *D*

18 Which statement about embryonic organ development in humans is accurate?

(1) It is affected primarily by the eating habits and general health of the father.
(2) It may be affected by the diet and general health of the mother.
(3) It will not be affected by any medication taken by the mother in the second month of pregnancy.
(4) It is not affected by conditions outside the embryo.

19 Experiments revealed the following information about a certain molecule:

— It can be broken down into amino acids.
— It can break down proteins into amino acids.
— It is found in high concentrations in the small intestine of humans.

This molecule is most likely

(1) an enzyme
(2) an inorganic compound
(3) a hormone
(4) an antigen

20 The diagram below represents a structure involved in cellular respiration.

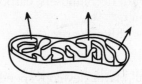

Mitochondrion

The release of which substance is represented by the arrows?

(1) glucose   (3) carbon dioxide
(2) oxygen   (4) DNA

21 Scientists have genetically altered a common virus so that it can destroy the most lethal type of brain tumor without harming the healthy tissue nearby. This technology is used for all of the following *except*

(1) treating the disease
(2) curing the disease
(3) controlling the disease
(4) diagnosing the disease

22 Many species of plants interact with harmless underground fungi. The fungi enable the plants to absorb certain essential minerals and the plants provide the fungi with carbohydrates and other nutrients. This describes an interaction between a

(1) parasite and its host
(2) predator and its prey
(3) scavenger and a decomposer
(4) producer and a consumer

23 In an ocean, the growth and survival of seaweed, small fish, and sharks depends on abiotic factors such as

(1) sunlight, temperature, and minerals
(2) sunlight, pH, and type of seaweed
(3) number of decomposers, carbon dioxide, and nitrogen
(4) number of herbivores, carbon, and food

24 A basketball player develops speed and power as a result of practice. This athletic ability will *not* be passed on to her offspring because

(1) muscle cells do not carry genetic information
(2) mutations that occur in body cells are not inherited
(3) gametes do not carry complete sets of genetic information
(4) base sequences in DNA are not affected by this activity

25 Carbon dioxide containing carbon-14 is introduced into a balanced aquarium ecosystem. After several weeks, carbon-14 will most likely be present in

(1) the plants, only
(2) the animals, only
(3) both the plants and animals
(4) neither the plants nor animals

26 Which situation is a result of human activities?

(1) decay of leaves in a forest adds to soil fertility
(2) acid rain in an area kills fish in a lake
(3) ecological succession following volcanic activity reestablishes an ecosystem
(4) natural selection on an island changes gene frequencies

27 Which human activity will most likely have a *negative* effect on global stability?

(1) decreasing water pollution levels
(2) increasing recycling programs
(3) decreasing habitat destruction
(4) increasing world population growth

28 Which process helps reduce global warming?

(1) decay
(2) industrialization
(3) photosynthesis
(4) burning

29 Which phrase belongs in box *X* of the flowchart below?

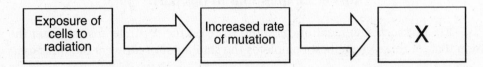

(1) Increased chance of cancer
(2) Increase in the production of functional gametes
(3) Decrease in genetic variability of offspring
(4) Decreased number of altered genes

30 The data in the table below indicate the presence of specific reproductive hormones in blood samples taken from three individuals. An *X* in the hormone column indicates a positive lab test for the appropriate levels necessary for normal reproductive functioning in that individual.

Data Table

Individuals	Hormones Present		
	Testosterone	Progesterone	Estrogen
1		X	X
2			X
3	X		

Which processes could occur in individual 3?

(1) production of sperm, only
(2) production of sperm and production of eggs
(3) production of eggs and embryonic development
(4) production of eggs, only

Directions (31–40): For *each* statement or question, write on the separate answer sheet the *number* of the word or expression that, of those given, best completes the statement or answers the question.

31 While viewing a specimen under high power of a compound light microscope, a student noticed that the specimen was out of focus. Which part of the microscope should the student turn to obtain a clearer image under high power?

(1) eyepiece   (3) fine adjustment
(2) coarse adjustment   (4) nosepiece

32 The diagram below shows the relative concentration of molecules inside and outside of a cell.

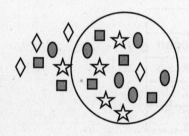 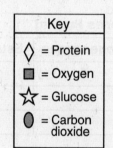

Which statement best describes the general direction of diffusion across the membrane of this cell?

(1) Glucose would diffuse into the cell.
(2) Protein would diffuse out of the cell.
(3) Carbon dioxide would diffuse out of the cell.
(4) Oxygen would diffuse into the cell.

33 Which statement most accurately describes scientific inquiry?

(1) It ignores information from other sources.
(2) It does not allow scientists to judge the reliability of their sources.
(3) It should never involve ethical decisions about the application of scientific knowledge.
(4) It may lead to explanations that combine data with what people already know about their surroundings.

34 The diagram below represents a pyramid of energy that includes both producers and consumers.

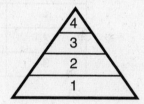

The greatest amount of available energy is found at level

(1) 1   (3) 3
(2) 2   (4) 4

35 How much water should be removed from the graduated cylinder shown below to leave 5 milliliters of water in the cylinder?

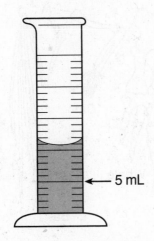

← 5 mL

(1) 6 mL   (3) 11 mL
(2) 7 mL   (4) 12 mL

36 The diagram below represents a food web.

A Meadow Environment

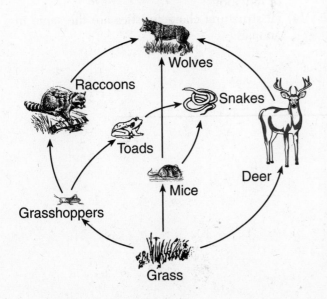

Two of the herbivores represented in this food web are

(1) toads and snakes
(2) deer and mice
(3) wolves and raccoons
(4) grasshoppers and toads

37 Compounds containing phosphorus that are dumped into the environment can upset ecosystems because phosphorus acts as a fertilizer. The graph below shows measurements of phosphorus concentrations taken during the month of June at two sites from 1991 to 1997.

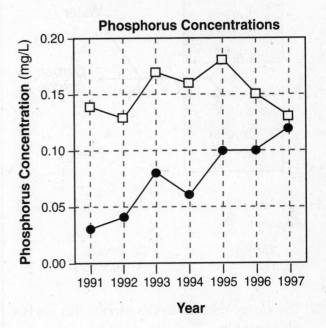

Which statement represents a valid inference based on information in the graph?

(1) There was no decrease in the amount of compounds containing phosphorus dumped at site 2 during the period from 1991 to 1997.
(2) Pollution controls may have been put into operation at site 1 in 1995.
(3) There was most likely no vegetation present near site 2 from 1993 to 1994.
(4) There was a greater variation in phosphorous concentration at site 1 than there was at site 2.

Base your answers to questions 38 and 39 on the diagram below and on your knowledge of biology. The diagram illustrates a process by which energy is released in organisms.

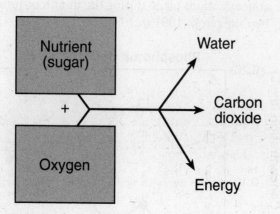

38 Cells usually transfer the energy that is released directly to

(1) glucose   (3) oxygen
(2) ATP   (4) enzymes

39 The energy released in this process was originally present in

(1) sunlight and then transferred to sugar
(2) sunlight and then transferred to oxygen
(3) the oxygen and then transferred to sugar
(4) the sugar and then transferred to oxygen

Base your answer to question 40 on the diagram below and on your knowledge of biology.

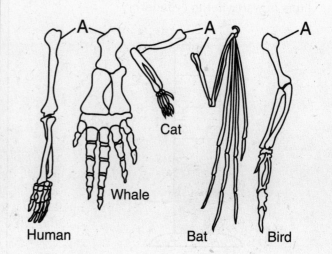

40 The similarities of the bones labeled A provide evidence that

(1) the organisms may have evolved from a common ancestor
(2) all species have one kind of bone structure
(3) the cells of the bones contain the same type of mutations
(4) all structural characteristics are the same in animals

Part B–2

Answer all questions in this part. [15]

Directions (41–55): For those questions that are followed by four choices, circle the *number* of the choice that best completes the statement or answers the question. For all other questions in this part, follow the directions given in the question.

Base your answers to questions 41 and 42 on the information below and on your knowledge of biology.

> A biology student was given three unlabeled jars of pond water from the same source, each containing a different type of mobile unicellular organism: euglena, ameba, and paramecium. The only information the student has is that the ameba and paramecium are both heterotrophs and the euglena can be either heterotrophic or autotrophic, depending on its environment.

41 State *one* way the euglena's two methods of nutrition provide a survival advantage the other unicellular organisms do *not* have. [1]

_____

_____

_____

41 ☐

42 Which procedure and resulting observation would help identify the jar that contains the euglena?

(1) Expose only one side of each jar to light. After 24 hours, only in the jar containing euglena will most of organisms be seen on the darker side of the jar.

(2) Expose all sides of each jar to light. After 48 hours, the jar with the highest dissolved carbon dioxide content will contain the euglena.

(3) Over a period of one week, determine the method of reproduction used by each type of organism. If mitotic cell division is observed, the jar will contain euglena.

(4) Prepare a wet-mount slide of specimens from each jar and observe each slide with a compound light microscope. Only the euglena will have chloroplasts.

42 ☐

Base your answers to questions 43 through 46 on the passage below and on your knowledge of biology.

Decline of the Salmon Population

Salmon are fish that hatch in a river and swim to the ocean where their body mass increases. When mature, they return to the river where they were hatched and swim up stream to reproduce and die. When there are large populations of salmon, the return of nutrients to the river ecosystem can be huge. It is estimated that during salmon runs in the Pacific Northwest in the 1800s, 500 million pounds of salmon returned to reproduce and die each year. Research estimates that in the Columbia River alone, salmon contributed hundreds of thousands of pounds of nitrogen and phosphorus compounds to the local ecosystem each year. Over the past 100 years, commercial ocean fishing has removed up to two-thirds of the salmon before they reach the river each year.

43 Identify the process that releases the nutrients from the bodies of the dead salmon, making the nutrients available for other organisms in the ecosystem. [1]

_____

43 ☐

44 Identify *one* organism, other than the salmon, that would be present in or near the river that would most likely be part of a food web in the river ecosystem. [1]

_____

44 ☐

45 Identify *two* nutrients that are returned to the ecosystem when the salmon die. [1]

_____

_____

45 ☐

46 State *one* impact, other than reducing the salmon population, that commercial ocean fishing has on the river ecosystem. [1]

_____

_____

46 ☐

Base your answers to questions 47 through 51 on the information and data table below and on your knowledge of biology.

Biologists investigated the effect of the presence of aluminum ions on root tips of a variety of wheat. They removed 2-mm sections of the tips of roots. Half of the root tips were placed in a nutrient solution with aluminum ions, while the other half were placed in an identical nutrient solution without aluminum ions. The length of the root tips, in millimeters, was measured every hour for seven hours. The results are shown in the data table below.

Data Table

Time (hr)	Length of Root Tips in Solution With Aluminum Ions (mm)	Length of Root Tips in Solution Without Aluminum Ions (mm)
0	2.0	2.0
1	2.1	2.2
2	2.2	2.4
3	2.4	2.8
4	2.6	2.9
5	2.7	3.2
6	2.8	3.7
7	2.8	3.9

Directions (47–49): Using the information in the data table, construct a line graph on the grid *on the next page*, following the directions below.

47 Mark an appropriate scale on each labeled axis. [1]

48 Plot the data for root tips in the solution with aluminum ions on the grid. Surround each point with a small circle and connect the points. [1]

Example:

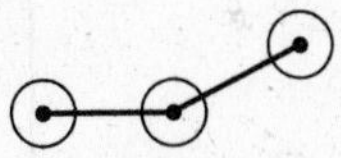

49 Plot the data for root tips in the solution without aluminum ions on the grid. Surround each point with a small triangle and connect the points. [1]

Example:

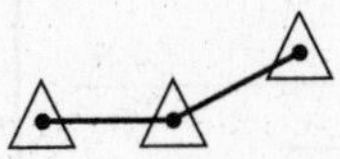

Growth of Wheat Root Tips

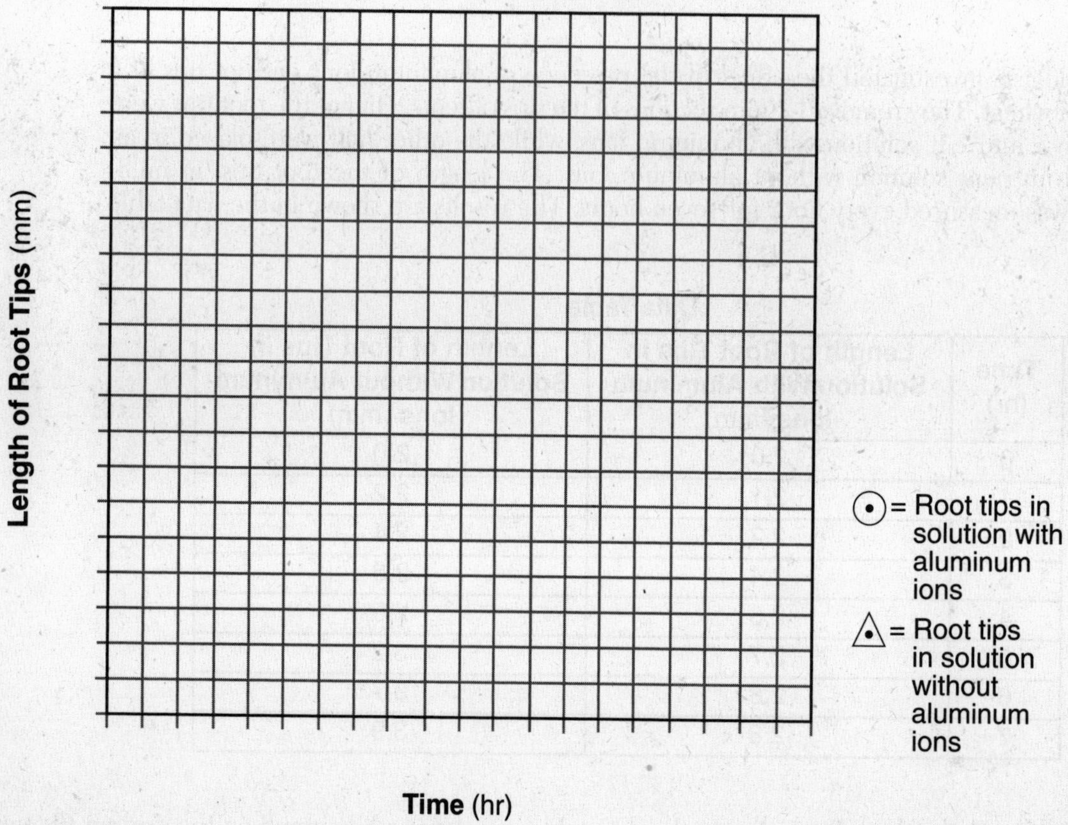

Length of Root Tips (mm) (vertical axis)

Time (hr) (horizontal axis)

⊙ = Root tips in solution with aluminum ions

△• = Root tips in solution without aluminum ions

47 ☐

48 ☐

49 ☐

50 The aluminum ions most likely affected

(1) photosynthetic rate

(2) the union of gametes

(3) mitotic cell division

(4) starch absorption from the soil

50 ☐

51 Describe the effect of aluminum ions on the growth of the root tips of wheat. [1]

_____

_____

51 ☐

Base your answers to questions 52 and 53 on the information below and on your knowledge of biology.

A pond in the Adirondack Mountains of New York State was once a fishing spot visited by many people. It was several acres in size, and fishermen in boats were a common sight. Over time, the pond has become smaller in area and depth. Places where there was once open water are now covered by grasses and shrubs. Around the edges of the pond there are cattails and other wetland plants.

52 Identify the ecological process responsible for the changes to this pond. [1]

_____

52 ☐

53 Predict what will most likely happen to this pond area over the next hundred years if this process continues. [1]

_____

_____

53 ☐

Base your answers to questions 54 and 55 on the statement below and on your knowledge of biology.

The use of nuclear fuel can have positive and negative effects on an ecosystem.

54 State *one* positive effect on an ecosystem of using nuclear fuel to generate electricity. [1]

_____

_____

54 ☐

55 State *one* negative effect on an ecosystem of using nuclear fuel to generate electricity. [1]

_____

_____

55 ☐

Part C

Answer all questions in this part.   [17]

Directions (56–65): Record your answers in the spaces provided in this examination booklet.

Base your answers to questions 56 and 57 on the statement below and on your knowledge of biology.

> Selective breeding has been used to improve the racing ability of horses.

56 Define selective breeding and state how it would be used to improve the racing ability of horses. [2]

_____

_____

_____

_____

56 ☐

57 State *one disadvantage* of selective breeding. [1]

_____

_____

57 ☐

58 State *one* specific way the removal of trees from an area has had a *negative* impact on the environment. [1]

_____

_____

58 ☐

Base your answers to questions 59 through 61 on the information below and on your knowledge of biology.

It has been discovered that plants utilize chemical signals for communication. Some of these chemicals are released from leaves, fruits, and flowers and play various roles in plant development, survival, and gene expression. For example, bean plant leaves infested with spider mites release chemicals that result in an increase in the resistance to spider mites in uninfested leaves on the same plant and the expression of self-defense genes in uninfested bean plants nearby.

Plants can also communicate with insects. For example, corn, cotton, and tobacco under attack by caterpillars release chemical signals that simultaneously attract parasitic wasps to destroy the caterpillars and discourage moths from laying their eggs on the plants.

59 Identify the specialized structures in the cell membrane that are involved in communication. [1]

_____

59 ☐

60 Explain why chemicals released from one plant species may not cause a response in a different plant species. [1]

_____

_____

_____

60 ☐

61 State *two* advantages of relying on chemicals released by plants rather than using man-made chemicals for insect control. [2]

_____

_____

_____

_____

61 ☐

Base your answers to questions 62 through 64 on the information below and on your knowledge of biology.

Cells of the immune system and the endocrine system of the human body contribute to the maintenance of homeostasis. The methods and materials these two systems use as they carry out this critical function are different.

62 State *two* ways cells of the immune system fight disease. [2]

_____

_____

62 ☐

63 Identify the substance produced by the cells of all the endocrine glands that helps maintain homeostasis. [1]

_____

63 ☐

64 Identify *one* specific product of one of the endocrine glands and state how it aids in the maintenance of homeostasis. [1]

_____

_____

_____

64 ☐

65 A certain plant has white flower petals and it usually grows in soil that is slightly basic. Sometimes the plant produces flowers with red petals. A company that sells the plant wants to know if soil pH affects the color of the petals in this plant. Design a controlled experiment to determine if soil pH affects petal color. In your experimental design be sure to:

- state the hypothesis to be tested in the experiment   [1]
- state *one* way the control group will be treated differently from the experimental group   [1]
- identify *two* factors that must be kept the same in both the control group and the experimental group   [1]
- identify the dependent variable in the experiment   [1]
- state *one* result of the experiment that would support the hypothesis   [1]

65 □

Part D

Answer all questions in this part. [13]

Directions (66–76): For those questions that are followed by four choices, circle the *number* of the choice that best completes the statement or answers the question. For all other questions in this part, follow the directions given in the question.

Base your answers to questions 66 and 67 on the information and data table below and on your knowledge of biology

Two students collected data on their pulse rates while performing different activities. Their average results are shown in the data table below.

Data Table

Activity	Average Pulse Rate (beats/min)
sitting quietly	70
walking	98
running	120

66 State the relationship between activity and pulse rate. [1]

_____

_____

66 ☐

67 State *one* way that this investigation could be improved. [1]

_____

_____

67 ☐

Base your answers to questions 68 through 71 on the information below and on your knowledge of biology.

For Teacher Use Only

To demonstrate techniques used in DNA analysis, a student was given two paper strip samples of DNA. The two DNA samples are shown below.

Sample 1: ATTCCGGTAATCCCGTAATGCCGGATAATACTCCGGTAATATC

Sample 2: ATTCCGGTAATCCCGTAATGCCGGATAATACTCCGGTAATATC

The student cut between the C and G in each of the shaded CCGG sequences in sample 1 and between the As in each of the shaded TAAT sequences in sample 2. Both sets of fragments were then arranged on a paper model of a gel.

68 The action of what kind of molecules was being demonstrated when the DNA samples were cut? [1]

________________________________ 68

69 Identify the technique that was being demonstrated when the fragments were arranged on the gel model. [1]

________________________________ 69

70 The results of this type of DNA analysis are often used to help determine

(1) the number of DNA molecules in an organism

(2) if two species are closely related

(3) the number of mRNA molecules in DNA

(4) if two organisms contain carbohydrate molecules 70

71 State *one* way that the arrangement of the two samples on the gel model would differ. [1]

____

____ 71

____

Base your answers to questions 72 and 73 on the information below and on your knowledge of biology.

In birds, the ability to crush and eat seeds is related to the size, shape, and thickness of the beak. Birds with larger, thicker beaks are better adapted to crush and open seeds that are larger.

One species of bird found in the Galapagos Islands is the medium ground finch. It is easier for most of the medium ground finches to pick up and crack open smaller seeds rather than larger seeds. When food is scarce, some of the birds have been observed eating larger seeds.

72 Describe *one* change in beak characteristics that would most likely occur in the medium ground finch population after many generations when an environmental change results in a permanent shortage of small seeds. [1]

_____

_____

72 ☐

73 Explain this long-term change in beak characteristics using the concepts of:

- competition [1]
- survival of the fittest [1]
- inheritance [1]

_____

_____

_____

_____

_____

73 ☐

_____

Base your answers to questions 74 and 75 on the information and diagram below and on your knowledge of biology. The diagram represents some cells on a microscope slide before and after a substance was added to the slide.

Before	After

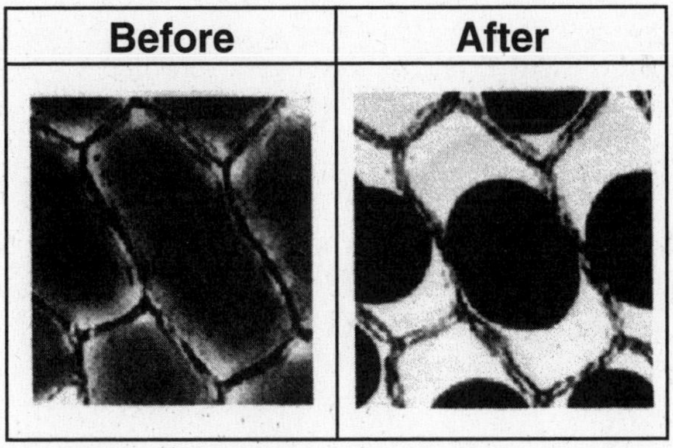

74 Identify a substance that was most likely added to the slide to cause the change observed. [1]

_____

75 Describe a procedure that could be used to add this substance to the cells on the slide without removing the coverslip. [1]

_____

_____

_____

76 In the *Diffusion Through a Membrane* lab, the model cell membranes allowed certain substances to pass through based on which characteristic of the diffusing substance?

(1) size

(2) shape

(3) color

(4) temperature

Part A

Answer all questions in this part. [30]

Directions (1–30): For *each* statement or question, write on your separate answer sheet the *number* of the word or expression that, of those given, best completes the statement or answers the question.

1 Which statement describes a role of fungi in an ecosystem?

(1) They transfer energy to decaying matter.
(2) They release oxygen into the ecosystem.
(3) They recycle chemicals from dead organisms.
(4) They synthesize organic nutrients from inorganic substances.

2 Which diagram best represents the levels of organization in the human body?

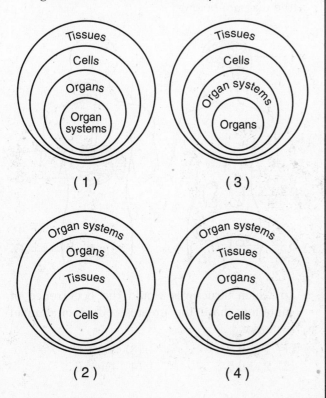

(1)   (3)

(2)   (4)

3 Which situation indicates that a disruption of homeostasis has taken place?

(1) the presence of hormones that keep the blood sugar level steady
(2) the maintenance of a constant body temperature
(3) cell division that is involved in normal growth
(4) a rapid rise in the number of red blood cells

4 A protein on the surface of HIV can attach to proteins on the surface of healthy human cells. These attachment sites on the surface of the cells are known as

(1) receptor molecules   (3) molecular bases
(2) genetic codes   (4) inorganic catalysts

5 Contractile vacuoles maintain water balance by pumping excess water out of some single-celled pond organisms. In humans, the kidney is chiefly involved in maintaining water balance. These facts best illustrate that

(1) tissues, organs, and organ systems work together to maintain homeostasis in all living things
(2) interference with nerve signals disrupts cellular communication and homeostasis within organisms
(3) a disruption in a body system may disrupt the homeostasis of a single-celled organism
(4) structures found in single-celled organisms can act in a manner similar to tissues and organs in multicellular organisms

6 Which statement best explains the observation that clones produced from the same organism may *not* be identical?

(1) Events in meiosis result in variation.
(2) Gene expression can be influenced by the environment.
(3) Differentiated cells have different genes.
(4) Half the genetic information in offspring comes from each parent.

7 A change in the base subunit sequence during DNA replication can result in

(1) variation within an organism
(2) rapid evolution of an organism
(3) synthesis of antigens to protect the cell
(4) recombination of genes within the cell

8 The diagram below represents a yeast cell that is in the process of budding, a form of asexual reproduction.

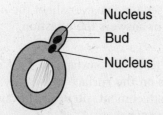

Nucleus
Bud
Nucleus

Which statement describes the outcome of this process?

(1) The bud will develop into a zygote.
(2) The two cells that result will each contain half the species number of chromosomes.
(3) The two cells that result will have identical DNA.
(4) The bud will start to divide by the process of meiotic cell division.

9 Two proteins in the same cell perform different functions. This is because the two proteins are composed of

(1) chains folded the same way and the same sequence of simple sugars
(2) chains folded the same way and the same sequence of amino acids
(3) chains folded differently and a different sequence of simple sugars
(4) chains folded differently and a different sequence of amino acids

10 Even though each body cell in an individual contains the same DNA, the functions of muscle cells and liver cells are *not* the same because

(1) mutations usually occur in genes when muscle cells divide
(2) liver tissue develops before muscle tissue
(3) liver cells produce more oxygen than muscle cells
(4) liver cells use different genes than muscle cells

11 The flounder is a species of fish that can live in very cold water. The fish produces an "antifreeze" protein that prevents ice crystals from forming in its blood. The DNA for this protein has been identified. An enzyme is used to cut and remove this section of flounder DNA that is then spliced into the DNA of a strawberry plant. As a result, the plant can now produce a protein that makes it more resistant to the damaging effects of frost. This process is known as

(1) sorting of genes
(2) genetic engineering
(3) recombination of chromosomes
(4) mutation by deletion of genetic material

12 Some human body structures are represented in the diagram below.

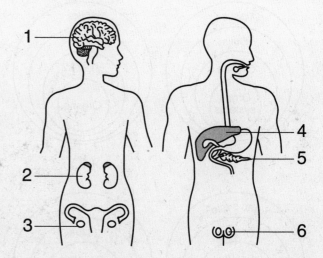

In which structures would the occurrence of mutations have the greatest effect on human evolution?

(1) 1 and 3   (3) 3 and 6
(2) 2 and 5   (4) 4 and 6

13 A single pair of goldfish in an aquarium produced a large number of offspring. These offspring showed variations in body shape and coloration. The most likely explanation for these variations is that the

(1) offspring were adapting to different environments
(2) offspring were produced from different combinations of genes
(3) parent fish had not been exposed to mutagenic agents
(4) parent fish had not reproduced sexually

14 A certain species has little genetic variation. The rapid extinction of this species would most likely result from the effect of

(1) successful cloning
(2) gene manipulation
(3) environmental change
(4) genetic recombination

15 Which two structures of a frog would most likely have the same chromosome number?

(1) skin cell and fertilized egg cell
(2) zygote and sperm cell
(3) kidney cell and egg cell
(4) liver cell and sperm cell

16 Tissues develop from a zygote as a direct result of the processes of

(1) fertilization and meiosis
(2) fertilization and differentiation
(3) mitosis and meiosis
(4) mitosis and differentiation

17 The human female reproductive system is adapted for

(1) production of zygotes in ovaries
(2) external fertilization of gametes
(3) production of milk for a developing embryo
(4) transport of oxygen through a placenta to a fetus

18 The letters in the diagram below represent structures in a human female.

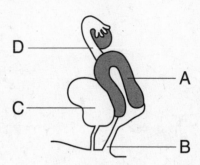

Estrogen and progesterone increase the chance for successful fetal development by regulating activities within structure

(1) A   (3) C
(2) B   (4) D

19 Which part of a molecule provides energy for life processes?

(1) carbon atoms   (3) chemical bonds
(2) oxygen atoms   (4) inorganic nitrogen

20 Energy from organic molecules can be stored in ATP molecules as a direct result of the process of

(1) cellular respiration
(2) cellular reproduction
(3) diffusion
(4) digestion

21 Which statement best describes how a vaccination can help protect the body against disease?

(1) Vaccines directly kill the pathogen that causes the disease.
(2) Vaccines act as a medicine that cures the disease.
(3) Vaccines cause the production of specific molecules that will react with and destroy certain microbes.
(4) Vaccines contain white blood cells that engulf harmful germs and prevent them from spreading throughout the body.

22 The diagram below represents four different species of wild birds. Each species has feet with different structural adaptations.

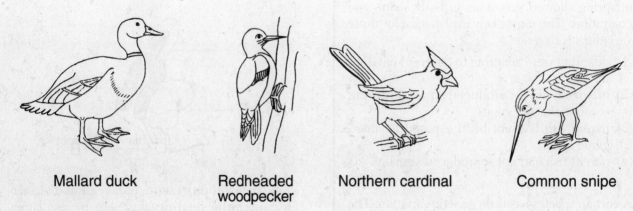

Mallard duck   Redheaded woodpecker   Northern cardinal   Common snipe

The development of these adaptations can best be explained by the concept of

(1) inheritance of resistance to diseases that affect all these species
(2) inheritance of characteristics acquired after the birds hatched from the egg
(3) natural selection
(4) selective breeding

23 The diagram below represents a nucleus containing the normal chromosome number for a species.

Which diagram bests illustrates the normal formation of a cell that contains all of the genetic information needed for growth, development, and future reproduction of this species?

(1)

(2)

(3)

(4)

24 The diagram below represents events associated with a biochemical process that occurs in some organisms.

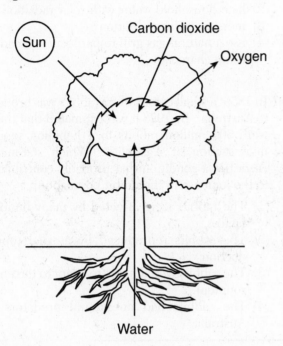

Water

Which statement concerning this process is correct?

(1) The process represented is respiration and the primary source of energy for the process is the Sun.
(2) The process represented is photosynthesis and the primary source of energy for the process is the Sun.
(3) This process converts energy in organic compounds into solar energy which is released into the atmosphere.
(4) This process uses solar energy to convert oxygen into carbon dioxide.

25 In the transfer of energy from the Sun to ecosystems, which molecule is one of the first to store this energy?

(1) protein   (3) DNA
(2) fat   (4) glucose

26 The diagram below represents two molecules that can interact with each other to cause a biochemical process to occur in a cell.

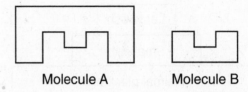

Molecule A   Molecule B

Molecules *A* and *B* most likely represent

(1) a protein and a chromosome
(2) a receptor and a hormone
(3) a carbohydrate and an amino acid
(4) an antibody and a hormone

27 The graph below represents the amount of available energy at successive nutrition levels in a particular food web.

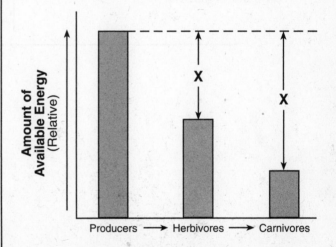

The *X*s in the diagram represent the amount of energy that was most likely

(1) changed into inorganic compounds
(2) retained indefinitely by the herbivores
(3) recycled back to the producers
(4) lost as heat to the environment

28 The diagram below represents an energy pyramid constructed from data collected from an aquatic ecosystem.

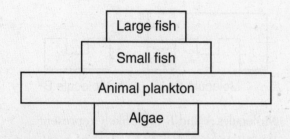

Which statement best describes this ecosystem?

(1) The ecosystem is most likely unstable.
(2) Long-term stability of this ecosystem will continue.
(3) The herbivore populations will continue to increase in size for many years.
(4) The producer organisms outnumber the consumer organisms.

29 In order to reduce consumption of nonrenewable resources, humans could

(1) burn coal to heat houses instead of using oil
(2) heat household water with solar radiation
(3) increase industrialization
(4) use a natural-gas grill to barbecue instead of using charcoal

30 In 1859, a small colony of 24 rabbits was brought to Australia. By 1928 it was estimated that there were 500 million rabbits in a 1-million square mile section of Australia. Which statement describes a condition that probably contributed to the increase in the rabbit population?

(1) The rabbits were affected by many limiting factors.
(2) The rabbits reproduced by asexual reproduction.
(3) The rabbits were unable to adapt to the environment.
(4) The rabbits had no natural predators in Australia.

Directions (31–42): For *each* statement or question, write on the separate answer sheet the *number* of the word or expression that, of those given, best completes the statement or answers the question.

31 What is the approximate length of the earthworm shown in the diagram below?

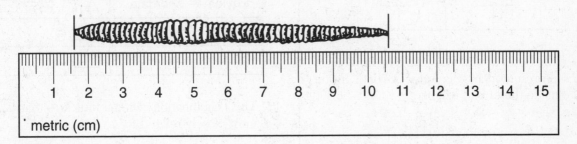

(1) 9 mm   (3) 10.6 cm
(2) 90 mm   (4) 106 cm

32 Information concerning the diet of crocodiles of different sizes is contained in the table below.

Percentage of Crocodiles of Different Lengths and Their Food Sources

Food Source	Group A 0.3–0.5 Meter	Group B 2.5–3.9 Meters	Group C 4.5–5.0 Meters
mammals	0	18	65
reptiles	0	17	48
fish	0	62	38
birds	0	17	0
snails	0	25	0
shellfish	0	5	0
spiders	20	0	0
frogs	35	0	0
insects	100	2	0

Which statement is *not* a valid conclusion based on the data?

(1) Overharvesting of fish could have a negative impact on group *C*.
(2) The smaller the crocodile is, the larger the prey.
(3) Group *B* has no preference between reptiles and birds.
(4) Spraying insecticides would have the most direct impact on group *A*.

33 The diagram below represents an incomplete section of a DNA molecule. The boxes represent unidentified bases.

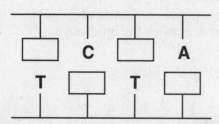

When the boxes are filled in, the total number of bases represented by the letter A (both inside and outside the boxes) will be

(1) 1
(2) 2
(3) 3
(4) 4

34 The graph below shows the growth of a population of bacteria over a period of 80 hours.

Growth of a Population of Bacteria

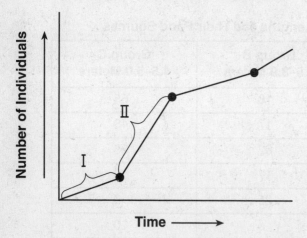

Which statement best describes section II of the graph?

(1) The population has reached the carrying capacity of the environment.
(2) The rate of reproduction is slower than in section I.
(3) The population is greater than the carrying capacity of the environment.
(4) The rate of reproduction exceeds the death rate.

35 A classification system is shown in the table below.

Classification	Examples
Kingdom — animal	△, ○, ◻, ☆, ▭, ◇, ℰ, ▽
Phylum — chordata	△, ◻, ℰ, ☆, ▭
Genus — *Felis*	▭, ℰ
Species — *domestica*	▭

This classification scheme indicates that ▭ is most closely related to

☆   △   ◻   ℰ
(1)   (2)   (3)   (4)

36 Information concerning nests built in the same tree by two different bird species over a ten-year period is shown in the table below.

Distance of Nest Above Ground (m)	Total Number of Nests Built by Two Different Species	
	A	B
less than 1	5	0
1–5	10	0
6–10	5	0
over 10	0	20

What inference best describes these two bird species?

(1) They most likely do not compete for nesting sites because they occupy different niches.
(2) They do not compete for nesting sites because they have the same reproductive behavior.
(3) They compete for nesting sites because they build the same type of nest.
(4) They compete for nesting sites because they nest in the same tree at the same time.

37 The diagram below shows the effect of spraying a pesticide on a population of insects over three generations.

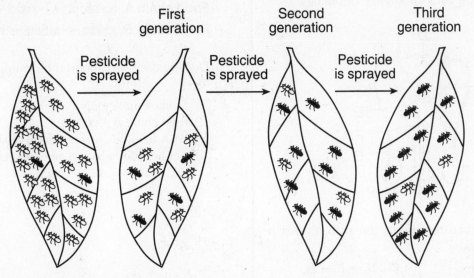

First generation

Second generation

Third generation

Pesticide is sprayed

Pesticide is sprayed

Pesticide is sprayed

Which concept is represented in the diagram?

(1) survival of the fittest

(2) dynamic equilibrium

(3) succession

(4) extinction

38 In an ecosystem, the herring population was reduced by fishermen. As a result, the tuna, which feed on the herring, disappeared. The sand eels, which are eaten by herring, increased in number. The fishermen then overharvested the sand eel population. Cod and seabirds then decreased. Which food web best represents the feeding relationships in this ecosystem?

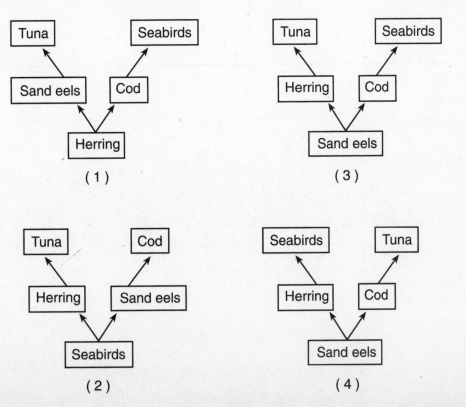

(1)

(2)

(3)

(4)

Base your answers to questions 39 through 41 on the diagram below, which represents systems in a human male and on your knowledge of biology.

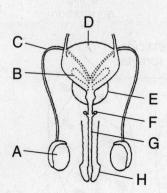

39 Which sequence represents the path of sperm leaving the body?

(1) $A \rightarrow C \rightarrow G$ (3) $E \rightarrow F \rightarrow H$

(2) $A \rightarrow C \rightarrow B$ (4) $D \rightarrow F \rightarrow G$

40 Which structures aid in the transport of sperm by secreting fluid?

(1) A and H (3) C and D

(2) B and E (4) D and H

41 Which structure has both reproductive and excretory functions?

(1) A (3) C

(2) G (4) D

42 Two food chains are represented below.

Food chain A: aquatic plant → insect → frog → hawk

Food chain B: grass → rabbit → hawk

Decomposers are important for supplying energy for

(1) food chain A, only
(2) food chain B, only
(3) both food chain A and food chain B
(4) neither food chain A nor food chain B

Part B–2

Answer all questions in this part. [13]

Directions (43–55): For those questions that are followed by four choices, circle the *number* of the choice that, of those given, best completes the statement or answers the question. For all other questions in this part, follow the directions given in the question and record your answers in the spaces provided.

Base your answers to questions 43 through 45 on the diagrams below and on your knowledge of biology. The diagrams represent two different cells and some of their parts. The diagrams are not drawn to scale.

Cell A   Cell B

43 Identify an organelle in cell *A* that is the site of autotrophic nutrition. [1]

_____

44 Identify the organelle labeled *X* in cell *B*. [1]

_____

45 Which statement best describes these cells?

(1) Cell *B* lacks vacuoles while cell *A* has them.

(2) DNA would not be found in either cell *A* or cell *B*.

(3) Both cell *A* and cell *B* use energy released from ATP.

(4) Both cell *A* and cell *B* produce antibiotics.

Base your answers to questions 46 through 48 on the diagram below and on your knowledge of biology.

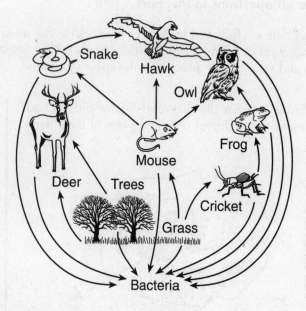

46 What is an appropriate title for this diagram?

(1) Energy Flow in a Community

(2) Ecological Succession

(3) Biological Evolution

(4) A Food Chain

46 ☐

47 Which organism carries out autotrophic nutrition?

(1) hawk

(2) cricket

(3) grass

(4) deer

47 ☐

48 State what would most likely happen to the cricket population if all of the grasses were removed. [1]

_____

_____

48 ☐

Base your answers to questions 49 through 53 on the information and diagrams below and on your knowledge of biology.

The laboratory setups represented below were used to investigate the effect of temperature on cellular respiration in yeast (a single-celled organism). Each of two flasks containing equal amounts of a yeast-glucose solution was submerged in a water bath, one kept at 20°C and one kept at 35°C. The number of gas bubbles released from the glass tube in each setup was observed and the results were recorded every 5 minutes for a period of 25 minutes. The data are summarized in the table below.

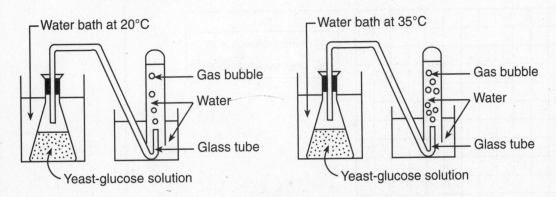

Data Table

Time (minutes)	Total Number of Bubbles Released	
	20°C	35°C
5	0	5
10	5	15
15	15	30
20	30	50
25	45	75

Directions (49–51): Using the information in the data table, construct a line graph on the grid on the next page, following the directions below.

49 Mark an appropriate scale on each axis. [1]

50 Plot the data for the total number of bubbles released at 20°C on the grid on the next page. Surround each point with a small circle and connect the points. [1]

Example: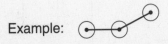

51 Plot the data for the total number of bubbles released at 35°C on the grid. Surround each point with a small triangle and connect the points. [1]

Example:

The Effect of Temperature on Respiration in Yeast

Total Number of Bubbles Released (y-axis)

Time (minutes)

Key
⊙ Yeast respiration at 20°C
△ Yeast respiration at 35°C

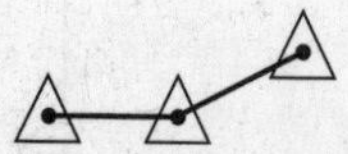

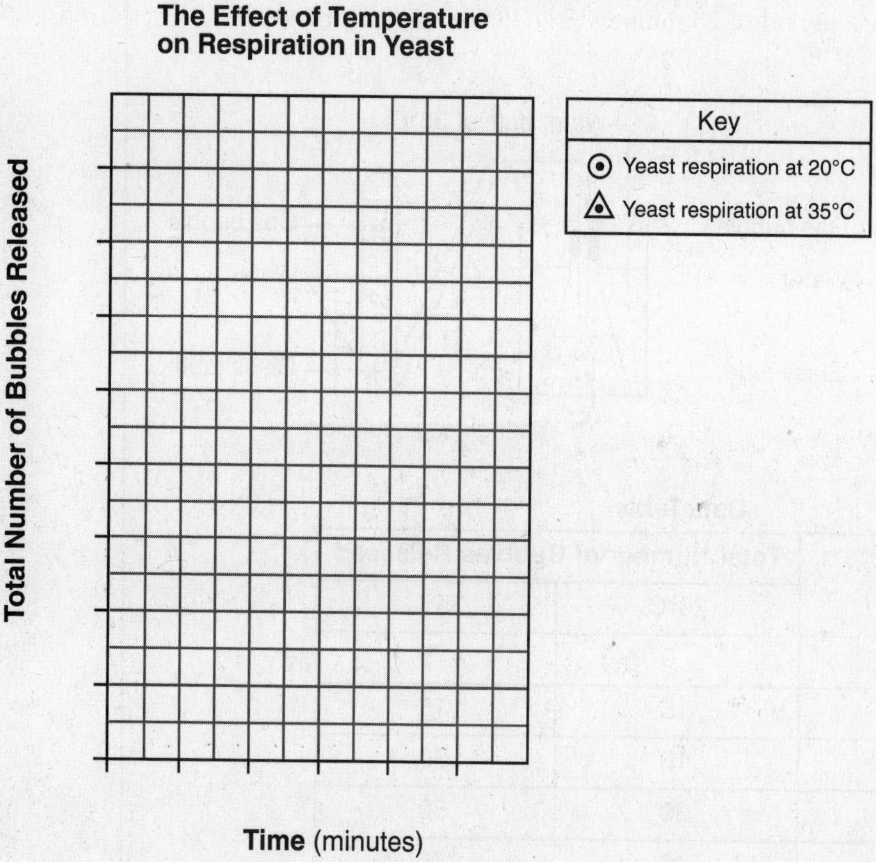

49 ☐

50 ☐

51 ☐

52 State *one* relationship between temperature and the rate of gas production in yeast. [1]

_____

_____

52 ☐

53 Identify the gas that would be produced by the process taking place in both laboratory setups. [1]

_____

_____

53 ☐

Base your answers to questions 54 and 55 on the diagram below and on your knowledge of biology.

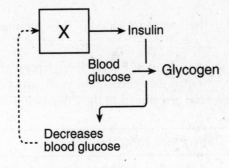

54 Identify the organ labeled X.   [1]

_____

55 The dashed line in the diagram represents

(1) a digestive process

(2) a feedback mechanism

(3) cellular differentiation

(4) recycling of organic chemicals

54 ☐

55 ☐

Part C

Answer all questions in this part. [17]

Directions (56–61): Record your answers in the spaces provided in this examination booklet.

56 An experiment was carried out to determine how competition for living space affects plant height. Different numbers of plants were grown in three pots, *A*, *B*, and *C*. All three pots were the same size. The data collected are shown in the table below.

Average Daily Plant Height (mm)							
	Day 1	Day 2	Day 3	Day 4	Day 5	Day 6	Day 7
Pot A—5 plants	2	4	6	8	10	14	16
Pot B—10 plants	2	4	6	8	10	12	12
Pot C—20 plants	2	2	2	6	6	8	8

Analyze the experiment that produced the data shown in the table. In your answer be sure to:

- state a hypothesis for the experiment [1]
- identify *one* factor, other than pot size, that should have been kept the same in each experimental group [1]
- identify the dependent variable [1]
- state whether the data supports or fails to support your hypothesis and justify your answer [1]

56

57 In many investigations, both in the laboratory and in natural environments, the pH of substances is measured. Explain why pH is important to living things. In your explanation be sure to:

- identify *one* example of a life process of an organism that could be affected by a pH change   [1]
- state *one environmental* problem that is directly related to pH   [1]
- identify *one* possible cause of this environmental problem   [1]

_____

_____

_____

_____

_____

_____

_____

_____

57 ☐

_____

Base your answer to question 58 on the information below and on your knowledge of biology.

Cargo ships traveling to the Great Lakes from the Caspian Sea in Eurasia often carry water in tanks known as ballast tanks. This water helps the ships to be more stable while crossing the ocean. Upon arrival in the Great Lakes, this water is pumped out of the ships. Often this water contains species that are not native to the Great Lakes environment. The zebra mussel is one species that was introduced into the Great Lakes in this way.

Although large numbers of zebra mussels often clog water intake pipes of power plants and other industries, the mussels have a benefit. Each mussel filters about a quart of water per day, absorbing cancer-causing PCB's from lake water in the process.

The goby, a bottom-feeding fish from Europe, was introduced into the Great Lakes in a similar way a few years later. The gobies have become a dominant species in the Great Lakes, eating small zebra mussels and the eggs and young of other fish. Gobies are eaten by large sport fish. These sport fish have been tested and PCB's have been found in their tissues. Recommendations have been made that people limit the number of sport fish they eat.

58 Explain how the introduction of foreign species can often cause environmental problems. In your answer be sure to:

- state how the zebra mussels and gobies were introduced into the United States [1]
- state *one* way either the zebra mussels *or* gobies have become a problem in their new environment [1]
- describe how *both* zebra mussels and gobies contribute to increasing the concentration of PCB's in sport fish [2]

_____

_____

_____

_____

_____

_____

_____

_____

_____

58 ☐

59 Knowledge of human genes gained from research on the structure and function of human genetic material has led to improvements in medicine and health care for humans.

- state *two* ways this knowledge has improved medicine and health care for humans [2]
- identify *one* specific concern that could result from the application of this knowledge [1]

_____

_____

_____

_____

_____

_____

59

Base your answers to questions 60 and 61 on the information below and on your knowledge of biology.

> You are the owner of a chemical company. Many people in your community have been complaining that rabbits are getting into their gardens and eating the flowering plants and vegetables they have planted. Your company is developing a new chemical product called Bunny Hop-Away that repels rabbits. This product would be sprayed on the plants to prevent the rabbits from eating them. Certain concerns need to be considered before you make the product available for public use.

60 State *two* environmental concerns that should be considered before the product is sold and used by the public. [2]

_____

_____

_____

_____

60

61 State *one* safety procedure that should be followed when the product is sprayed on plants. [1]

_____

_____

61

Part D

Answer all questions in this part. [13]

Directions (62–73): For those questions that are followed by four choices, circle the *number* of the choice, that, of those given, best completes the statement or answers the question. For all other questions in this part, follow the directions given in the questions and record your answers in the spaces provided.

62 Students were asked to determine if they could squeeze a clothespin more times in a minute after resting than after exercising. An experiment that accurately tests this question should include all of the following *except*

(1) a hypothesis on which to base the design of the experiment

(2) a large number of students

(3) two sets of clothespins, one that is easy to open and one that is more difficult to open

(4) a control group and an experimental group with equal numbers of students of approximately the same age

63 Which statement best describes a controlled experiment?

(1) It eliminates the need for dependent variables.

(2) It shows the effect of a dependent variable on an independent variable.

(3) It avoids the use of variables.

(4) It tests the effect of a single independent variable.

64 Which statement best describes a change that usually takes place in the human body when the heart rate increases as a result of exercise?

(1) More oxygen is delivered to muscle cells.

(2) Blood cells are excreted at a faster rate.

(3) The rate of digestion increases.

(4) No hormones are produced.

62 ☐

63 ☐

64 ☐

Base your answers to questions 65 through 67 on the diagram below and on your knowledge of biology. The diagram shows the results of a technique used to analyze DNA.

DNA Samples

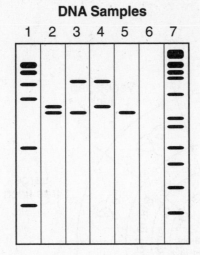

65 This technique used to analyze DNA directly results in

(1) synthesizing large fragments of DNA

(2) separating DNA fragments on the basis of size

(3) producing genetically engineered DNA molecules

(4) removing the larger DNA fragments from the samples

65 ☐

66 This laboratory technique is known as

(1) gel electrophoresis

(2) DNA replication

(3) protein synthesis

(4) genetic recombination

66 ☐

67 State *one* specific way the results of this laboratory technique could be used. [1]

_____

_____

67 ☐

68 The cactus finch, warbler finch, and woodpecker finch all live on one island. Based on the information in the diagram below, which one of these finches is *least* likely to compete with the other two for food? Support your answer with an explanation.   [1]

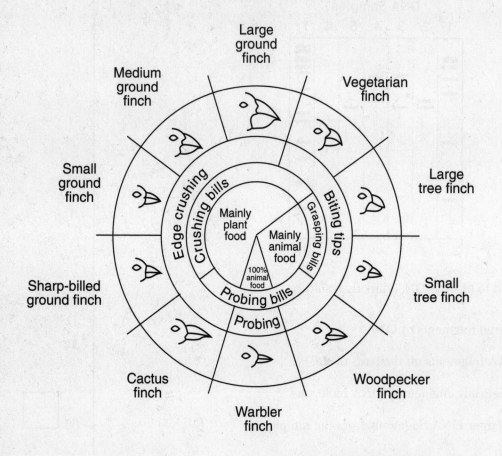

From: *Galapagos: A Natural History Guide*

Variations in Beaks of Galapagos Islands Finches

_____

_____

_____

68 ☐

Base your answers to questions 69 and 70 on the information below and on your knowledge of biology.

Evolutionary changes have been observed in beak size in a population of medium ground finches in the Galapagos Islands. Given a choice of small and large seeds, the medium ground finch eats mostly small seeds, which are easier to crush. However, during dry years, all seeds are in short supply. Small seeds are quickly consumed, so the birds are left with a diet of large seeds. Studies have shown that this change in diet may be related to an increase in the average size of the beak of the medium ground finch.

69 The most likely explanation for the increase in average beak size of the medium ground finch is that the

(1) trait is inherited and birds with larger beaks have greater reproductive success

(2) birds acquired larger beaks due to the added exercise of feeding on large seeds

(3) birds interbred with a larger-beaked species and passed on the trait

(4) lack of small seeds caused a mutation which resulted in a larger beak

69 ☐

70 In exceptionally dry years, what most likely happens in a population of medium ground finches?

(1) There is increased cooperation between the birds.

(2) Birds with large beaks prey on birds with small beaks.

(3) The finches develop parasitic relationships with mammals.

(4) There is increased competition for a limited number of small seeds.

70 ☐

Base your answers to questions 71 and 72 on the diagram below and on your knowledge of biology. The diagram shows the changes that occurred in a beaker after 30 minutes. The beaker contained water, food coloring, and a bag made from dialysis tubing membrane.

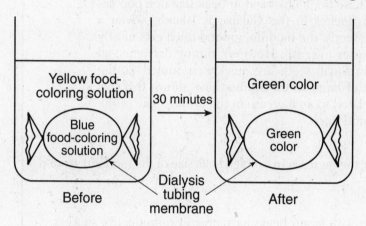

71 When the colors yellow and blue are combined, they produce a green color. Which statement most likely describes the relative sizes of the yellow and blue food-coloring molecules in the diagram?

(1) The yellow food-coloring molecules are small, while the blue food-coloring molecules are large.

(2) The yellow food-coloring molecules are large, while the blue food-coloring molecules are small.

(3) Both the yellow food-coloring molecules and the blue food-coloring molecules are large.

(4) Both the yellow food-coloring molecules and the blue food-coloring molecules are small.

72 Which statement best explains the changes shown?

(1) Molecular movement was aided by the presence of specific carbohydrate molecules on the surface of the membrane.

(2) Molecular movement was aided by the presence of specific enzyme molecules on the surface of the membrane.

(3) Molecules moved across the membrane without additional energy being supplied.

(4) Molecules moved across the membrane only when additional energy was supplied.

73 Cell *A* shown below is a typical red onion cell in water on a slide viewed with a compound light microscope.

— Cell A

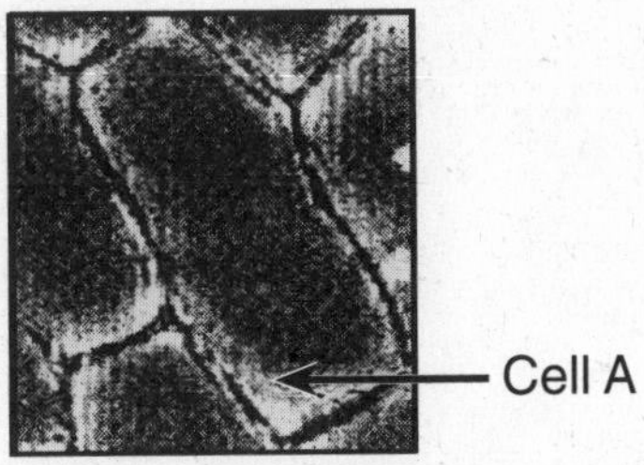

Draw a diagram of how cell *A* would most likely look after salt water has been added to the slide and label the cell membrane in your diagram. [2]

73 ☐

A

acid precipitation: rain, snow, sleet, or fog with a pH below 5.6; causes the deterioration of forests, lakes, statues, and buildings.

active transport: energy-expending process by which cells transport materials across the cell membrane against a concentration gradient.

adaptation (a dap TAY shun): evolution of a structure, behavior, or internal process that enables an organism to respond to environmental factors and live to produce offspring.

adenosine triphosphate (ATP) (uh DEH nuh seen • tri FAHS fayt): energy-storing molecule in cells composed of an adenosine molecule, a ribose sugar and three phosphate groups; energy is stored in the molecule's chemical bonds and can be used quickly and easily by cells.

aerobic: chemical reactions that require the presence of oxygen.

alcoholic fermentation: anaerobic process in which cells convert pyruvic acid into carbon dioxide and ethyl alcohol; carried out by many bacteria and fungi such as yeasts.

alveoli (al VEE uh li): sacs in the lungs where oxygen diffuses into the blood and carbon dioxide diffuses into the air.

amino acids: basic building blocks of protein molecules.

amylase: digestive enzyme found in saliva and pancreatic juices; breaks starches into smaller molecules such as disaccharides and monosaccharides.

anaerobic: chemical reactions that do not require the presence of oxygen.

antibodies (AN tih bahd eez): proteins in the blood plasma produced in reaction to antigens that react with and disable antigens.

antigens: foreign substances that stimulate an immune response in the body.

aorta: largest blood vessel in the body; transports oxygen-rich blood from the left ventricle of the heart to the arteries.

artificial selection: process of breeding organisms with specific traits in order to produce offspring with identical traits.

asexual reproduction: type of reproduction where one parent produces one or more identical offspring without the fusion of gametes.

precipitación ácida: Lluvia, nieve, granizo o neblina con un pH menor de 5.6; causa el deterioro de los bosques, los lagos, las estatuas y los edificios.

transporte activo: Proceso que requiere energía y mediante el cual la célula transporta materiales a través de la membrana celular contra un gradiente de concentración.

adaptación: Evolución de una estructura, comportamiento o proceso interno que permite a un organismo responder a los factores ambientales y sobrevivir para producir progenie.

trifosfato de adenosina (ATP): Moléculas que almacenan la energía de la célula, compuestas de una molécula de adenosina, un azúcar ribosa y tres grupos fosfato. La energía es almacenada en los enlaces químicos de la molécula y puede ser usada rápida y fácilmente por la célula.

aeróbica: Reacciones químicas que requieren la presencia de oxígeno.

fermentación alcohólica: Proceso anaeróbico en que las células convierten el ácido pirúvico a dióxido de carbono y alcohol etílico; la llevan a cabo muchas bacterias y hongos como las levaduras.

alvéolos: Sacos de los pulmones a través de los cuales el oxígeno se difunde hacia la sangre y el dióxido de carbono se difunde en el aire.

aminoácidos: Componentes básicos de las moléculas de proteínas.

amilasa: Enzima digestiva que se encuentra en la saliva y en los jugos pancreáticos. Descompone los almidones en moléculas más pequeñas como disacáridos y monosacáridos.

anaeróbico: Reacciones químicas que no requieren la presencia de oxígeno.

anticuerpos: Proteínas del plasma sanguíneo que son producidas en reacción a la presencia de antígenos, los cuales reaccionan y destruyen a dichos antígenos.

antígenos: Sustancias extrañas que estimulan la respuesta inmunológica del cuerpo.

aorta: El vaso sanguíneo más grande del cuerpo; transporta sangre rica en oxígeno desde el ventrículo izquierdo del corazón hacia las arterias.

selección artificial: Proceso de cría de organismos que poseen rasgos específicos para producir progenies con rasgos idénticos.

reproducción asexual: Tipo de reproducción en la cual un solo progenitor produce una o más crías idénticas sin la fusión de gametos.

atria: two upper chambers of the mammalian heart through which blood enters.

automatic nervous system (ANS): in humans, portion of the peripheral nervous system that carries impulses from the central nervous system to internal organs; produces involuntary responses.

autotrophs (AW tuh trohfs): organisms that use energy from the sun or energy stored in chemical compounds to manufacture their own nutrients.

auriculas: Las dos cavidades superiores del corazón de los mamíferos a través de las cuales entra la sangre al corazón.

sistema nervioso autónomo (SNA): En los humanos, la porción del sistema nervioso periférico que lleva impulsos desde el sistema nervioso central hacia los órganos internos. Produce respuestas involuntarias.

autótrofos: Organismos que utilizan la energía del sol o la energía almacenada en los compuestos químicos para producir sus propios nutrientes.

B

biodiversity: variety of life in an area; usually measured as the number of species that live in an area.

biodiversidad: La variedad de vida en un área; por lo común se mide como el número de especies que viven en un área.

C

cardiac muscle: type of involuntary muscle found only in the heart; composed of interconnected cardiac muscle fibers; adapted to generate and conduct electrical impulses for muscle contraction.

carrying capacity: number of organisms of one species that an environment can support indefinitely; populations below carrying capacity tend to increase; those above carrying capacity tend to decrease.

cartilage: tough flexible material making up the skeletons of agnathans, sharks, and their relatives, as well as portions of bony-animal skeletons.

cell: basic unit of all organisms; all living things are composed of cells.

cellular respiration: chemical process where mitochondria break down food molecules to produce ATP; the three stages of cellular respiration are glycolysis, the citric acid cycle, and the electron transport chain.

central nervous system (CNS): in humans, the central control center of the nervous system made up of the brain and spinal cord.

cerebellum (ser uh BE lum): rear portion of the brain; controls balance, posture, and coordination.

cerebrum (suh REE brum): largest part of the brain, composed of two hemispheres connected by bundles of nerves; controls conscious activities, intelligence, memory, language, skeletal muscle movements, and the senses.

músculo cardíaco: Tipo de músculo involuntario que se encuentra solo en el corazón; está compuesto por fibras musculares cardíacas interconectadas; está adaptado para generar y transmitir impulsos nerviosos para la contracción muscular.

capacidad de carga: Número de organismos de una especie que un ambiente puede mantener indefinidamente; las poblaciones que están por debajo de la capacidad de carga tienden a aumentar; aquellas que están sobre la capacidad de carga tienden a disminuir.

cartílago: Material flexible y fuerte que compone el esqueleto de los agnatos, los tiburones y sus parientes, además de porciones del esqueleto de los animales con huesos.

célula: Unidad básica de todos los organismos; todos los seres vivos están compuestos de células.

respiración celular: Proceso químico durante el cual la mitocondria descompone las moléculas de alimento para producir ATP; las tres etapas de la respiración celular son la glicólisis, el ciclo del ácido cítrico y la cadena de transporte electrónico.

sistema nervioso central (SNC): En los humanos, el centro de control central del sistema nervioso, compuesto por el cerebro y la médula espinal.

cerebelo: Porción posterior del cerebro; controla el equilibrio, la postura y la coordinación.

cerebro: La parte más grande de la masa cerebral, compuesto por dos hemisferios conectados por grupos de nervios; controla las actividades conscientes, la inteligencia, la memoria, el lenguaje, los movimientos de los músculos esqueléticos y los sentidos.

chlorophyll: light-absorbing pigment in plants and some protists that is required for photosynthesis; absorbs most wavelengths of light except for green.

chloroplasts: chlorophyll-containing organelles found in the cells of plants and some protists; capture light energy and converted it to chemical energy.

citric acid cycle: in cellular respiration, series of chemical reactions that break down glucose and produce ATP; energizes electron carriers that pass the energized electrons on to the electron transport chain.

cloning: creating genetically identical copies of an organism or gene.

commensalism (kuh MEN suh lih zum): symbiotic relationship in which one species benefits and the other species is neither harmed nor benefited.

compound light microscope: instrument that uses light and a series of lenses to magnify objects in steps; can magnify an object up to 1500 times its original size.

conservation biology: field of biology that studies methods and implements plans to protect biodiversity.

control: in an experiment, the standard against which results are compared.

cytoplasm: clear, gelatinous fluid in cells that is the site of numerous chemical reactions; in eukaryotic cells, it suspends the cell's organelles.

cytoskeleton: cellular framework found within the cytoplasm composed of microtubules and microfilaments.

clorofila: Pigmento que absorbe la luz, presente en las plantas y algunos protistas, que se requiere para la fotosíntesis; absorbe la mayoría de las longitudes de onda de luz excepto el verde.

cloroplastos: Organelos que contienen clorofila; se encuentran en las células de las plantas y algunos protistas; capturan la energía luminosa y la convierten en energía química.

ciclo del ácido cítrico: En la respiración celular, la serie de reacciones químicas que descomponen la glucosa y producen ATP; provee energía a los portadores de electrones que transfieren estos electrones energizados en la cadena de transporte electrónico.

clonación: Copias idénticas de la información genética de un organismo o de un gene.

comensalismo: Relación simbiótica en la cual una de las especies se beneficia y la otra especie ni sufre daño ni se beneficia.

microscopio de luz compuesto: Instrumento que utiliza la luz y una serie de lentes para aumentar gradualmente el tamaño de los objetos; puede aumentar el tamaño de un objeto hasta 1500 veces su tamaño original.

biología de la conservación: Campo de la biología que estudia los métodos e implementa planes para proteger la biodiversidad.

control: En un experimento, es la norma contra la cual se comparan los resultados.

citoplasma: Fluido gelatinoso de las células donde ocurren numerosas reacciones químicas. Es el fluido en el que se encuentran suspendidos los organelos de las células eucariotas.

citoesqueleto: Armazón celular que se encuentra dentro del citoplasma, compuesto de micro-túbulos y microfilamentos.

D

data: information obtained from experiments, sometimes called experimental results.

decomposers: organisms, such as fungi and bacteria, that break down and absorb nutrients from dead organisms.

deoxyribonucleic acid (DNA): a nucleic acid; the master copy of an organism's information code that contains the instructions used to form all of an organism's enzymes and structural proteins.

dependent variable: in an experiment, the condition that results from changes in the independent variable.

datos: Información que se obtiene de los experimentos, llamada a veces resultados experimentales.

descomponedores: Organismos como los hongos y las bacterias que descomponen y absorben los nutrientes de organismos muertos.

ácido desoxirribonucleico (DNA): Ácido nucleico; la copia maestra del código de información de un organismo y que contiene las instrucciones que se usan para formar todas las enzimas y proteínas estructurales del organismo.

variable dependiente: En un experimento, es la condición que resulta de los cambios introducidos en la variable independiente.

development: all of the changes that take place during the life of an organism; a characteristic of all living things.

diaphragm (DI uh fram): in mammals, the sheet of muscles located beneath the lungs that separates the chest cavity from the abdominal cavity; expands and contracts the chest cavity, which increases the amount of oxygen entering the body.

diffusion: net, random movement of particles from an area of higher concentration to an area of lower concentration, eventually resulting in even distribution.

diploid: cell with two of each kind of chromosome; is said to contain a diploid, or $2n$, number of chromosomes.

dynamic equilibrium: result of diffusion where there is continuous movement of particles but no overall change in concentration.

desarrollo: Todos los cambios que ocurren durante la vida de un organismo; una característica de todos los seres vivos.

diafragma: En los mamíferos, lámina muscular localizada por debajo de los pulmones que separa la cavidad torácica de la cavidad abdominal; expande y contrae la cavidad torácica, lo que hace aumentar la cantidad de oxígeno que entra al cuerpo.

difusión: Movimiento neto y al azar de partículas desde un área de mayor concentración hacia un área de menor concentración, lo que resulta a la postre en la distribución homogénea de las partículas.

diploide: Aquella célula que posee dos de cada tipo de cromosomas, se dice que es diploide, o con un número $2n$ de cromosomas.

equilibrio dinámico: Resultado de la difusión donde hay un movimiento constante de partículas sin que ocurra un cambio en la concentración.

E

ecology: scientific study of interactions between organisms and their environments.

ecosystem: interactions among populations in a community; the community's physical surroundings, or abiotic factors.

electron transport chain: series of proteins embedded in a membrane along which energized electrons are transported; as electrons are passed from molecule to molecule, energy is released.

endangered species: a species in which the number of individuals falls so low that extinction is possible.

endocrine glands: series of ductless glands that make up the endocrine system; release chemicals directly into the bloodstream where they relay messages to other parts of the body.

enzymes: type of protein found in all living things that changes the rate of chemical reactions.

epididymis (e puh DIH duh mus): in human males, the coiled tube within the scrotum in which the sperm complete maturation.

epiglottis (ep uh GLAH tus): flap of cartilage that closes over the opening of the respiratory tract during swallowing; prevents food from entering the respiratory tract.

evolution (e vuh LEW shun): gradual change in a species through adaptations over time.

ecología: Estudio científico de las interacciones entre los organismos y sus ambientes.

ecosistema: Interacciones entre las poblaciones de una comunidad; el ambiente físico de la comunidad, o sea, los factores abióticos.

cadena de transporte de electrones: Serie de proteínas inmersas en una membrana que se encargan de transportar electrones; a medida que los electrones pasan de una molécula a la siguiente, se libera energía.

especie en peligro de extinción: Una especie en la cual el número de individuos se reduce tanto que existe peligro de que se extinga.

glándulas endocrinas: Serie de glándulas que no poseen conductos y que forman el sistema endocrino; liberan sustancias químicas directamente al torrente sanguíneo por medio del cual llevan mensajes a otras partes del cuerpo.

enzimas: Tipo de proteína presente en todos los seres vivos que modifica la tasa de las reacciones químicas.

epidídimo: En los machos humanos, el tubo enroscado dentro del escroto en que los espermatozoides terminan de madurar.

epiglotis: Lámina de cartílago que al tragar, cierra la entrada del tracto respiratorio; evita que el alimento entre al tracto respiratorio.

evolución: Cambio gradual en una especie resultado de adaptaciones a lo largo del tiempo.

exotic species: nonnative species in an area; may take over niches of native species in an area and eventually replace them.

experiment: procedure that tests a hypothesis by collecting information under controlled conditions.

extinction (ek STINGK shun): the disappearance of a species when the last of its members dies.

especies exóticas: Especies no nativas de un área; pueden tomar los nichos de las especies nativas de un área y a la postre reemplazarlas.

experimento: Procedimiento que pone a prueba una hipótesis por medio de la recolección de información bajo condiciones controladas.

extinción: La desaparición de una especie; ocurre cuando el último miembro de una especie muere.

F

fertilization: fusion of male and female gametes.

fetus: a developing mammal from nine weeks to birth.

follicle: in human females, group of epithelial cells that surround a developing egg cell.

fossil: physical evidence of an organism that lived long ago that scientists use to study the past; evidence may appear in rocks, amber, or ice.

fecundación: Fusión de los gametos femenino y masculino.

feto: Un mamífero en desarrollo desde las nueve semanas hasta el nacimiento.

folículo: En las mujeres, grupo de células epiteliales que rodean a la célula óvulo en desarrollo.

fósil: Prueba física de un organismo que vivió hace mucho tiempo que los científicos utilizan para estudiar el pasado; evidencia que puede aparecer en las rocas, el ámbar o el hielo.

G

gametes: male and female sex cells; sperm and eggs.

gene: segment of DNA that controls the protein production and the cell cycle.

genetic engineering: method of cutting DNA from one organism and inserting the DNA fragment into a host organism of the same or a different species.

genetic recombination: major source of genetic variation among organisms caused by reassortment or crossing-over during meiosis.

glycolysis (gli KAH lih sis): in cellular respiration, series of anaerobic chemical reactions in the cytoplasm that breaks down glucose into pyruvic acid; forms a net profit of two ATP molecules.

guard cells: cells that control the opening and closing of the stomata; regulate the flow of water vapor from leaf tissue.

gametos: Las células sexuales masculinas y femeninas; espermatozoides y óvulos.

gene: Segmento del DNA que controla la producción de proteínas y el ciclo celular.

ingeniería genética: Método de cortar el DNA de un organismo e insertar el fragmento en el DNA de otro organismo huésped de la misma especie o de una especie diferente.

recombinación genética: La fuente más importante de variabilidad entre los organismos causada por el reacomodo o el entrecruzamiento durante la meiosis.

glicólisis: En la respiración celular, la serie de reacciones químicas anaeróbicas del citoplasma las cuales descomponen la glucosa en ácido pirúvico; produce una ganancia neta de dos moléculas de ATP.

células guardianas: Células que controlan el cerrarse y el abrirse de los estomas; regulan el flujo de vapor de agua en los tejidos de la hoja.

H

habitat corridors: natural strips of land that allow the migration of organisms from one wilderness area to another.

corredores de hábitat: Franjas naturales de terreno que permiten la migración de los organismos de un área silvestre a otra.

habitat fragmentation: separation of wilderness areas from each other; may cause problems for organisms that need large areas for food or mating.

haploid: cell with one of each kind of chromosome; is said to contain a haploid or *n*, number of chromosomes.

hemoglobin (HEE muh gloh bun): iron-containing protein molecule in red blood cells that binds to oxygen and carries it from the lungs to the body's cells.

heterotrophs (HE tuh ruh trohfs): organisms that cannot make their own food and must feed on other organisms for energy and nutrients.

homeostasis (hoh mee oh STAY sus): organism's regulation of its internal environment to maintain conditions suitable for survival; a characteristic of all living things. process of maintaining equilibrium in cells' internal environments.

homologous chromosomes (hoh MAH luh gus): paired chromosomes with genes for the same traits arranged in the same order.

homologous structures: structures with common evolutionary origins; can be similar in arrangement, in function, or both; provides evidence of evolution from a common ancestor; forelimbs of crocodiles, whales, and birds are examples.

hormone: chemical produced in one part of an organism and transported to another part, where it causes a physiological change.

hybrid: offspring formed by parents having different forms of a trait.

hypothesis (hi pahth us sus): explanation for a question or a problem that can be formally tested.

fragmentación del hábitat: Separación de las áreas silvestres; puede causar problemas a los organismos que requieren de grandes áreas para su alimentación o apareamiento.

haploide: Célula que tiene uno de cada tipo de cromosomas; se dice que contiene un número haploide, o *n*, de cromosomas.

hemoglobina: Molécula de proteína de los glóbulos rojos que contiene hierro que se enlaza al oxígeno y lo lleva desde los pulmones hasta las células del cuerpo.

heterótrofos: Organismos que no pueden producir su propio alimento y deben alimentarse de otros organismos para obtener energía y nutrientes.

homeostasis: Regulación del organismo de su ambiente interno para mantener las condiciones adecuadas para la sobrevivencia; característica de todos los seres vivos. el proceso que permite que las células mantengan el equilibrio de sus condiciones internas.

cromosomas homólogos: Pares de cromosomas con genes para los mismos rasgos acomodados en el mismo orden.

estructuras homólogas: Estructuras que tienen el mismo origen evolutivo; pueden ser similares en su localización, su función, o en ambas; proporcionan evidencias sobre la evolución a partir de un antepasado común; las extremidades delanteras de los cocodrilos, las ballenas y las aves son ejemplos.

hormona: Compuesto químico producido en una parte del organismo y transportado a otra parte en donde causa un cambio fisiológico.

híbrido: Progenie de progenitores que tienen formas diferentes para un rasgo.

hipótesis: Explicación para una pregunta o problema que puede ser puesta formalmente a prueba.

I

independent variable: in an experiment, the condition that is tested because it affects the outcome of the experiment.

variable independiente: La condición que se prueba en un experimento porque afecta el resultado del experimento.

J

joints: point where two or more bones meet; can be fixed or facilitate movement of bones in relation to one another.

articulaciones: Sitios donde dos o más huesos se juntan; pueden ser fijas o facilitar el movimiento de un hueso en relación con los otros.

L

lactic acid fermentation: series of anaerobic chemical reactions in which pyruvic acid uses NADH to form lactic acid and NAD^+, which is then used in glycolysis; supplies energy when oxygen for aerobic respiration is scarce.

ligament: tough band of connective tissue that attaches one bone to another; joints are often held together and enclosed by ligaments.

light-dependent reactions: phase of photosynthesis where light energy is converted to chemical energy in the form of ATP; results in the splitting of water and the release of oxygen.

light-independent reactions: phase of photosynthesis where energy from light-dependent reactions is used to produce glucose and additional ATP molecules.

lymph: tissue fluids composed of water and dissolved substances from the blood that have collected and entered the lymph vessels.

lysosomes: organelles that contain digestive enzymes; digest excess or worn out organelles, food particles, and engulfed viruses or bacteria.

fermentación del ácido láctico: Serie de reacciones químicas anaeróbicas en las cuales el ácido pirúvico utiliza NADH para formar ácido láctico y NAD^+, el cual es utilizado a continuación en la glicólisis; provee energía cuando el oxígeno para la respiración aeróbica es escaso.

ligamento: Banda fuerte de tejido conectivo que adhiere un hueso al otro; las articulaciones están a menudo rodeadas y sostenidas en su lugar por los ligamentos.

reacciones dependientes de la luz: Fase de la fotosíntesis en la cual la energía luminosa es convertida a energía química en forma de ATP; resulta en el rompimiento del agua y la liberación de oxígeno.

reacciones independientes de la luz: Fase de la fotosíntesis en la cual la energía proveniente de las reacciones dependientes de la luz se utiliza para producir glucosa y moléculas adicionales de ATP.

linfa: Fluidos de los tejidos compuestos de agua y sustancias disueltas provenientes de la sangre que han sido recogidas y han entrado a los vasos de la linfa.

lisosomas: Organelos que contienen enzimas digestivas; digieren los organelos gastados o extras, las partículas de alimento y rodean e ingieren los virus o las bacterias.

M

medulla oblongata (muh DU luh • ah blon GAH tuh): part of the brain stem that controls involuntary activities such as breathing and heart rate.

meiosis (mi OH sus): type of cell division where one body cell produces four gametes, each containing half the number of chromosomes as a parent's body cell.

menstrual cycle: in human females, the monthly cycle that includes the production of an egg, the preparation of the uterus to receive an egg, and the shedding of an egg if it remains unfertilized.

messenger RNA (mRNA): RNA that transports information from DNA in the nucleus to the cell's cytoplasm.

mitochondria: eukaryotic membrane-bound organelles that transform energy stored in food molecules; has a highly folded inner membrane that produces energy-storing molecules.

bulbo raquídeo: Parte del tronco encefálico que controla las actividades involuntarias como la respiración y el ritmo cardíaco.

meiosis: Tipo de división celular en la cual las células del cuerpo producen gametos, cada uno de los cuales contiene la mitad del número de cromosomas de una célula corporal del progenitor.

ciclo menstrual: En las mujeres, el ciclo mensual que incluye la producción de un óvulo, la preparación del útero para recibir el óvulo y la descarga del óvulo si no ha sido fecundado.

RNA mensajero (mRNA): RNA que transporta información desde el DNA en el núcleo hasta el citoplasma de la célula.

mitocondrias: Organelos eucariotas membranosos que transforman la energía almacenada en las moléculas de los alimentos; poseen una membrana interna con muchos dobleces que se encarga de producir las moléculas que almacenan la energía.

mitosis (mi TOH sus): period of nuclear cell division in which two daughter cells are formed, each containing a complete set of chromosomes.

mutation: any change or random error in a DNA sequence.

mutualism (MYEW chuh wuh lih zum): a symbiotic relationship in which both species benefit.

mitosis: Período de la división nuclear en que se forman dos células hijas, cada una de las cuales contiene un grupo completo de cromosomas.

mutación: Cualquier cambio o error ocurrido al azar en la secuencia del DNA.

mutualismo: Relación simbiótica en la cual las dos especies se benefician.

N

natural selection: mechanism for change in populations; occurs when organisms with favorable variations survive, reproduce, and pass their variations to the next generation.

negative feedback system: internal feedback mechanism in which a substance is fed back to inhibit the original signal and reduce production of a substance; examples include hormones in the endocrine system.

nephron: individual filtering unit of the kidneys.

neurons (NYU ronz): basic unit of structure and function in the nervous system; conducts impulses throughout the nervous system; composed of dendrites, a cell body, and an axon.

neurotransmitters: chemicals released from an axon that diffuse across a synapse to the next neuron's dendrites to initiate a new impulse.

niche (neesh): role or position a species has in its environment; includes all biotic and abiotic interactions as an animal meets its needs for survival and reproduction.

nucleus (NEW klee us): positively charged center of an atom composed of neutrons and positively charged protons, and surrounded by negatively charged electrons. in eukaryotic cells, the central membrane-bound organelle that manages cellular functions and contains DNA.

selección natural: Mecanismo de cambio en las poblaciones; ocurre cuando los organismos con variaciones favorables sobreviven, se reproducen y transfieren sus variaciones a la siguiente generación.

sistema de retroalimentación negativa: Mecanismo interno de retroalimentación en el que una sustancia es enviada de regreso para inhibir la señal original y reducir la producción de una sustancia; ejemplos incluyen las hormonas del sistema endocrino.

nefrón: Unidad individual de filtración de los riñones.

neuronas: Unidades básicas de estructura y función del sistema nervioso; conducen los impulsos a través del sistema nervioso; están compuestas por las dendritas, el cuerpo celular y el axón.

neurotransmisores: Sustancias químicas liberadas desde el axón que se difunden en el área de sinapsis hacia las dendritas de la próxima neurona para iniciar un nuevo impulso.

nicho: La función o la posición de un organismo en su ambiente; incluye todas las interacciones bióticas y abióticas necesarias para que el organismo pueda satisfacer sus necesidades de sobrevivencia y reproducción.

núcleo: Centro del átomo con carga positiva compuesto por neutrones y protones de carga positiva, el cual está rodeado por electrones de carga negativa. en las células eucariotas es el organelo membranoso central y está a cargo de las funciones celulares y contiene el DNA.

O

organ: group of two or more tissues organized to perform complex activities within an organism.

organelles: membrane-bound structures with particular functions within eukaryotic cells.

órgano: Grupo de dos o más tejidos organizados para llevar a cabo actividades complejas dentro del organismo.

organelos: Estructuras membranosas con funciones específicas localizadas dentro de las células eucariotas.

organism: anything that possesses all the characteristics of life; all organisms have an orderly structure, produce offspring, grow, develop, and adjust to changes in the environment.

organ system: multiple organs that work together to perform a specific life function.

osmosis (ahs MOH sus)**:** diffusion of water across a selectively permeable membrane depending on the concentration of solutes on either side of the membrane.

ovary: in plants, the bottom portion of a flowers's pistil that contains one or more ovules each containing one egg.

oviduct: in females, the tube that transports eggs from the ovary to the uterus.

ovulation: in females, the process of an egg rupturing through the ovary wall and moving into the oviduct.

ozone layer: layer of the atmosphere that helps to protect living organisms on Earth's surface from damaging doses of ultraviolet radiation from the Sun.

organismo: Cualquier cosa que posea todas las características de la vida; todos los organismos tienen una estructura ordenada, producen progenies, crecen, se desarrollan y se adaptan a los cambios del ambiente.

sistema de órganos: Órganos múltiples que trabajan juntos para llevar a cabo una actividad vital específica.

osmosis: Difusión del agua a traves de una membrana de permeabilidad selectiva que depende de la concentración de solutos en cualquiera de los dos lados de la membrana.

ovario: En las plantas es la porción inferior del pistilo que contiene uno o más huevos, cada uno de los cuales contiene un óvulo.

oviducto: Es el tubo que transporta los óvulos desde el ovario hasta el útero en las hembras.

ovulación: En las mujeres, el proceso de salida de un óvulo a través de la pared del ovario y su entrada al oviducto.

capa de ozono: Capa de la atmósfera que ayuda a proteger a los organismos vivos en la superficie de la Tierra de dosis dañinas de radiación ultravioleta proveniente del sol.

P

parasitism (PER uh suh tih zum)**:** symbiotic relationship in which one organism benefits at the expense of another, usually another species.

pathogens: disease-producing agents such as bacteria, protozoans, fungi, viruses, and other parasites.

pepsin: enzyme found in gastric juices; begins the chemical digestion of proteins in food; most effective in acidic environments.

peripheral nervous system (puh RIH frul) (PNS)**:** division of the nervous system made up of all the nerves that carry messages to and from the central nervous system.

peristalsis (per uh STAHL sus)**:** series of involuntary smooth muscle contractions along the walls of the digestive tract that move food through the digestive tract.

pH: measure of how acidic or basic a solution is; the scale ranges from below 0 to above 14; solution with pH above 7 is basic and a pH below 7 is acidic.

phagocytes (FAG uh sites)**:** white blood cells that destroy pathogens by surrounding and engulfing them; include macrophages, neutrophils, monocytes, and eosinophils.

parasitismo: Relación simbiótica en la cual un organismo se beneficia de otro, a menudo de otra especie.

patógenos: Agentes productores de enfermedades, como las bacterias, los protozoarios, los hongos, los virus y otros parásitos.

pepsina: Enzima que se encuentra en los jugos gástricos; comienza la digestión química de las proteínas en el alimento; es más eficiente en medios ácidos.

sistema nervioso periférico (SNP): División del sistema nervioso compuesta por los nervios que transportan mensajes desde y hacia el sistema nervioso central.

peristalsis: Serie de contracciones involuntarias del músculo liso a lo largo de las paredes del tracto digestivo que hace que se mueva el alimento a lo largo del tracto digestivo.

pH: Medida de la acidez o la basicidad de una solución; la escala varía entre menos de 0 a más de 14. Las soluciones con pH mayor que 7 son básicas y las soluciones con pH menor que 7 son ácidas.

fagocitos: Glóbulos blancos sanguíneos que destruyen a los patógenos rodeándolos y tragándoselos; incluye a los macrófagos, los neutrófilos, los monocitos y los eosinófilos.

pharynx (FAHR inx): in planarians, the tubelike, muscular organ that extends from the mouth; aids in feeding and digestion.

photolysis (fo TAH luh sis): reaction taking place in the thylakoid membranes of a chloroplast during light-dependent reactions where two molecules of water are split to form oxygen, hydrogen ions, and electrons.

photosynthesis: process by which autotrophs, such as algae and plants, trap energy from sunlight with chlorophyll and use this energy to convert carbon dioxide and water into simple sugars.

pigments: molecules that absorb specific wavelengths of sunlight.

placenta (pluh SEN tuh): organ that provides food and oxygen to and removes waste from young inside the uterus of placental mammals.

plasma membrane: flexible boundary between the cell and its environment; allows materials such as water and nutrients to enter and waste products to leave.

plasmid: small ring of DNA found in a bacterial cell that is used as a biological vector.

population: group of organisms all of the same species, which interbreed and live in the same place at the same time.

punctuated equilibrium: idea that periods of speciation occur relatively quickly with long periods of genetic equilibrium in between.

faringe: En las planarias, el órgano muscular parecido a un tubo que se extiende desde la boca; ayuda en la alimentación y la digestión.

fotólisis: Reacción que sucede en las membranas tilacoides del cloroplasto durante las reacciones dependientes de la luz, en la cual dos moléculas de agua se rompen y forman oxígeno, iones de hidrógeno y electrones.

fotosíntesis: Proceso por medio del cual los organismos autótrofos, como las algas y las plantas, atrapan la energía solar por medio de la clorofila y utilizan esta energía para convertir el dióxido de carbono y el agua en azúcares simples.

pigmentos: Moléculas que absorben longitudes de onda específicas de la luz solar.

placenta: Órgano que provee alimento y oxígeno a la cría en desarrollo en el útero de los mamíferos placentarios, además de eliminar sus desechos.

membrana plasmática: Frontera flexible entre una célula y su ambiente; permite que los materiales como el agua y los nutrientes entren y los desechos salgan de la célula.

plasmidio: Pequeño anillo de DNA que se encuentra en las células bacterianas y se usa como vector biológico.

población: Grupo de organismos, todos ellos de la misma especie, que se entrecruzan y viven en el mismo sitio al mismo tiempo.

equilibrio interrumpido: La idea de que los períodos de especiación ocurren relativamente rápido, separados por largos períodos de equilibrio genético.

R

receptors: binding sites on target cells that bind with specific hormones.

recombinant DNA (ree KAHM buh nunt): DNA made by recombining fragments of DNA from different sources.

reflex (REE fleks): simple, automatic response in an animal that involves no conscious control; usually acts to protect an animal from serious injury. automatic response to a stimulus; reflex stimulus travels to the spinal column and sent directly back to the muscle.

reintroduction programs: programs that release organisms into an area where their species once lived in hopes of reestablishing naturally reproducing populations.

response: an organism's reaction to a change in its internal or external environment.

receptores: Sitios de adherencia en las células asignadas en donde se enlazan hormonas específicas.

DNA recombinante: DNA que se produce al combinar fragmentos de DNA de diferentes fuentes.

reflejo: Respuesta simple automática de un animal que no está bajo control consciente; a menudo actúa para proteger al animal de daños serios. Respuesta automática a un estímulo; el estímulo reflejo viaja a la médula espinal y es devuelto directamente al músculo.

programas de reintroducción: Programas en los cuales se liberan organismos en áreas donde la especie solía vivir con la esperanza de restablecer poblaciones que se reproduzcan en forma natural.

respuesta: La reacción de un organismo a un cambio en su ambiente interno o externo.

restriction enzymes: DNA-cutting enzymes that can cut both strands of a DNA molecule at a specific nucleotide sequence.

retrovirus (reh tro VY rus): type of viral replication where a virus uses reverse transcriptase to make DNA from viral RNA; the retroviral DNA is then integrated into the host cell's chromosome.

ribosomes: nonmembrane-bound organelles in the nucleus where proteins are assembled.

enzimas restríctivas: Enzimas cortadoras del DNA que pueden cortar ambas hebras de la molécula de DNA cuando encuentran una secuencia específica de nucleótidos.

retrovirus: Tipo de replicación viral que utiliza la transcriptasa inversa para formar DNA a partir de RNA viral; el DNA del retrovirus es luego integrado al cromosoma de la célula huésped.

ribosomas: Organelos nucleares no membranosos en los que se arman las proteínas.

S

safety symbol: symbol that warns you about a danger that may exist from chemicals, electricity, heat, or experimental procedures.

scientific methods: procedures that biologists and other scientists use to gather information and answer questions; include observing and hypothesizing, experimenting, and gathering and interpreting results.

selective permeability: feature of the plasma membrane that maintains homeostasis within a cell by allowing some molecules into the cell while keeping others out.

semen: combination of sperm and fluids from the seminal vesicles, prostate gland, and bulbourethral glands.

seminal vesicles: in males, pair of glands located at the base of the urinary bladder that secrete a mucouslike fluid into the vas deferens.

sexual reproduction: pattern of reproduction that involves the production and subsequent fusion of haploid sex cells.

skeletal muscle: a type of voluntary muscle that is attached to and moves the bones of the skeleton.

smooth muscle: type of involuntary muscle found in the walls of internal organs and blood vessels; most common function is to squeeze, exerting pressure inside the tube or organ it surrounds.

somatic nervous system: portion of the nervous system composed of cranial nerves, spinal nerves, and all of their branches; voluntary pathway that relays information mainly between the skin, the CNS, and skeletal muscles.

species (SPEE sheez): group of organisms that can interbreed and produce fertile offspring in nature.

símbolo de seguridad: Símbolo que te advierte acerca de algún peligro, ya sean sustancias químicas, la electricidad, el calor o las maniobras realizadas durante el procedimiento experimental.

métodos científicos: Procedimientos que los biólogos y otros científicos utilizan para reunir información y contestar preguntas; incluyen la observación, la formación de hipótesis, la experimentación y la recolección y análisis de los resultados.

permeabilidad selectiva: Característica de la membrana celular que mantiene la homeostasis dentro de la célula al permitir la entrada de algunas moléculas y detener el paso de otras.

semen: Combinación de los espermatozoides con fluidos producidos por las vesículas seminales, la glándula próstata y las glándulas bulbouretrales.

vesículas seminales: En los machos, el par de glándulas localizadas en la base de la vejiga urinaria que secretan un fluido denso a menudo hacia los vasos deferentes.

reproducción sexual: Patrón de reproducción que implica la producción y luego la fusión de células sexuales haploides.

músculo esquelético: Tipo de músculo voluntario que se encuentra adherido a los huesos del esqueleto, a los cuales mueve.

músculo liso: Tipo de músculo involuntario que se encuentra en las paredes de los órganos internos y los vasos sanguíneos; su función más común es la de apretar, poniendo presión dentro del tubo u órgano que rodea.

sistema nervioso somático: Porción del sistema nervioso compuesto por los nervios craneales, los nervios de la espina dorsal y todas sus ramificaciones; es la ruta voluntaria que pasa la información sobre todo entre la piel, el CNS y los músculos esqueléticos.

especie: Grupo de organismos que pueden cruzarse y producir progenies fértiles bajo condiciones naturales.

stimulus: anything in an organism's internal or external environment that causes the organism to react.

synapse: tiny space between one neuron's axon and another neuron's dendrites over which a nerve impulse must pass.

estímulo: Cualquier condición del ambiente interno o externo de un organismo que ocasiona una reacción en el organismo.

sinapsis: Espacios diminutos entre el axón de una neurona y las dendritas de otra a través de los cuales debe pasar el impulso nervioso.

T

tendons: thick bands of connective tissue that attach muscles to bones.

theory: explanation of natural phenomenon supported by a large body of scientific evidence obtained from many different investigations and observations.

threatened species: when the population of a species is likely to become endangered.

tissue: groups of cells that work together to perform a specific function.

trachea (TRAY kee uh): tubelike passageway for air flow that connects with two bronchi tubes that lead into the lungs.

transcription (trans KRIHP shun): process in the cell nucleus where enzymes make an RNA copy of a DNA strand.

transfer RNA (tRNA): RNA that transports amino acids to the ribosomes to be assembled into proteins.

transgenic organisms: organisms that contain functional recombinant DNA from a different organism.

tendones: Bandas gruesas de tejido conectivo que adhieren los músculos a los huesos.

teoría: Explicación de un fenómeno natural que tiene el apoyo de un gran cuerpo de evidencia científica obtenida de muchos experimentos y observaciones diferentes.

especies amenazadas: Ocurre cuando la población de una especie se encuentra a punto de desaparecer.

tejido: Grupo de células que trabajan juntas para llevar a cabo una función específica.

tráquea: Pasaje tubular para el flujo de aire que se conecta con los dos bronquios que llegan a los pulmones.

transcripción: Proceso que ocurre en el núcleo de la célula, en que las enzimas hacen una copia de RNA a partir de una hebra de DNA.

RNA de transferencia (tRNA): El RNA que transporta los aminoácidos a los ribosomas para armar las proteínas.

organismos transgénicos: Organismos que contienen DNA recombinante en estado funcional, proveniente de organismos diferentes.

U

umbilical cord: ropelike structure that attaches the embryo to the wall of the uterus; supplies a developing embryo with oxygen and nutrients and removes waste products.

ureter: tube that transports urine from each kidney to the urinary bladder.

urethra (yoo REE thruh): tube through which urine is passed from the urinary bladder to the outside of the body.

uterus (YEWT uh rus): in females, the hollow, muscular organ in which the offspring of placental mammals develop.

cordón umbilical: Estructura parecida a una cuerda que ata al embrión a la pared del útero; provee al embrión en desarrollo de oxígeno y nutrientes y elimina los productos de desecho.

uréter: Tubo que transporta la orina desde cada riñón hacia la vejiga urinaria.

uretra: Tubo a través del cual la orina es llevada desde la vejiga urinaria hacia el exterior del cuerpo.

útero: En las hembras, el órgano muscular hueco en donde se desarrollan las crías de los mamíferos placentarios.

V

vaccine: substance consisting of weakened, dead, or incomplete portions of pathogens or antigens that produce an immune response when injected into the body.

vacuole: membrane-bound space in the cytoplasm of cells used for the temporary storage of materials.

vas deferens (VAS • DE fuh renz): in males, duct that transports sperm from the epididymis towards the ejaculatory ducts of the urethra.

vector: means by which DNA from another species can be carried into the host cell; may be biological or mechanical.

ventricles: two lower chambers of the mammalian heart; receive blood from the atria and send it to the lungs and body.

villus: single projection on the lining of the small intestine that functions in the absorption of digested food; they increase the surface area of the small intestine and increase the absorption rate.

vacuna: Sustancia compuesta de patógenos muertos o debilitados, de sus fragmentos, o de antígenos, que producen una respuesta inmunológica cuando se inyectan dentro del cuerpo.

vacuola: Espacio en el citoplasma de las células rodeado por una membrana y que se utiliza para el almacenamiento temporal de materiales.

conductos deferentes: En los machos, conductos que transportan los espermatozoides desde el epidídimo hacia los conductos eyaculatorios de la uretra.

vector: Vehículo por medio del cual el DNA de otra especie puede ser llevado a la célula huésped; puede ser biológico o mecánico.

ventrículos: Las dos cavidades inferiores del corazón de los mamíferos; reciben la sangre proveniente de las aurículas y la envían a los pulmones y al resto del cuerpo.

microvellosidad: Proyección individual del recubrimiento del intestino delgado que funciona en la absorción del alimento digerido; aumenta el área de superficie del intestino delgado lo que aumenta la tasa de absorción.

Z

zygote (ZI goht): diploid cell formed when a sperm fertilizes an egg.

cigoto: Célula diploide que se forma cuando el espermatozoide fecunda el óvulo.

Index

Index

Index

Index

Index

Stereomicroscopes, 146
Stereoscope, 146
Stimulus, 14, 43
Stomach
    organ of digestive system, 98
Stroma, 27
Substrates, 33
Succession, 118–*119*
    after environmental disturbances, 119
Sun, 25, 114, 115
Sweat glands, 100
    perspiration, 100
Symbiotic relationships, 119–120
    commensalism, 120
    mutualism, 119
    parasitism, 120
Synapse, 101
    chemicals diffuse across, 101

T

Temperature
    measurement of, 144
Tendon, 102
    attaches muscles to bones, 102
Testes, 104
Testosterone, 104
Theory, 1, 7, 8
    spontaneous generation, 1
Threatened species, 133, 138
Thylakoid discs, 26
Thylakoid membrane, 26, 27, 29
Thylakoids, 18
Thymine (T), 60
Tissue, 15
    using stem cells to repair, 77
Tongue
    organ of digestive system, 97
Trachea, 99
Traits, 55
    acquired without a change in DNA, 87
    desirable, 73
    dominant, 63
    proteins and, 62
    relationship among DNA, proteins, and, *63*
Transcription, 62
Transfer RNA (tRNA), 62
Transplant rejection, 49
Transportation of molecules. *See* Cellular
    transport
Trypsin, 33

U

Umbilical cord, 105, 106
Uracil (U), 62
Ureter, 100
Urethra, 100
Urinary bladder, 100
Urinary system, 100–*101*
    kidneys, 100
    ureters, 100
    urethra, 100
    urinary bladder, 100
Urine, 100
Uterus, 104

V

Vaccine, 48
    recommended childhood, 48 table
Vacuoles, 17
van Helmont, Jean Baptiste, 1
Variables
    dependent, 5
    independent, 4
Vas deferens, 104
Vectors, 76
Vegetative propagation, 57
Veins, 99
Ventricles, 99
Villus, 98
Vitamin deficiencies, 50 table
Volume
    measurement of, 144

W

Water pollution, 131
    damage to aquatic ecosystems, 131
    effects on food webs, 131
Wet-mount slide, 147
    preparing, 147
White blood cells, 98
    fights infection, 98
    formed in bone marrow and lymph tissue, 98
    lymphocytes, 98
    phagocytes, 98

Z

Zygote, 57, 105
    in cloned mammal, 77

Photo Credits

Cover (cr)McDonald Wildlife Photography/Animals Animals, (others)PhotoDisc;

vi CORBIS;

2–3 Getty Images;

8 Will & Deni McIntyre/Photo Researchers;

25 Bob Mullenix/KS Studios;

65 Lester V. Bergman/CORBIS;

74 (t)Frank Gorski/Peter Arnold Inc., (b)Arthur M. Siegelman/Visuals Unlimited;

89 Stuart Westmoreland/Norbert Wu Productions;

111 John Winnie Jr./DRK Photo;

123 (bl)Tom & Pat Leeson/Photo Researchers, (bc)Patti Murray/Earth Scenes, (br)Don & Pat Valenti/DRK Photo;

130 Will & Deni McIntyre/Photo Researchers;

132 Michael Fredericks Jr./Animals Animals;

133 (tl)G. Carleton Ray/Photo Researchers, (tr)Scott Camazine/Photo Researchers;

135 Chris Smith, NYSERDA;

136 Courtesy W.H. Freeman and Company;

146 Matt Meadows.